Sweet Little Neville:

May out here in the Philippines, for your eighth birthday, Daddy and Mother give you this Geography to be the first book in the Library you are going to build from now on.

May you get to see most of the countries described in this beautiful book and learn to look upon these different people with love and understanding. This is the greatest wish for you from

Herman N. Archer.

and Alice W. Archer,

Manila, P.I. October 29th 1939.

D1087158

LIST OF BOOKS OF HENDRIK WILLEM VAN LOON

TRANSLATIONS

These books have been translated and published in the following foreign countries.

Ancient Man: England, Holland.

*The Story of Mankind: England, Holland, Germany, Sweden, Denmark, China, Japan, India, Russia, Spain, Italy, Poland, Hungary, Czecho-Slovakia, Greece, Palestine. There also have been translations into Esperanto and Braille.

**The Story of the Bible: Sweden, England, Finland, Holland.

*Tolerance: Sweden, England, Holland.

*America: Germany, England, Spain, Italy, Holland.

·Man the Miracle Maker: England, Germany, Holland.

*Rembrandt van Rijn: Germany, Holland, Norway.

**van Loon's Geography is now being translated into German and Dutch and French and being adapted for those who speak the King's rather than the President's English. Negotiations for five other translations of the Geography are under way at the moment of printing.

*Now available in Star Edition.
**De luxe Edition, Garden City Publishing Co., Inc.

The Will to Live

VAN LOON'S GEOGRAPHY

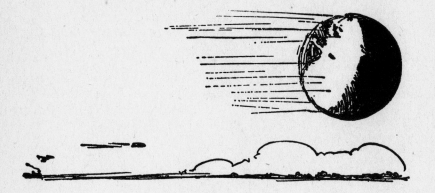

THE STORY OF THE WORLD

WRITTEN AND ILLUSTRATED BY

Hendrik Willem van Loon

De Luxe Edition

GARDEN CITY PUBLISHING CO., INC.

GARDEN CITY   NEW YORK

1937
GARDEN CITY PUBLISHING CO., INC.

Ten years ago you sent me a letter and today you get your answer. What you wrote (I am quoting from the original) was this:

". . . Yes, but how about geography? No, I don't merely want a new geography. I want a geography of my own, a geography that shall tell me what I want to know and omit everything else and I want you to write it for me. I went to a school where they took the subject very seriously. I learned all about the different countries and how they were bounded and about the cities and how many inhabitants they had and I learned the names of all the mountains and how high they were and how much coal was exported every year, and I forgot all these things just as fast as I had learned them. They failed to connect. They resolved themselves into a jumble of badly digested recollections, like a museum too full of pictures or a concert that has lasted too long. And they were of no earthly value to me, for every time I needed some concrete fact, I had to look it up on maps and in atlases and encyclopedias and blue books. I suppose that many others have suffered in the same way. On behalf of all these poor victims, will you please give us a new geography that will be of some use? Put all the mountains and the cities and the oceans on your maps and then tell us only about the people who live in those places and why they are there and where they came from and what they are doing—a sort of human interest story applied to geography. And please stress the countries that are really interesting and don't pay quite so much attention to the others that are merely names, for then we will be able to remember all about them, but otherwise . . ."

And I, eager as always to oblige when I receive a command from your hands, turn around and say, "My dear, here it is!"

HENDRIK WILLEM VAN LOON.

TABLE OF CONTENTS

Air

Coffey Cook

TABLE OF CONTENTS

LIST OF ILLUSTRATIONS

LIST OF COLORED AND WASH ILLUSTRATIONS

xix

xx COLORED AND WASH ILLUSTRATIONS

VAN LOON'S GEOGRAPHY

"History is the Fourth Dimension of Geography.
It gives it both time and meaning."

I

AND THESE ARE THE PEOPLE WHO LIVE IN THE WORLD WE LIVE IN

IT SOUNDS incredible, but nevertheless it is true. If everybody in this world of ours were six feet tall and a foot and a half wide and a foot thick (and that is making people a little bigger than they usually are), then the whole of the human race (and according to the latest available statistics there are now nearly 2,000,000,000 descendants of the original Homo Sapiens and his wife) could be packed into a box measuring half a mile in each direction. That, as I just said, sounds incredible, but if you don't believe me, figure it out for yourself and you will find it to be correct.

If we transported that box to the Grand Canyon of Arizona and balanced it neatly on the low stone wall that keeps people from breaking their necks when stunned by the incredible beauty of that silent witness of the forces of Eternity, and then called little Noodle, the dachshund, and told him (the tiny beast is very intelligent and loves to oblige) to give the unwieldy contraption a slight push with his soft brown nose, there would be a moment of crunching and ripping as the wooden planks loosened stones and shrubs and trees on their downward path, and then a low and even softer bumpity-bumpity-bump and a sudden splash when the outer edges struck the banks of the Colorado River.

Then silence and oblivion!

The human sardines in their mortuary chest would soon be forgotten.

The Canyon would go on battling wind and air and sun and rain as it has done since it was created.

3

The world would continue to run its even course through the uncharted heavens.

The astronomers on distant and nearby planets would have noticed nothing out of the ordinary.

A century from now, a little mound, densely covered with vegetable matter, would perhaps indicate where humanity lay buried.

And that would be all.

I can well imagine that some of my readers will not quite like this story and will feel rather uncomfortable when they see their own proud race reduced to such proportions of sublime insignificance.

There is however a different angle to the problem—an angle which makes the very smallness of our numbers and the helplessness of our puny little bodies a matter of profound and sincere pride.

Here we are, a mere handful of weak and defenceless mammals. Ever since the dawn of the first day we have been surrounded on all sides by hordes and swarms of creatures infinitely better prepared for the struggle of existence than we are ourselves. Some of them were a hundred feet long and weighed as much as a small locomotive while others had teeth as sharp as the blade of a circular saw. Many varieties went about their daily affairs clad in the armor of a medieval knight. Others were invisible to the human eye but they multiplied at such a terrific rate that they would have owned the entire earth in less than a year's time if it had not been for certain enemies who were able to destroy them almost as fast as they were born. Whereas man could only exist under the most favorable circumstances and was forced to look for a habitat among the few small pieces of dry land situated between the high mountains and the deep sea, these fellow-passengers of ours considered no summit too high and found no sea too deep for their ambitions. They were apparently made of the stuff that could survive regardless of its natural surroundings.

When we learn on eminent authority that certain varieties of insects are able to disport themselves merrily in petroleum (a substance we would hardly fancy as the main part of our daily diet) and that others manage to live through such changes in temperature as would kill all of us within a very few minutes; when we discover to our gruesome dismay that those little brown beetles, who seem so fond of literature that they are forever racing around in our bookcases, continue the even tenor of their restless days minus two or three or four legs, while we ourselves are disabled by a mere pin-prick on one of our toes, then we sometimes begin to realize against what sort of competitors we have been forced to hold our own, ever since we made our first appearance upon this whirling bit of rock, lost somewhere in the darkest outskirts of an indifferent universe.

What a side-splitting joke we must have been to our pachydermous contemporaries who stood by and watched this pinkish sport of nature indulge in its first clumsy efforts to walk on its hind legs without the help of a convenient tree-trunk or cane!

But what has become of those proud and exclusive owners of almost 200,000,000 square miles of land and water (not to mention the unfathomable oceans of air) who ruled so sublime by that right of eminent domain which was based upon brute force and sly cunning?

The greater part of them has disappeared from view except where as "Exhibit A" or "B" we have kindly given them a little parking space in one of our museums devoted to natural history. Others, in order to remain among those present, were forced to go into domestic service and today in exchange for a mere livelihood they favor us with their hides and their eggs and their milk and the beef that grows upon their flanks, or drag such loads as we consider a little too heavy for our own lazy efforts. Many more have betaken themselves to out-of-the-way places where we permit them to browse and graze and perpetuate their species because, thus far, we have not thought it worth our while to remove them from the scene and claim their territory for ourselves.

In short, during only a couple of thousands of centuries (a mere second from the point of view of eternity), the human race has made itself the undisputed ruler of every bit of land and at present it bids fair to add both air and sea as part of its domains. And all that, if you please, has been accomplished by a few hundred million creatures who enjoyed not one single advantage over their enemies except the divine gift of Reason.

Even there I am exaggerating. The gift of Reason in its more sublime form and the ability to think for one's self is restricted to a mere handful of men and women. They therefore become the masters who lead. The others, no matter how much they may resent the fact, can only follow. The result is a strange and halting procession, for no matter how hard people may try, there are ten thousand stragglers for every true pioneer.

Whither the route of march will eventually lead us, that we do not know. But in the light of what has been achieved during the last four thousand years, there is no limit to the sum total of our potential achievements—unless we are tempted away from the path of normal development by our strange inherent cruelty which makes us treat other members of our own species as we would never have dared to treat a cow or a dog or even a tree.

The earth and the fullness thereof has been placed at the disposal of Man. Where it has not been placed at his disposal, he has taken possession by right of his superior brain and by the strength of his foresight and his shot-guns.

This home of ours is a good home. It grows food enough for all of us. It has abundant quarries and clay beds and forests from which all of us can be provided with more than ample shelter. The patient sheep of our pastures and the waving flax fields with their myriads of blue flowers, not to forget the industrious little silk-worm of China's mulberry trees—they all contribute to shelter our bodies against the cold of winter and protect them against the scorching heat of summer. This home of ours is a good home. It produces all these benefits in so abundant measure that every man, woman and child could have his or her share with a little extra supply thrown in for the inevitable days of rest.

But Nature has her own code of laws. They are just, these laws, but they are inexorable and there is no court of appeal.

Nature will give unto us and she will give without stint, but in return she demands that we study her precepts and abide by her dictates.

A hundred cows in a meadow meant for only fifty spells disaster—a bit of wisdom with which every farmer is thoroughly familiar. A million people gathered in one spot where there should be only a hundred thousand causes congestion, poverty and unnecessary suffering, a fact which apparently has been overlooked by those who are supposed to guide our destinies.

That, however, is not the most serious of our manifold errors. There is another way in which we offend our generous foster-mother. Man in the only living organism that is hostile to its own kind. Dog does not eat dog—tiger does not eat tiger —yea, even the loathsome hyena lives at peace with the members of his own species. But Man hates Man, Man kills Man, and in the world of today the prime concern of every nation is to prepare itself for the coming slaughter of some more of its neighbors.

This open violation of Article I of the great Code of Creation which insists upon peace and good will among the members of the same species has carried us to a point where soon the human race may be faced with the possibility of complete annihilation. For our enemies are ever on the alert. If Homo Sapiens (the all-too-flattering name given to our race by a cynical scientist, to denote our intellectual superiority over the rest of the animal world)—if Homo Sapiens is unable or unwilling to assert himself as the master of all he surveys, there are thousands of other candidates for the job and it ofttimes seems as if a world dominated by cats or dogs or elephants or some of the more highly organized insects (and how they watch their opportunity!) might offer very decided advantages over a planet top-heavy with battle-ships and siege-guns.

What is the answer and what is the way out of this hideous and shameful state of affairs?

In a humble way this little book hopes to point to the one and only way out of that lugubrious and disastrous blind-alley into which we have strayed through the clumsy ignorance of our ancestors.

It will take time, it will take hundreds of years of slow and painful education to make us find the true road of salvation. But that road leads towards the consciousness that we are all of us fellow-passengers on one and the same planet. Once we have got hold of this absolute verity—once we have realized and grasped the fact that for better or for worse this is our common home—that we have never known another place of abode—that we shall never be able to move from the spot in space upon which we happened to be born—that it therefore behooves us to behave as we would if we found ourselves on board a train or a steamer bound for an unknown destination—we shall have taken the first but most important step towards the solution of that terrible problem which is at the root of all our difficulties.

We are all of us fellow-passengers on the same planet and the weal and woe of everybody else means the weal and woe of ourselves!

Call me a dreamer and call me a fool—call me a visionary or call for the police or the ambulance to remove me to a spot where I can no longer proclaim such unwelcome heresies. But mark my words and remember them on that fatal day when the human race shall be requested to pack up its little toys and surrender the keys of happiness to a more worthy successor.

The only hope for survival lies in that one sentence:

WE ARE ALL OF US FELLOW-PASSENGERS ON THE SAME PLANET AND WE ARE ALL OF US EQUALLY RESPONSIBLE FOR THE HAPPINESS AND WELL-BEING OF THE WORLD IN WHICH WE HAPPEN TO LIVE.

II

A DEFINITION OF THE WORD GEOGRAPHY AND HOW I SHALL APPLY IT IN THE PRESENT VOLUME

BEFORE we start out upon a voyage, we usually try to find out more or less definitely whither we are bound and how we are supposed to get there. The reader who opens a book is entitled to a little information of the same sort and a short definition of the word "Geography" will therefore not be out of order.

I happen to have the "Concise Oxford Dictionary" on my desk and that will do as well as any other. The word I am looking for appears at the bottom of page 344, edition of 1912.

> "Geography: the science of the earth's surface, form, physical features, natural and political divisions, climate, productions and population."

I could not possibly hope to do better, but I shall stress some of the aspects of the case at the expense of others, because I intend to place man in the center of the stage. This book of mine will not merely discuss the surface of the earth and its physical features, together with its political and natural boundaries. I would rather call it a study of man in search of food and shelter and leisure for himself and for his family and an attempt to find out the way in which man has either adapted himself to his background or has reshaped his physical surroundings in order to be as comfortable and well nourished and happy as seemed compatible with his own limited strength.

It has been truly said that the Lord hath some very strange customers among those who love Him, and indeed we shall find our planet inhabited by a weird and extraordinary variety of

9

fellow-boarders. Many of them, upon first acquaintance, will appear to be possessed of very objectionable personal habits and of general characteristics which we would rather not encounter in our own children. But two billion human beings, even if they do not cut much of a figure when packed in a small wooden box, are still a very respectable number of people and among so many there is of course the widest possible scope for all sorts of experiments of an economic and social and cultural nature. It seems to me that those experiments deserve our attention before anything else. For a mountain is after all merely a mountain until

The Human Touch

it has been seen by human eyes and has been trod by human feet and until its slopes and valleys have been occupied and fought over and cultivated by a dozen generations of hungry settlers.

The Atlantic Ocean was just as wide and deep and as wet and salty before the beginning of the thirteenth century as after, but it took the human touch to make it what it is today—a bridge between the New World and the Old, the highway for the commerce between East and West.

For thousands of years the endless Russian plains lay ready to offer their abundant harvests to whomsoever should take the trouble to sow the first grain. But the aspect of that country today would be a very different one if the hand of a German or a Frank, rather than that of a Slav, had guided the iron-pointed stick that plowed the first furrows.

The islands of Nippon would shake and quake just as incessantly, whether they happened to be inhabited by aboriginal Japanese or by the remnants of the now defunct Tasmanian race, but in the latter case they would hardly be able to feed 60,000,000 people. While the British Isles, if they had been overrun by Neapolitans or Berbers instead of having been conquered by the restless fighters from northern Europe, would never have become the center of an empire one hundred and fifty times as large as the mother country and containing one-sixth of all the human beings now assembled on our planet.

Generally speaking, I have paid more attention to the purely "human" side of geography than to the commercial problems which are held to be of such great importance in a day and age devoted to mass production.

But experience has taught me that no matter how eloquent you wax upon the subject of importing and exporting, and the output of coal mines and oil reservoirs and bank deposits, you will never be able to tell your reader something which he can remember from one page to the next. Whenever he has need of such figures he will be obliged to look them up once more and verify them with the help of a dozen contradictory (and often self-contradictory) handbooks on commercial statistics.

Man comes first in this geography.

His physical environment and background come next.

The rest is given whatever space remains.

III

OUR PLANET: ITS HABITS, CUSTOMS AND MANNERS

LET us begin with an old and trusted definition. "The world is a small, dark object, entirely surrounded by space."

It is not a "sphere" or a ball but a "spheroid", which means first cousin to a sphere and consists of a ball slightly flattened at the poles. The so-called "poles" you can find for yourself by sticking a knitting needle through the center of an apple or an orange and holding the object straight in front of you. Where the knitting needle sticks out of the apple or the orange, there the poles are located, one in the middle of a deep sea (the North Pole) and the other on top of a high mountain plateau.

As for the "flatness" of the polar regions, which goes with the definition of a spheroid, it need not disturb you in the least. For the axis of the earth from pole to pole is only $\frac{1}{300}$ shorter than the diameter taken at the equator. In other words, if you were the proud possessor of a globe of three feet in diameter (and few globes that you can buy in our stores are as large as that —you would have to go to a museum to find one), the axis would be only $\frac{1}{8}$ of an inch shorter than the equatorial diameter, and it would hardly show unless the workmanship had been of exceptional fineness.

Nevertheless the fact is of considerable interest to explorers who are trying to find their way through the polar regions and to those who make a study of the higher forms of geography. But for the purposes of the present book it is sufficient that I have mentioned it. Your physics professor has probably one of those little contraptions in his laboratory that will show you how the poles could not help becoming flat as soon as our speck

13

of dust began to revolve around its own axis. Ask him to let you see it. That will save you a trip to the home of all the meridians.

The earth, as we all know, is a planet. We have inherited the word from the Greeks who had observed (or thought they had observed) that certain stars were forever moving across the skies while others apparently stood still. They therefore called the former "planets" or "wanderers" and the latter "fixed stars" because, having no telescopes, they could not follow them on their peregrinations. As for the word "star", we do not know its origin but it probably has something to do with a Sanskrit root which was in turn connected with the verb "to strew". If that be true the stars would then be the little flames "strewn" all over the heavens, a description which is quite pretty and fits the case admirably.

The earth turns around the sun and depends upon the sun for its light and heat. As the sun is more than seven hundred times as large as all the planets put together, and as the temperature of the sun near the surface is about 6000° Fahrenheit, the earth need not feel apologetic about borrowing her humble little portion of comfort from a neighbor who can so easily spare these few charitable rays and will never know the difference.

In the olden days the people believed that the earth was situated in the center of the universe, a small, flat disc of dry land entirely surrounded by the waters of the ocean and suspended in the air like the coffin of Mohammed or a toy balloon that has escaped the hand of a child. A few of the more enlightened Greek astronomers and mathematicians (the first people who dared to think for themselves without asking the permission of their priests) seem to have had a very definite suspicion that this theory must be wrong. After several centuries of very hard and very straight thinking, they came to the conclusion that the earth was not flat, but round, and that it did not hang quietly suspended in the air and in the exact center of the universe, but that it floated through space and was flying at a

Space

considerable rate of speed round a much larger object which was called the sun.

At the same time they suggested that those other shining little orbs which seemed to revolve around us against a common background of so-called "fixed stars" were merely our fellow-planets, children of the same mother-sun and subject to the identical laws of behavior which regulated our own daily conduct—such as getting up and going to bed at certain regular hours, and being obliged to follow a track which had been laid out for us at the day of our birth and from which we could not stray without running the risk of instant doom.

During the last two hundred years of the Roman Empire the thinking part of the population had accepted this hypothesis as something so self-evident that it could no longer be considered a subject for debate. But when the Church became all-powerful, shortly after the beginning of the fourth century, it was no longer safe to harbor such ideas, least of all that one which proclaimed the earth to be round. We should not judge them too harshly. In the first place the earliest converts to Christianity generally belonged to those classes of society that had been the least exposed to the current learning of the times. And furthermore they were firmly convinced that the end of the world was near at hand when Christ would return to the former scene of His sufferings to separate the good from the evil. He would return in the midst of all His glory and for every one to behold. But, so they reasoned, and quite correctly from their own point of view, if this were to be the case (and they had no doubt upon the subject) then the world must be flat. For otherwise Christ would have to make His re-appearance twice—once for the benefit of the people on the western hemisphere and once for the benefit of those on the other side of the world. Such a procedure, of course, would be absurd and undignified and therefore entirely out of the question.

The Church, therefore, for almost a thousand years insisted upon teaching once again that the earth was a flat disc and that it was the center of the universe. In learned circles, among the scientists of a few of the monasteries and among the astronomers of some of the rapidly growing cities, the old Greek conception of a round world, revolving around the sun together with a number of other planets, was never quite discarded. Only the men who held this to be true did not openly dare to talk about the subject, but kept their ideas strictly to themselves. For they knew that a public discussion would merely upset the peace and quiet of millions of their less intelligent fellow-citizens while it would do absolutely nothing to bring the solution of the problem any nearer.

Since then, the Church people too, with very few exceptions, have been forced to accept the notion that the planet on which we live must be a ball. By the end of the fifteenth century the evidence in favor of this ancient Greek theory had become too overwhelming to be refuted any longer. And it was and is based upon the following observations:

In the first place, there was the fact that when we approach a mountain or a ship at sea, we first of all notice the summit or the top of the mast and only very gradually, as we come nearer, are we able to see the rest of the object under observation.

In the second place, no matter where we are, the scene all around us appears to be a circle. Our eyes therefore must be equally removed from every part of the land or sea under observation and the further we get away from the surface of the earth in a balloon or on top of a tower, the larger that circle gets. If the earth happened to be egg-shaped, we would find ourselves in the middle of a large oval. If it were a square or a triangle, the horizon would be a square or a triangle too.

In the third place, when a partial eclipse of the moon takes place, the shadow of the earth on the moon is a circle and only a ball will cause a circular shadow.

In the fourth place, the other planets and stars too are spheres and why should we alone among so many billions be an exception?

In the fifth place, when the ships of Magellan had sailed long enough in a westerly direction, they finally returned to the

Only round objects give round shadows

place from which they had left and when Captain Cook did the same thing, going from west to east, the survivors of his expedition also came back to the port from which they had sailed.

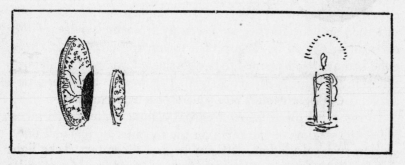

Eclipse

And finally, when we travel northward towards the poles, the familiar constellations of the stars (the signs of the Zodiac of the ancients) disappear lower and lower below the horizon, but they arise again and come higher and higher, the nearer we return to the equator.

I hope that I have brought forward enough undisputable facts to prove that the planet on which we happen to live must be round. But should the evidence be insufficient to satisfy you, go to any reliable professor of physics. He will take one of those stones that are forever falling from high towers and he will let it do tricks with the law of gravity which prove beyond the shadow of a doubt that the earth must be a sphere. If he uses very simple words and does not talk too fast, you may be able to understand him, but only if you know a great deal more about mathematics and physics than I do.

Here I could indulge in a great many very learned statistics, none of which however would be of the slightest use to you. The average mind (the author's mind included) is simply not fit to

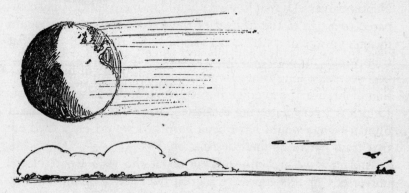

Our speed through space is much faster than that of the fastest cannon-ball

follow such calculations with any degree of comfort. Take light for example. Light travels at the rate of speed of 186,000 miles per second. It goes seven times around the earth while you snap your fingers once. And yet the light from the nearest of the fixed stars (Alpha Centauri, if you want the correct address) must travel four and one-third years at the rate of 186,000 miles per

second ere it strikes our eyes. The sun can reach us in eight minutes and Jupiter in three minutes, but the Polar Star, which
plays such an important role in the science of navigation, would
need forty years to send us a single ray of light.

Alas, most of us get slightly dizzy when we are asked to
"imagine" such a distance, and the very idea of a light-year, or
the distance covered by a ray of light in a single year, or
$365 \times 24 \times 60 \times 60 \times 186,000$ miles becomes something so
enormous that as a rule we say "Oh, yes", and then go out and
play with the cat or turn on the radio.

But all of us are familiar with railroad trains. Let us try it
that way:

An ordinary passenger train, going day and night without
stops, would need five-sevenths of a year to reach the moon.
But if it started today it would not get to the sun until A. D. 2232.
It would need 8,300 years to get to the suburbs where the planet
Neptune lives. All that however would be mere child's play compared to a trip to the nearest of the fixed stars, for that would
mean a voyage of 75,000,000 years. As for the Polar Star, that
train would need 700,000,000 years to get there and 700,000,-
000 years is a long time, a very long time. If we put the dura-
tion of life for the average human being at about seventy years
(which is a very flattering estimate), 10,000,000 generations of
human beings would have been born and would have died ere
that train got to its final destination.

And now we are only talking about the visible part of the
universe. Our telescopes are a great deal better than the funny
little contraptions with which the contemporaries of Galileo
searched the sky and incidentally made some of the most remarkable discoveries. Even so, they are still very imperfect and
until we improve our lenses a thousand-fold we shall not make
much headway. Therefore, when we talk about the universe,
what we really mean is "that small part of the universe which
is visible and which has come under our own personal observation or under the observation of those sensitive photographic
plates which are substituted nowadays for the human eye". As

Those few specks—and that is all we know of our universe

for the rest of the universe, the still invisible part, alas, we know nothing about it. And what is worse, we dare not even guess.

Among all these millions of stars, fixed and otherwise, which are our more immediate neighbors, there are only two which influence our own existence in a very direct and noticeable fashion, and those two are the sun and the moon. The sun, because once every twenty-four hours she provides one-half of our planet with heat and light. And the moon, because she is near enough to us to influence the behavior of the ocean and to cause that strange aquatic phenomenon which we know as the "tides".

The moon is really quite near to us. Therefore, although it is much smaller than the sun (if we represent the sun by our familiar out-sized globe of three feet diameter, the earth would be a green pea and the moon the mere point of a pin) the moon has a much stronger "pull" on the surface of the earth than the sun.

If the earth consisted entirely of solid matter, that pull of the moon would hardly make itself felt. But three-fourths of the surface of the earth consists of water and that water follows the moon on its peregrination across the earth, just as iron filings spread out across a piece of paper will follow the toy magnet you pass across the table.

All day and all night long a broad strip of water, several

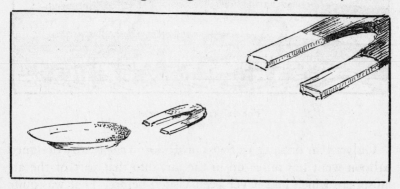

The Tides

hundred miles wide, is following in the wake of the moonlight. When it enters bays and harbors and the mouths of rivers and becomes greatly condensed, it causes the tides of twenty or thirty or forty feet difference which make navigation in those waters such a very difficult feat. When the sun and the moon happen to be on the same side of the earth, the pull is of course much stronger than when the moon is there alone, and then we get a so-called "spring-tide"; and a spring-tide in many parts of the world is something very much akin to a small inundation.

The earth is entirely surrounded by a layer of nitrogen and oxygen which we call the atmosphere or the "air". This layer is supposed to be about 300 miles thick and it turns around together with the earth just as the skin of an orange turns around with the inside of the orange which it protects.

The layers of atmosphere

Only a year or so ago a Swiss professor in a specially designed balloon went ten miles up in the air, into that part of the atmosphere which had never been visited before. That was quite a feat, but 290 miles still remain to be explored.

Earthquakes

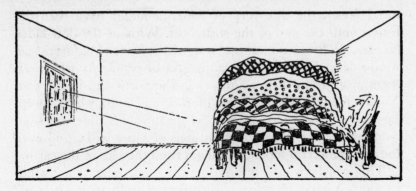

They keep us warm like so many blankets

The atmosphere, together with the surface of the earth and the sea, is the laboratory in which all our different sorts of weather, our winds and our rainstorms and blizzards and our dry periods, are manufactured. As these influence our happiness and well-being every hour of our lives, we ought to discuss them here in considerable detail.

The three factors which make our climate what it is (but rarely, alas, what it should be) are the temperature of the soil, the prevailing wind and the amount of moisture which is present in the air. Originally "climate" meant the "slope of the earth". For the Greeks had noticed that as the surface of the earth "sloped" further and further towards the poles, both the temperature and the humidity of the spots they visited also changed, and in that way "climate" came to mean the atmospheric condition of any given region rather than its exact geographic position.

Today when we speak of the "climate" of a country, we mean the average weather conditions which prevail there during the different parts of the year and it is in that sense that I shall use the word.

First of all let me say something about those mysterious winds which have played such a great role in the civilization of mankind. For without the regular "trade-winds" of the equatorial ocean, the discovery of America might have been deferred until the age of the steamboat. Without the dew-laden breezes, California and the countries of the Mediterranean would never have reached that degree of prosperity which sets them apart from their neighbors in the north and in the east. Not to mention the particles of rock and sand which, swept forward by the wind, will act as gigantic, invisible sheets of sand-paper, and which after millions of years will grind even the most powerful mountain ranges from the face of the earth.

This word "wind" means literally something that "winds its way". A wind, therefore, is a current of air "winding its way" from one place to another. But why does a current of air wind its way from one place to another? Because some of the air is usually warmer than the rest and therefore lighter and has a tendency to rise as high as it can go. When that happens, there is a vacuum. The cold air, being heavier, rushes into that vacuum, because, as the Greeks had already discovered two thousand years ago, "Nature abhors a vacuum", and air is just as much of a vacuum-hater as water or the human race.

We know of course how we can produce hot air in any given room—by the simple expedient of lighting a fire. Among the planets the sun is the stove and the planets are the rooms which are to be heated. The greatest amount of heat will of course be nearest to the stove (along the equator) and the smallest amount of heat will be found furthest removed from the stove (near the North and South Poles).

Now a stove causes a considerable commotion in the air—a circular commotion. The hot air will rise towards the ceiling. As soon as it gets there, it will be further removed from the original source of heat than it was before, and as a result it will begin to cool off. The cooling process will cause it to lose its lightness and to fall back towards the earth. But as soon as it gets a little lower, it will once more get in touch with the stove. Once more it will grow warmer and lighter and once more it will begin to rise. And so on and so forth, until the stove goes out. But then the walls of the room, which have absorbed considerable heat while

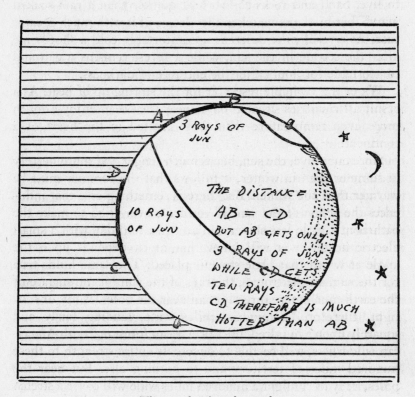

The sun heating the earth

the stove was burning, will keep the room warm for a shorter or longer time, depending upon the material of which they are made.

These walls may be compared to the soil on which we happen to live. Sand and rocks absorb heat quicker than a rain-soaked marsh, but by the same token they let go of it with much greater ease. As a result, the desert is uncomfortably cold a short time after the setting of the sun, while a forest remains warm and comfortable for hours after the entrance of darkness.

Water is a veritable reservoir for the storing up of heat. As a result all countries situated on or near the ocean enjoy a much more even temperature than those located in the heart of a continent.

Since our stove, the sun, burns much longer and more fiercely in summer than in winter, it follows that the summer must be warmer than the winter. But there is something else that influences the action of the sun. If you have ever tried to make the bathroom a little less shivery on an extra cold day with a small electric heater, you will know that much depends upon the angle at which that little stove is placed. The same holds true for the sun. In the tropics, the rays of the sun hit the surface of the earth much more directly than near the poles. A ray of sunlight, therefore, a hundred miles wide, landing fairly and squarely upon a hundred miles of African forest or South American wilderness, will be able to devote its entire strength to these hundred miles of territory and to nothing else. But near the poles, a ray of sunlight a hundred miles wide will cover a stretch of land or ice that is twice as wide (as the picture will show you much more easily than a thousand words could hope to do), and the heating power of those hundred miles of sunlight near the poles will therefore be cut exactly in half, just as an oil-burner which is supposed to keep a six-room apartment at a comfortable temperature will prove a failure when called upon to perform a similar service for a twelve-room flat.

What makes the job of our celestial stove even more complicated is the fact that the sun must also keep the atmosphere

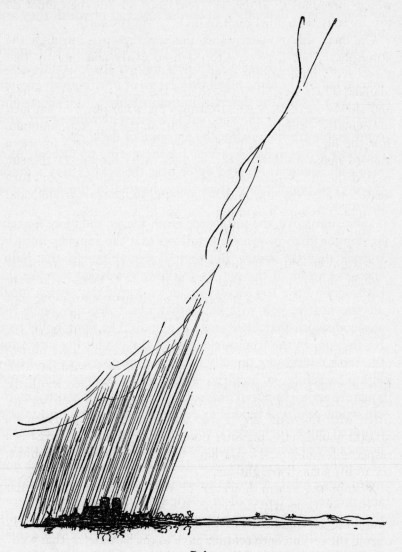

Rain

which surrounds us at an even temperature. But she cannot do this directly. She must do it indirectly, via the earth.

On their way to our planet the sun rays pass through the atmosphere, but they pass through so easily and quickly that they hardly influence the temperature of that faithful terrestrial blanket. Then they hit the earth and the earth stores up the heat and slowly surrenders part of it into the atmosphere. That fact, incidentally, explains why it is so cold on the top of a mountain. For the higher we get, the less the heat of the earth has been able to make itself felt. If (as used to be supposed) the sun heated the atmosphere directly and the atmosphere in its turn heated the earth, it would be just the other way around and our mountain tops would not be covered with snow.

And now we come to the most difficult part of the problem. Air is not just "air" in our sense of the word. It has both substance and weight. The lower layers of air therefore are under a much higher pressure than the higher ones. When you want to flatten out a leaf or a flower you put it between the pages of a book and then put twenty other volumes on top of it because you know that the pressure will be greatest in the book that is at the bottom of the pile. The pressure under which we human beings live is considerably more than most of us suspect. It is fifteen pounds per square inch. That means that we would be crushed flat except for the fortunate circumstance that we are filled with the same air as that which surrounds us. Even so, 30,000 pounds (the pressure upon a body of average size) is a respectable amount. If you have any doubts upon the subject, try to lift a small freight-car.

Within the realm however of the atmosphere itself that pressure is constantly changing. We know this through the invention of Evangelista Torricelli, a pupil of Galileo, who early during the seventeenth century gave us the barometer, that well-known instrument by which we are able to measure the pressure of the air at any time of day or night.

As soon as the first of these Torricellian tubes had been placed upon the market, people began to experiment with them. They noticed that the pressure fell by about an inch for every 900 feet one ascended above sea-level. Then followed another discovery which did so much to make meteorology, the study of atmospheric phenomena, such a reliable science in forecasting the weather.

Certain physicists and geographers began to suspect that there was a definite connection between the pressure of the air and the direction of the prevailing winds or vice versa. But in order to establish some irrefutable law regulating the behavior of all air-currents, it was first of all necessary to spend several centuries collecting the data from which to draw a few definite conclu-

Rainstorms after all are only local affairs

sions. When this had been done, it was shown that certain parts of the world enjoyed an air pressure well above that of the mean sea-level, while others had pressures far below the mean sea-level. The first of these were then called high-pressure areas and the second low-pressure areas. Next it was definitely established that winds would always tend to blow from high-pressure areas to low-pressure areas and that the velocity and strength of the wind would depend upon the highness of the high-pressure area and the lowness of the low-pressure area. And when the high-pressure was very high and the low-pressure was very low, then we would have a very violent wind—a storm, a cyclone or a hurricane.

The winds not only keep our living quarters, the earth, decently ventilated, but they also play a great role in the distribution of that rain without which a normal development of plant life and animal life would be completely impossible.

Rain is merely evaporated water from the oceans and from the inland seas and from the inland snow-fields, which is carried along by the air in the form of vapor. As hot air can hold much more vapor than cold air, the water-vapor will be carried along without much difficulty until the air grows colder. Then part of it gets condensed and falls back again upon the surface of the earth in the form of rain or hail or snow.

The rainfall of any given region therefore will depend almost entirely upon the winds to which it is exposed. If we have a sea-coast separated from the mainland by mountains (a very common occurrence) the coastal region will be wet and damp. For the wind, being forced to rise into higher regions (where the pressure is lower), will cool off as it gets further and further away from the sea-level and it will shed its vapor in the form of rain and snow and will reappear on the other side of the mountain range as a dry wind without a drop of moisture.

The rainfall of the tropics is both regular and abundant because the enormous heat of the land makes the air rise to a great height, where it gets cooled off and is obliged to let go of most of its vapor, which thereupon returns to earth in the form of heavy sheets of rain. But as the sun does not always stand right over the equator, but moves slightly from north to south, most of the equatorial regions enjoy four seasons, two seasons during which there are terrific rainstorms and two seasons during which the weather is dry.

But those regions which are exposed to steady air-currents running from colder to warmer regions are by far the worst off. For as the winds pass from the cold area to the hot one, their capacity for absorption becomes steadily greater and they are unable to release the vapor they carry, causing many parts of this earth to be turned into deserts where it may not rain more than once or twice every ten years.

So much for the general subject of wind and rain. A detailed discussion will follow when we describe each individual country.

And now a few words about the earth itself, and about that thin crust of hardened rock on which we live.

There are a great many theories about the true inner nature of our planet, but our definite knowledge upon the subject is still exceedingly vague.

Let us be honest. How high have we ever been up in the air or how low down into the bowels of the earth?

On a globe of three feet in diameter, the highest mountain in the world, Mt. Everest, would show about as thick as a thin piece of tissue paper and the deepest hole in the ocean, just east of the Philippine Islands, would be represented by a dent of the size and shape of a postage stamp. Well, we have never yet descended to the bottom of the ocean and we have never yet climbed Mt. Everest. We have been a little higher than the top of this Himalayan giant in balloons and flying machines, but when all is said and done, even after the recent successful flight of the Swiss Professor Piccard, $^{29}/_{30}$ of the atmosphere still remain to be explored. As for the water, we have never yet descended below $^{1}/_{40}$ of the total depth of the Pacific Ocean, and incidentally, the depth of the deepest sea is greater than the height of the highest mountain. Why this should be we do

The crust of the earth is as full of holes as a sponge

not know, but if we dumped the highest mountains of the different continents into the deepest part of the ocean, the tops of Mt. Everest and Aconcagua would still be several thousand feet below the surface of the sea.

In the light of our present-day knowledge however these puzzling facts prove nothing at all about the origin and the subsequent development of the crust of the earth. Neither (as our grandfathers so fondly hoped) need we turn to our vol- canoes for an answer about the true inner nature of our planet, for we have come to realize that those are not outlets for the hot substance that is supposed to fill the interior of the earth. If the comparison were not quite so unsavory, I would like to compare them to boils on the skin of the earth, nasty afflictions but purely local affairs which never penetrate very deep into the body of the patient.

In round numbers there are still some 320 active volcanoes left. There used to be 400 others on the active list, but these have since been retired and pensioned off with the rank of ordinary or common mountains.

The great majority of all these volcanoes are situated near the sea-coast. Indeed, the most restless part of the world's crust, Japan (where the seismograph shows a slight volcanic disturbance four times every day or 1,447 times a year) is an island, and so were Martinique and Krakatoa, the most tragic victims of recent volcanic outbursts.

In view of the close proximity of sea to volcano, it was quite

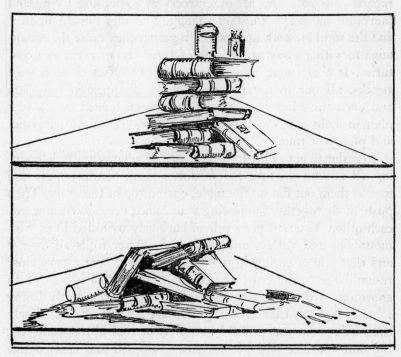

Why not make your own earthquakes?

natural that people should have tried to explain all volcanic eruptions as the result of water seeping into the inner part of the earth, thereby causing a sort of gigantic boiler explosion with the well-known disastrous results of an overflow of lava and steam and what have you. But since then we have discovered several very busy volcanoes hundreds of miles away from the sea, and that theory too has therefore come to naught. Ask me again about all this two centuries hence for at the present moment we can only shake our heads and repeat, "We do not know."

Meanwhile, what about the surface of the earth itself? We used to talk so glibly about the rock of ages that would forever defy the changes of time. Modern science is less confident and regards this rock and all other rocks as something living and therefore subject to constant change. The rain raineth upon it and the wind bloweth upon it and together they cause the mountains to wither away at the rate of three inches every ten centuries. If there were no counter-moves to offset these erosive attacks, all our mountains would have disappeared long ago and even the Himalayas would have been turned into a vast plain in about 116,000,000 years. But there are counter-activities and plenty of them.

In order to get at least a vague idea of what is really happening all around us, take half a dozen clean handkerchiefs and spread them out flat on the table, one on top of the other. Then push all six together by moving your hands very slowly towards each other. You will get a pile of curiously wrinkled linen with mountains and valleys and folds and counter-folds all over it and that pile of curiously wrinkled linen will bear a very close resemblance to the crust of the earth. That crust is part of an enormous structure racing through space and constantly losing some of its heat. Like all things that are cooling off, it is slowly contracting. As you probably know, when an object contracts, the outer surface will get curiously rumpled and creased like a couple of handkerchiefs being pushed together.

The best guess at the present moment (but remember that it

The Rise and Fall of All Mountains

is only a guess) tells us that the diameter of the earth has shrunk some thirty miles since the beginning of our independent existence as a planet. That does not seem very much when you think of it as a straight line. But remember the tremendous scope of the curved planes with which we are dealing. The surface of the world is 196,950,000 square miles. A sudden change of only a few yards in diameter would be enough to cause a catastrophe which none of us would survive.

Nature therefore works very slowly her wonders to perform. She insists upon maintaining a proper balance in everything she does. When she allows one sea to run dry (our own Salt Lake is rapidly dwindling away, the Lake of Constance in Switzerland will be gone in another 100,000 years) she starts another one in some other part of the world; and when she permits certain mountain-ranges to disappear (the Alps in central Europe will be as flat as our prairies in another 60,000,000 years) then another part of the crust in a totally different corner of the globe is slowly being reshaped and wrinkled into a fresh mountain-range. That, at least, we believe to be the case, although as a rule the process is by far too slow and gradual to allow us to make any concrete observations of the changes that are taking place.

There is however an exception to this general rule. When left to herself, Nature is in no particular hurry. But when aided and abetted by man, she sometimes proves herself an uncomfortably fast worker. And ever since man became truly civilized and invented his little steam-engines and his little sticks of dynamite, the surface of the earth has been transformed so rapidly that our great-grandparents would hardly recognize their own pastures and gardens, were they to come back to us for a little holiday. Our greed for timber and the ruthlessness with which we have denuded whole mountain-ranges of their blanket of forests and shrubs have turned vast regions into primeval wildernesses. For as soon as the forests were gone, that fertile soil which for so many years had faithfully clung to the rocky surface of the hill-sides was brutally washed away and the barren slopes became a menace to the surrounding country-side. The rain was then no longer held captive by the turf and by the roots of the trees, but was able to rush down towards the plains in torrents and cataracts, destroying everything it met on its way towards the valleys and plains.

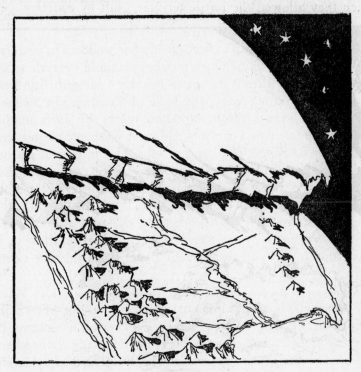

The Glaciers in America

And this unfortunately is not said in a flight of high rhetorical exaggeration. We don't have to go back to the glacial periods when, for reasons as yet unexplained, the whole of northern Europe and northern America lay buried beneath a heavy blanket of ice and snow which dug such dangerous grooves through entire mountain-ranges. We need only go as far back as the era of the Romans, who were first-rate exploiters (weren't they the

"practical men" of antiquity?) and who in less than five generations completely changed the climate of their own peninsula by
the senseless destruction of everything that had thus far helped
to make Italy a country of well-balanced and even temperature.
And what the Spaniards did to the mountains of South America,
when they allowed the fertile terraces, built by countless gen-

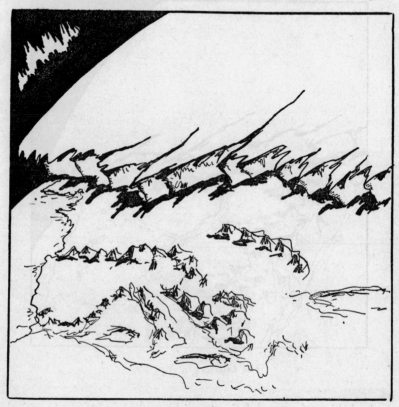

The Glaciers in Europe

erations of patient little Indians, to go to ruin, is a fact of such
recent occurrence as to need no further elucidation.

Of course that was the easiest way to deprive the natives of
their livelihood and reduce them to obedience by way of starva-

50,000,000 B. C. and A. D. 1932

tion—just as the extinction of the buffaloes by our own government was the most practical method of turning fierce warriors
into dirty, slovenly reservation-parishioners. But these cruel
and senseless measures carried their own punishment with them,
as any one familiar with our plains or the Andes will tell you.

Fortunately this is one of the few problems of practical
geographical importance which has at last penetrated to the
consciousness of those who sit in the seats of the mighty. No government today would any longer tolerate such scandalous interference with the soil upon which all of us depend for our well-
being. We have no control over the cosmic changes which take
place in the crust of our planet. But to a certain extent we can
control a vast number of details which make for a greater or
smaller rainfall in any given territory and which will prevent
fertile regions from being turned into howling deserts. We
may not know anything about the inside of this earth, but we
have at least learned a great many things about the outside. And
every day we add to the sum total of this useful bit of information and use it wisely for the benefit of all.

But I regret to say that we have no such control over the
greater part of the earth's surface—that part which we call the
oceans and the seas. Almost three-quarters of our globe are
uninhabitable because they are covered by a layer of water,
differing in depth from a couple of feet (near the shore) to
almost 35,000 feet in the famous "deep hole" just east of the
Philippines.

This layer of water can be roughly divided into three main
parts. The most important of these is the Pacific Ocean which
covers 68,500,000 square miles. The Atlantic Ocean covers 41,-
000,000 square miles and the Indian Ocean 29,000,000. Inland
seas account for another 2,000,000 square miles, while lakes
and rivers take up about 1,000,000 square miles of their own.
All this submerged territory was and is and always will remain
lost to us as a place of residence, unless we are able to redevelop
those gills which our ancestors of a few million years ago pos-

If we dumped the highest mountains of the world into the deepest part of the ocean (34,210 feet) situated between the Philippines and Japan, even Mount Everest would be more than 5,000 feet under water and the others in proportion. They are: 1–Everest (29,141). 2–Kinchinjinga, also in Asia near Nepal (28,225). 3–Aconcagua in the Argentine (22,834). 4–Chimborazo in Ecuador (20,702). 5–McKinley in Alaska (20,300), the highest mountain in North America. 6–Kilimanjaro in Africa (19,710). 7–Logan in Canada (19,850). 8–Elbruz in the Caucasus (18,465), the highest mountain in Europe. 9–Popocatepetl in Mexico (17,543). 10–Ararat in Armenia (17,090), the mountain on which Noah's ark stranded. 11–Mont Blanc in the French Alps (15,781). 12–Fujiyama in Japan (12,395). (Incidentally, there are twelve more mountains in the Himalayas which are higher than Aconcagua, but I do not mention them here because no one has ever heard of them.)

The highest spot on which human beings live all the year is the village of Gartok (13) in Tibet (14,518). The highest lake is Titicaca (14) in Peru (12,545). The highest cities are (15) Quito (9,343) and (16) Bogota (8,563) in South America. The cloister of the Saint Bernard Pass (17) in Switzerland is the highest spot where people live all the year around in Europe (8,111) while Mexico City (18) is the highest town in North America (7,415). Finally there is the Dead Sea (19) in Palestine, which is 1,290 feet below sea-level.

If the highest mountains should get dumped into the
deepest part of the ocean!

sessed and of which we still show the traces on the day of our birth.

This abundant supply of water may at first seem a complete waste of perfectly good territory and it may make us regret that our planet is as wet as it happens to be. For when we remember that 5,000,000 square miles of the land that is at our disposal are desert and that 19,000,000 square miles are steppes or plains of the semi-useless Siberian variety, while a considerable number of other millions of square miles are uninhabitable because they are either too high for us to live in (like the Himalayas and the Alps) or too cold (like the territory around the North and South Poles) or too wet (like the swamps of South America) or too densely covered with forests (like the forests of central Africa) and must therefore be deducted from the 57,-510,000 square miles that are listed as "land", we feel that we could make excellent use of a few more miles of added territory.

But it is extremely doubtful whether we could exist at all if it were not for this vast reservoir of heat, which we call the sea. The geological remnants of prehistoric times show us conclusively that there have been times when there was more land and less water than today, but invariably these were periods of intense cold. The present balance of 1 : 4 between water and land is an ideal one if our present climate is to continue indefinitely, and we shall all of us be much better off if it does not get disturbed.

This vast ocean which encircles the entire globe (in this respect the ancients had guessed right) is, like the solid crust of the earth, in constant motion. The moon and the sun, through their power of gravity, attract it and cause it to rise to a considerable height. Then there is the heat of the day which takes part of it away in the form of vapor. The cold of the polar regions covers it with ice. But from a practical point of view as something directly affecting our own well-being, the air-currents or winds must be accorded first rank for their influence upon the surface of the ocean.

When you blow long enough on your plate of soup, you will notice that the soup begins to move in the direction away from

The Gulf Stream

your mouth. When certain air-currents hit the surface of the ocean for years and years in succession, they will cause "drifts" which will move in a direction away from that particular current. Whenever there are a number of air-currents blowing from different directions, these different "drifts" will neutralize each other. But when the winds are steady, as they are for example on both sides of the equator, the drifts become veritable currents and these currents have played a very important role in the history of the human race and in making certain parts of the world inhabitable which otherwise would be as cold as Greenland's icy shores.

A map of these ocean rivers (for that is what many of those

Hundreds of millions of years ago the continents seem
to have been very different from today

currents really are) will show you where they are located. The Pacific Ocean has a number of such currents. The most important of these, as important in its way as the Gulf Stream of the Atlantic, is the Japan current or Kuro Siwo (which means the Blue Salt Current) which is caused by the north-east trade-winds. After having done its duty by Japan, it crosses the northern Pacific and bestows its blessings upon Alaska, which it keeps from being too cold for human habitation, and then, turning sharply towards the south, gives California its agreeable climate.

But when we speak of ocean currents, we think first of all of the Gulf Stream, that mysterious river, some fifty miles wide and 2000 feet deep, which for untold centuries has kept the northern part of Europe well supplied with the tropical heat of the Gulf of Mexico and which accounts for the fertility of England, Ireland and all the North Sea countries.

The Gulf Stream has an interesting career of its own. It begins with the famous North Atlantic Eddy, a drift rather than a current, which like a gigantic maelstrom turns around and around in the central part of the Atlantic and enfolds within itself that pool of semi-stagnant water which has become the home of billions of little fishes and floating plants and which, as the Sargasso or "Sea-Weed Sea", played a most important part in the history of early navigation. For once the trade-winds (the eastern winds that blew just north of the tropics) had blown your ship into the Sargasso Sea, you were lost. At least, that is what the sailors of the Middle Ages firmly believed. Your vessel would find itself caught by miles and miles of solid sea-weed and every one on board would slowly perish through hunger and thirst, while the ghastly wreck would remain forever bobbing up and down beneath the cloudless sky as a silent warning to others who might be tempted to defy the Gods.

When finally Columbus sailed placidly through the heart of this dullish stretch of water, it was shown that the fairy story about miles and miles of solid sea-weed had been grossly exaggerated. But even today there is something mysterious and uncanny to most people in that name, Sargasso Sea. It sounds medieval. It smacks of one of Dante's infernal circles. Actually, however, it is no more exciting than the swan-pond in Central Park.

But to return to the Gulf Stream. Part of the North Atlantic Eddy finally finds its way into the Caribbean Sea. There it is joined by a current that moves westward from the coast of Africa. These two currents, in addition to its own water, are too much for the Caribbean Sea. Like a cup that has been poured too full, it flows over into the Gulf of Mexico.

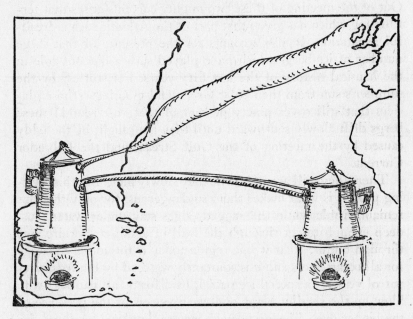

The gulf stream in your kitchen

The Gulf of Mexico has not got room for all this additional humidity and, using the straits between Florida and Cuba as a spigot, it pours forth a broad stream of hot water (80° Fahrenheit) which thereupon is called the Gulf Stream. When the Gulf Stream leaves the spigot, it flows at the rate of five miles an hour, which is one of the reasons why the old sailing vessels gave it a wide berth whenever they could and preferred to make a lengthy detour rather than try to navigate against a current which so severely delayed their own progress.

From the Gulf of Mexico the Gulf Stream moves up northward, following the American coast until finally it is deflected by the shape of the eastern shore, when it begins its voyage across the north Atlantic. Just off the Grand Banks of Newfoundland it meets its own offspring, the so-called Labrador Current, which, coming fresh from the glacial regions of Greenland, is as cold and uninviting as the Gulf Stream is warm and hospitable. Out of the meeting of these two mighty currents arises that terrible fog which has given that part of the Atlantic such a dreadful reputation. It also accounts for the presence of that large number of ice-bergs which have played such a hideous role in the nautical history of the last fifty years. For, cut off by the summer's sun from their solid Greenland moorings (those glaciers that still cover ninety percent of that vast island) these bergs drift slowly southward until they are caught by the eddy caused by the meeting of the Gulf Stream and the Labrador Current.

There they mill around while they slowly melt. But this melting process is what makes them so dangerous, for only the tops remain visible while the ragged edges stay under water, just deep enough to cut through the hull of a ship as a knife cuts through butter. That whole region today is forbidden territory for all ocean liners and it is constantly watched by United States patrol vessels (a special ice patrol, paid for by all nations) who blow up the smaller bergs and warn vessels of the presence of the bigger ones. Fishing boats, however, love this territory, for fishes who were born in the Arctic and were therefore accustomed to the cold temperature of the Labrador Current feel very unhappy in the tepid water of the Gulf Stream. While they are slowly making up their minds whether to go back to the Pole or try to swim across the warm Gulf Stream, they are caught by the nets of those French fishermen whose ancestors patronized the legendary Grand Banks of America hundreds of years before any one else. The two little islands of St. Pierre

Neighbors

and Miquelon, off the Canadian coast, are not only the last remaining remnants of that vast French empire which two centuries ago covered the greater part of the North American continent. They also bear silent witness to the courage of the Normandy fishermen who had visited our shores at least a hundred and fifty years before Columbus was born.

As for the Gulf Stream, after leaving the so-called Cold Wall (produced by the difference in temperature between the Gulf Stream and the Labrador Current) well to the north, it then leisurely moves across the Atlantic Ocean and spreads fan-wise over the coast of western Europe. It touches Spain and Portugal and France and England and Ireland and Holland and Belgium and Denmark and the Scandinavian peninsula, and bestows upon all these countries a much milder temperature than they would otherwise enjoy. Having thus done its duty by humanity, this strange current, carrying more water than all the rivers of the world combined, withdraws discreetly into the Arctic Sea. This sea thereupon finds itself so full of aquatic substance that it must find relief by sending out a current of its own, that Greenland Current which in turn is responsible for that Labrador Current I have just described.

It is a fascinating story.

It is such a fascinating story that I am sorely tempted to give by far too much space to this chapter alone. But that I must not do.

This chapter can only be a background—a general background of meteorology and oceanography and astronomy against which the actors in our play shall shortly act their part.

Now let us drop the curtain for a second.

When it rises, the stage is set for a new act.

That act will show you how men learned to find their way across those mountains and seas and deserts that had to be conquered ere we could truly call this world our home.

The curtain rises again.

Act II: Maps and methods of navigation.

IV

MAPS. A VERY BRIEF CHAPTER UPON A VERY BIG AND FASCI-
NATING SUBJECT. TOGETHER WITH A FEW OBSERVA-
TIONS ON THE WAY PEOPLE SLOWLY LEARNED
HOW TO FIND THEIR WAY ON THIS
PLANET OF OURS

WE ARE SO accustomed to maps that it is almost impossible
for us to imagine a time when there were no maps, when the
notion of travelling according to a map was as foreign to man's
conception of ultimate possibilities as the idea of traversing space
in the form of a mathematical formula would be to us today.

The ancient Babylonians, who were such excellent geome-
trists that they could make a cadastral survey of their entire
kingdom (that survey was made in 3800 B. C., or 2400 years
before Moses was born), have left us a few clay tablets containing what must have been an outline of their domains, but
these were hardly maps in our sense of the word. The Egyptians,
in order to get every penny of taxes they could sweat out of their
hard-working subjects, also made a survey of their kingdom,
which showed that they knew enough about practical mathematics to perform this difficult task. But no maps in the modern
sense of the word have so far been found in any of the royal
sepulchres.

The Greeks, the most curious-minded and nosey people of the
ancient world, wrote endless treatises upon the subject of geography, but we know next to nothing about their maps. Here and
there in some great commercial center there seem to have been
engraved bronze tablets showing the best route to be followed
if a merchant wanted to get from one part of the eastern Mediterranean to another. But none of these tablets has ever been

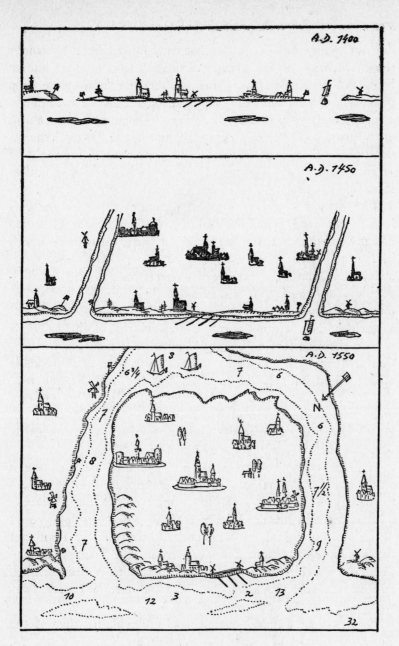

How Maps became Maps

dug up and we have no idea what they looked like. Alexander the Great, who covered greater distances than any other human being before him and very many after him, must have been possessed of a certain "geographical sense", for he maintained a special body of professional "pacers"—men who went ahead of the army and kept an accurate account of the distances the indefatigable Macedonians wandered on their search for the gold of India. But of regular maps, which would have been understandable to ourselves, not a vestige, not a scrap, not a line.

The Romans, who in quest of plunder (the most marvellously organized "systematic plunderers" of which the world has any account until the beginning of the great colonial epoch in Europe) went everywhere, lived everywhere, built roads everywhere, gathered taxes everywhere, hanged and crucified people everywhere, left the ruins of their temples and swimming-pools everywhere, seem to have been able to administer a world-empire without a single map worthy of the name. It is true their writers and orators quite frequently make mention of their maps and assure us that these were of remarkable accuracy and entirely dependable. But the only Roman map that has come down to us (if we except a small and insignificant piece of an ancient plan of Rome in the second century of our era) is something so primitive and clumsy that it is of no earthly value to modern man except as a historical curiosity.

It is known to historians as the Peutinger map because it was a man by the name of Conrad Peutinger, the town clerk to the city of Augsburg, who first conceived the idea of having it broadcasted by means of the recently invented printing-presses of Johann Gutenberg of Strassburg. Unfortunately Peutinger did not have the original to work from. The manuscript map he used was a thirteenth-century copy of a third-century original and during those thousand years, rats and mice had made away with a great many important details.

Even so, the general outline was undoubtedly that of the Roman original and if that was the best the Romans could do, they still had a great deal to learn. I will draw a copy of it here and let you judge for yourself. After a long and patient study of the document you will slowly begin to recognize what was in the mind of the Roman geographers. But you will also recognize that we have made enormous progress since the days when this spaghetti-shaped "world" was the last word in travel literature for a Roman general bound for England or the Black Sea.

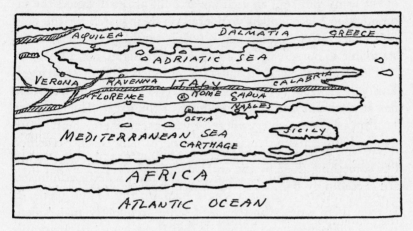

A Roman Map

As for the maps of the Middle Ages, we can pass them by without any special comment. The Church frowned upon all "useless scientific pursuits". The road to Heaven was more important than the shortest route from the mouth of the Rhine to the mouth of the Danube, and maps became mere funny pictures, full of headless monsters (the poor Eskimos, huddled in their furs until their heads were no longer visible, were the originals for this fanciful notion) and snorting unicorns and spouting whales and hippogrifs and krakens and mermaids and griffons and all the other denizens of a world bewildered by fear and superstition. Jerusalem was of course shown as the center of the world, and India and Spain were the ultimate limits, beyond which no man could hope to travel, and Scotland was a separate island, and the Tower of Babel was ten times as big as the entire city of Paris.

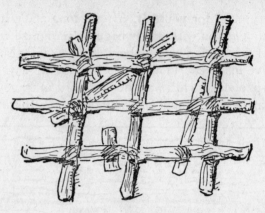

Polynesian Woven Map

Compared to these products of the medieval cartographers, the woven maps of the Polynesians (they look for all the world like something done by the children in a kindergarten, but they are exceedingly handy and very accurate) are veritable masterpieces of the navigator's ingenuity. Not to mention the work of the contemporary Arabs and Chinese, who however were ruled out as contemptible heathen. Nor was there any real improvement until the end of the fifteenth century when navigation was at last elevated to the rank of a science.

For then the Turks conquered the bridge-head connecting Europe with Asia, land traffic into the Orient was permanently interrupted, and it suddenly became necessary to find a new way to the Indies by way of the open sea. That meant an end to the old familiar system of sailing by the church-towers of the nearest mainland or sailing by the sound of the dogs barking along the water-front. And it was this necessity of finding one's way across the ocean without seeing anything at all for weeks at a time except sky and water which brought about the great improvement in the navigating methods of that day.

The Egyptians seem to have ventured as far as Crete but no further, and even then the visits to the big island seem to have been more a matter of having been blown out of one's course than the result of a well-planned voyage of discovery. The

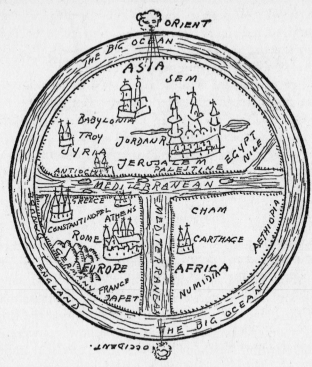

Medieval Map

Phoenicians and the Greeks were "church-tower sailors" at heart, although a few times they did quite remarkable things and even ventured forth as far as the Congo River and the Scilly Islands. Even then they undoubtedly hugged the shore as much as possible and at night pulled their boats up on dry land to escape being blown towards the open sea. As for the medieval merchants, they stuck to the Mediterranean, to the North Sea and to the Baltic, and were never for more than a few days without a glimpse of some distant mountain-range.

If they found themselves lost in the open, they had only one way in which to discover where the nearest land might be. For that purpose they always carried a few pigeons. They knew that pigeons would take the shortest route to the nearest bit of dry land. When they no longer knew what course to follow, they set one of their pigeons loose and observed the way it flew. Then they steered in that general direction taken by the bird until they saw the mountain tops and could make for the nearest harbor to ask where they might happen to be.

Of course during the Middle Ages even the average person was more familiar with the stars than we are today. He had to be because he lacked all sorts of information which nowadays comes to us in the printed form of almanacs and calendars. The more intelligent skippers therefore could find their way by studying the stars and by setting their course according to the Polar Star and the constellations. But in northern climes, where the sky was usually overcast, the stars were no great help. And navigation would have continued to be a painful and costly business of sailing by God and by guess (mostly the latter) if it had not been for a foreign invention which reached Europe shortly after the first half of the thirteenth century. But the origin and the history of the compass are still shrouded in deep mystery and what I tell you here is a matter of speculation rather than formal knowledge.

Genghis Khan, a little, slant-eyed Mongolian who during the first half of the thirteenth century ruled an empire slightly larger than any other that ever existed (it reached from the Yellow Sea to the Baltic and maintained itself in Russia until 1480) seems to have carried some sort of compass with him when he crossed the vast central Asiatic deserts, bound for the fleshpots of Europe. But it is impossible to say when the sailors of the Mediterranean had their first glimpse of this "blasphemous invention of the Devil", as the Church people called it, which soon afterwards was to carry their vessels to the ends of the earth.

Inventions of that sort, which are of world-wide importance, all seem to start in the same vague way. Some one returning from Jaffa or Famagusta probably brought a compass with him which he had bought from a merchant in Persia, who had told him that he had got it from some one who had just returned from India. The rumor spread through the ale-houses of the water-

Ice

fronts. Others wanted to see the funny little needle that had been bewitched by Satan and that would tell you where the north was, no matter where you happened to be. Of course, they did not believe such a thing could be true. Nevertheless, they asked their friend to bring them one too the next time he came back from the East. They even gave him the money, and six months later they had a little compass of their own. The darned thing worked! Then everybody must have a compass. Merchants in Damascus and Smyrna received hurry calls for more compasses. Instrument-makers in Venice and Genoa began to fabricate compasses on their own account. Suddenly we hear of compasses in every part of Europe. And within a few years the little glass-covered metal box had become such a commonplace sight that no one ever thought it worth while to write a book about an instrument that everybody had long since taken for granted.

So much for its career which must forever remain shrouded in mystery. But as for the compass itself, our knowledge about it has made great progress since the first sensitive needle guided the first Venetians from their lagoons to the delta of the Nile. For example, we have discovered that the needle of the compass does not point to the true north except on a few spots on the globe, while at all other places it points either a little to the east or a little to the west—a difference which is technically known as the "variation of the compass". This is due to the fact that the magnetic north and south poles do not coincide with the north and south poles of our planet but are several hundred miles toward the south and the north of the geographic poles. The northern magnetic pole is located in the island of Boothia Felix, an island to the north of Canada, where Sir James Ross first located it in 1831, and the southern magnetic pole is situated at 73° S. Lat. and 156° E. Long.

It follows therefore that it is not enough for a captain to have merely a compass on board. He must also have charts which show him the variations of his compass in different parts of the world. That however has to do with the science of navigation and the present volume is no handbook on navigation. Navigation is an exceedingly difficult and complicated branch of learning which refuses very positively to let itself be reduced to simple little words of one syllable. For our present purpose it is enough if you will kindly remember that the compass made its entry into Europe during the thirteenth and fourteenth centuries and that it was of tremendous help in making navigation a reliable science, and not merely a matter of fortunate guessing and hopelessly complicated calculations, which were far beyond the mental reach of most people.

But that was only a beginning.

One could now tell whether one were sailing north or north-by-east or north-north-east or north-east-by-north or north-east or north-east-by-east or in any of the other thirty-two "general directions" indicated by the compass. But for the rest, the medieval skipper had only two other instruments to help him find out in what part of the ocean he might happen to find himself.

In the first place, there was the lead-line. The lead-line was almost as old as the ships themselves. It would show the depth of the sea at any given point and if one had a chart indicating the different depths of the sea through which one was slowly wending one's way, the lead-line would give some indication of the approximate neighborhood in which one found one's self.

And then there was the log. The log originally was a small log of wood which was thrown overboard from the bow and which was then closely watched to see how long it would take before it passed the stern. As the length of the ship from stern to bow was of course known, one could then figure out how much time the vessel needed to pass a given point and that would show (more or less) how many miles the ship was making per hour.

The log of wood was gradually given up for the log-line, a long and thin but very strong piece of rope with a triangular piece of wood at the end. This rope had been beforehand divided into so many pieces by means of "knots" made at regular intervals and it was heaved overboard at the same time that another sailor started a sand-glass running. When all the sand had run through the glass (one knew of course beforehand how long that would take, two or three minutes) one pulled in the line and counted the knots that had run through one's hands while the sand-glass was emptying its contents from one bulb into the other. After that, a very simple calculation would show how fast the vessel was going, or as sailors used to say, "how many knots".

But even if the captain knew the speed of his ship and the general direction it was following, there were the currents and the tides and the winds to upset even the most careful of his calculations. As a result an ordinary ocean voyage, even long after the introduction of the compass, remained a most hazardous undertaking. The people who worked on the theoretical end of the problem realized that in order to make it something else, they would have to find a substitute for the old church-tower.

I am not trying to be funny when I say this. The church-tower or the tree on top of the high dune or the windmill on the dike or the barking of a watch-dog had been of such tremendous importance in the realm of navigation because it was a *fixed point*, something that would not change its position, no matter what happened. And given one such "fixed point", the sailor could then make his own deductions. "I must go further towards the east," he would say to himself, remembering the last time he had been in that part of the world, or "further towards the west or south or north to arrive where I want to be". And the mathematicians of that day (brilliant men, by the way, who, considering the scanty information and the faulty instruments at their disposal, did as good work as was ever done in their particular field) knew perfectly well where the crux of the situation lay. They must find a "fixed point" in nature to act as a substitute for the "fixed point" established by man.

They began their search about two centuries before Columbus (I am mentioning his name because 1492 is the one date every man, woman and child seems to know) and they have not finished it even in this day of wireless time-signals and under-water signals and mechanical steering-gears, when the "Iron Mike" has about driven the old helmsman out of his job.

Suppose you find yourself standing on a round ball at the foot of a tower on top of which there waves a flag. That flag will then be right straight over your head and as long as you remain at the foot of your tower it will be right straight over your head. But if you move away from it and try to look at it, you must lift your eyes at an angle, and that angle will depend upon the distance you are away from the tower, as you will see by studying this picture.

Church-tower navigation

And once this "fixed spot" had been discovered, the rest would be comparatively easy, for it would all be a matter of angles, and even the Greeks had known how to measure angles, for they had laid the foundation for the science of trigonometry which deals with the relationship between the sides and the angles of the triangle.

This brings us to the most difficult part of this chapter, indeed, I might say of the entire book—the search for what we now call latitude and longitude. The true method to establish one's latitude was discovered hundreds of years before longitude. Longitude (now that we know how to find it) looks much

The old conception of the World when the Earth
was the center of the Universe

simpler than latitude. But it offered certain almost insurmountable difficulties to our clockless ancestors. Whereas latitude, being
merely a matter of careful observation and even more careful figuring, was something they were able to solve at a comparatively early date. But enough of generalities. Here the
problem is, stated as simply as I know how.

You will notice a number of planes and angles. At D you
find yourself right beneath the top of the tower, just as you
will be standing almost right beneath the sun at 12 o'clock noon
if you happen to be on the equator. When you have moved to E

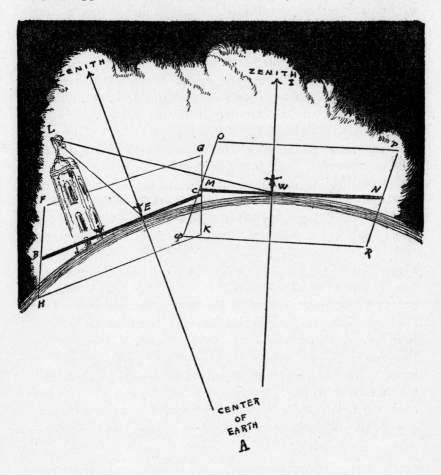

the matter becomes a little more complicated. The world on which you stand is round and you need a flat plane if you are to indulge in any figuring of angles. Therefore you draw a line from the imaginary center of the earth, called A, which runs through your own body and loses itself right above you in a spot called Zenith, the official astronomical name for the point of the heavens directly above the observer and which is the opposite of the Nadir, which is the point of the heavens directly under the observer.

Let us try to do this problem so that you can actually see it, for it is rather complicated. Stick a knitting-needle clean through the heart of an apple and imagine yourself on one side of that apple, sitting with your back leaning against the knitting-needle. The top of the knitting-needle is Zenith and the bottom is Nadir. Then imagine a plane that is at right angles with the place you are sitting or standing and the knitting-needle. When you are standing at E that plane will be the plane called FGKH and BC will be the line on that plane from which you are making your observation. Furthermore, for the sake of convenience and in order to make the problem a little easier, kindly imagine that your eyes are in your toes, on the exact spot where your feet touch the line BC. Then look up at the top of the flag-pole on your tower and measure the angle top-of-flag-pole (or L), the spot where you stand (or E), and the end of your imaginary line BC, which is part of the imaginary plane FGKH, which runs at right angles with the imaginary line Zenith-A, which connects the center of the earth with the point of the heavens directly above you, the observer. That angle, if you know anything about trigonometry, will tell you how far you are away from the tower. Move to W and repeat the process. W will become the point where you touch the imaginary line MN, which is part of the imaginary plane OPRQ, which runs at right angles with the line connecting the center of the earth A with the new Zenith (the Zenith of course changes every time you move an inch) which I shall call Zenith I. Meas-

ure the angle LWM and you know how much further you are
away from the tower.

You see, even in the simplest form it is still quite complicated, and that is why I shall only give you a general outline of
the basic principles upon which modern navigation is based. If
you intend to become a sailor, you will have to go to a special
school for a number of years to learn how to make the necessary
calculations; and then after you have handled your instruments
and your tables and charts for twenty or thirty years, your di-
rectors may even make you a captain and trust that you will be
able to take a ship from one port to the next. If you have no
such ambition, you will never understand all this anyway and
so you will pardon me if I make this chapter short and stick to
the general idea.

Since navigation was entirely an affair of angles, no possible
advance could be made in that science until trigonometry had
once more been rediscovered by the people of Europe. The
Greeks had laid the foundations for this science a thousand years
before, but after the death of Ptolemy (the famous geographer
from Alexandria in Egypt) trigonometry had been forgotten or
discarded as a superfluous luxury—something a little too clever
to be quite safe. But the people of India and after them the
Arabs of northern Africa and Spain had no such scruples and
they had nobly carried on where the Greeks had left off. These
words Zenith and Nadir (both of them pure Arabic) bear witness to the fact that when trigonometry was once more admitted
to the curriculum of the European schools (which happened
sometime during the thirteenth century) it was a Mohammedan
and not a Christian branch of learning. But during the next three
hundred years, the Europeans made up for lost time. For although they were once more able to work with angles and triangles, they still found themselves faced by the problem of discovering some definitely fixed point away from the earth to act
as a substitute for their church-tower.

The most reliable candidate for this sublime honor was the

North Star. The North Star was so far away from us that it never seemed to change its position and besides, it was so easy to locate that even the dumbest shrimp-fisherman could find it, once he had lost sight of land. All he had to do was to draw a straight line through the two stars that were furthest to the right in the Big Dipper, and he couldn't miss it. And, of course, there was always the sun, but its course had never been scientifically mapped out and only the most intelligent mariners could avail themselves of its assistance.

As long as people were forced to believe that the earth was flat, all calculations were bound to be hopelessly at odds with the true state of affairs. Early during the sixteenth century there came an end to these make-shift methods. The "disc" theory was discarded for the "sphere" theory and the geographers at last came into their own.

The first thing they did was to cut the earth into two equal halves which were divided by a plane running at right angles with the line connecting the North and the South Poles. The dividing line was called the equator. The equator therefore was everywhere equally far removed from both the North and the South Pole. Next the distance between the poles and the equator was divided into ninety equal parts. Next ninety parallel lines (circles, of course, for remember the earth was round at last) were drawn between the poles and the equator, each one about sixty-nine miles away from the next, since sixty-nine miles represented one-ninetieth of the supposed distance between the pole and the equator.

Geographers gave these circles numbers, beginning from the equator and going up (or down) to the poles. The equator itself became 0° and the poles 90°. Those lines were called degrees of Latitude (the L's of the picture will make you remember how they run) and a little ° placed at the right of the number was used as a convenient symbol for the word "degree" which was too long to be used in mathematical calculations.

All this meant an enormous step forward. But even so, the business of going to sea remained a very dangerous experience.

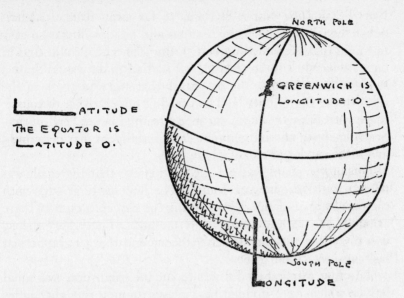

A dozen generations of mathematicians and sailors had to devote themselves to compiling data about the sun, giving its exact position for every day of every year and every clime before the average skipper was able to handle the latitude problem.

Then at last any reasonably intelligent sailor, provided he could read and write, was able to determine within a couple of miles how far away he was from the North Pole and from the equator, or in technical terms, in what N. Lat. (degree of latitude north of the equator) or S. Lat. he might find himself. It was not quite so easy once he had crossed the equator, for then he was no longer able to fall back upon the Polar Star which is not visible on the southern hemisphere. But that problem too was eventually solved by science, and after the end of the sixteenth century latitude ceased to be a matter of concern to those who went down to the sea in ships.

There remained however the difficulty of determining one's longitude (longitude to make it easy for you to remember that the longitudinal degrees run in a vertical direction) and it took two whole centuries more before that puzzle had been successfully solved. In trying to establish the different latitudes, the mathematicians had been able to start out with two fixed points —the North Pole and the South Pole. "Here," so they could say, "stands my church-tower, the North Pole (or the South Pole) and it will remain there until the end of time."

But there was no East Pole and no West Pole either, because the axis of the earth did not happen to run that way. Of course one could draw an endless number of meridians, circles going around the earth and crossing both poles. But which one of these millions of meridians was the one to choose as "The Meridian" that was to divide the world into halves, so that thereafter the sailor could say, "I am a hundred miles east or west of 'The Meridian' "? The old notion of Jerusalem as the center of the earth was still strong enough to make many people demand that the meridian running through Jerusalem be recognized as Long.° or our vertical equator. But national pride prevented this plan. Every country wanted to have Long.° run through its own capital and even today, when we are supposed to be a little more liberal-minded in this respect, there still are German, French and American maps which show Long.° running through Berlin, Paris and Washington. And in the end, as England was the country which happened to do most for the advancement of nautical knowledge during the seventeenth century (when the problem of longitude was finally solved) and as all nautical affairs were then under the supervision of the Royal Observatory, built in Greenwich near London in the year 1675, the meridian of Greenwich was finally adopted as the particular meridian which was to divide the world into longitudinal halves.

Then at last the sailor had his longitudinal church-tower, but he was still faced with another difficulty. How was he to discover how many miles he was either east or west of that Greenwich meridian, once he was out on the high seas? To settle this matter for good and all, the English government in the year 1713 appointed a special "Commission for the Discovery of Longitude at Sea" which was to solve the problem by the practical expedient of offering large rewards for the best method of "determining longitude on the high seas". A hundred thousand dollars was a lot of money, two centuries ago, and everybody set to work with a will. When the commission was finally disbanded during the first half of the nineteenth century it had spent more than $500,000 in the form of rewards for deserving inventions.

Most of their labors have long since been forgotten and the work they did has been dropped as obsolete. But two inventions, following in the wake of these generous monetary rewards, have proved to be of lasting benefit. The first of these was the sextant.

The sextant is a complicated instrument (a sort of miniature nautical observatory which one can carry under one's arm) which allows the sailor to measure all sorts of angular distances. It was direct heir to the clumsy medieval astrolabe and cross-staff and the quadrant of the sixteenth century, and, as so often happens when the whole world is looking for the same thing at the same moment, three men claimed to be the original inventors and fought bitterly for the honor.

But the excitement caused in nautical circles by the appearance of the first sextants was mild compared to the interest shown in the chronometer when that faithful and reliable time-piece made its appearance four years later, in 1735. The chronometer, invented by John Harrison, an horological genius (he was a carpenter until he became a watch-maker), was a clock which worked so accurately that it made it possible to carry Greenwich time to any part of the world in any clime and in any form, sort or mode of conveyance. This John Harrison had been able to do by providing his clock with something he called a "compensation curve". It altered the length of the balance-spring in proportion to the expansion or contraction caused by changes in temperature in such a way that his chronometer was practically weather-proof.

After endless and unseemly quarrels about the reward, Harrison received his hundred thousand dollars (in 1773, three years before his death). And today, no matter where a ship happens to be, provided it carries a chronometer, it will always know what time it is in Greenwich. And since the sun revolves around the earth in twenty-four hours (it is the other way around, but I am using the expression for the sake of convenience) and passes through fifteen degrees of longitude in one hour, all we need to do in order to determine just how far we have travelled east or west of The Meridian is to first determine what time it is on the spot where we ourselves happen to be and then compare our local time with Greenwich time and note the difference.

For example, if we find (after careful calculations which every ship's officer can make) that it is twelve o'clock where we are, but two o'clock by our chronometer (which gives us the exact Greenwich time), then we know that since the sun travels through fifteen degrees in one hour (which means four minutes for every single degree) and since there is a difference of two hours between our time and that of Greenwich, that we must have travelled exactly $2 \times 15° = 30°$. And we write down in the log-book (a little book so-called because before the general introduction of paper it used to be a piece of wood on which all such figures were written down with chalk) that on such and such a day at noon our ship found itself at Long. 30° West.

Today that startling invention of the year 1735 has lost a great deal of its importance. Every day at noon the Greenwich Observatory broadcasts the correct time all over the world. Chronometers are rapidly becoming superfluous luxuries. Indeed, if we are to believe our navigators, wireless telegraphy will eventually do away with all our complicated tables and our diligent calculations and computations. Then that lengthy chapter of finding one's way across those uncharted seas, where one wave looked so hopelessly much like the next that even the best of sailors could lose himself in less time than it takes to write down this sentence—then that marvellous chapter of courage and endurance and high intelligence will also have come to an end. The imposing man with the sextant will disappear from the bridge. He will sit in his cabin with a telephone clasped to his ear and he will ask, "Hello, Nantucket! (or Hello Cherbourg!)

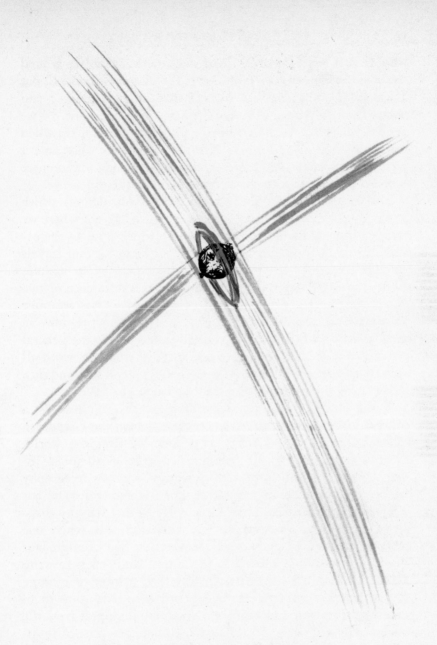

The new conception of the World in space

Where am I?" And Nantucket or Cherbourg will tell him. And that will be that.

But these twenty centuries of effort to make man's progress across the face of the earth safe and pleasant and profitable will not have been in vain. For they were one of the first successful experiments in international coöperation. Chinese, Arabs, Indians, Phoenicians, Greeks, Englishmen, Frenchmen, Dutchmen, Spaniards, Portuguese, Italians, Norwegians, Swedes, Danes, Germans, they all of them did their share to help the good work along.

That particular chapter in the history of coöperation has now been closed. But there remain enough others to keep us busy for quite a long time.

V

THE SEASONS AND HOW THEY HAPPEN

OUR word season is of Latin origin and it comes from the verb "serere" which means "to sow". "Season" should therefore be used only to indicate the spring—the "sowing time". But very early in the Middle Ages "season" lost that exclusive connotation. Three other seasons were added to divide the year into four equal parts: the winter, or wet season; the autumn, the period of increase (the same root as in "augmentation" or "august" which is not only the "month of the increase" but also a "person of augmented importance"); and the summer, which was the old Sanskrit name for the entire year.

Aside from their practical and their romantic interest to the human race, the four seasons have a most prosaic astronomical background, for they are the direct result of the earth's behavior on its yearly peregrination around the sun, as I shall tell you as briefly and as dully as the subject allows.

The earth turns around its own axis in 24 hours. The earth turns around the sun in about $365\frac{1}{4}$ days. To get rid of that $\frac{1}{4}$ day and keep the calendar more or less pure (no, it is not correct, but it is extremely doubtful whether the nations just now would find time in which to agree upon a decent revision) we have a year of 366 days, or leap-year, every four years except in the years which end with two zeros, such as 900, 1100, 1300 or 1900. But the years which can be divided by 400 are an exception to this exception. The last exception was Anno Domini 1600. The next one will be the year of grace 2000.

The earth does not describe a perfect circle on its way around the sun, but an ellipse. It is not much of an ellipse, but enough to make the study of the earth on its course through space a great

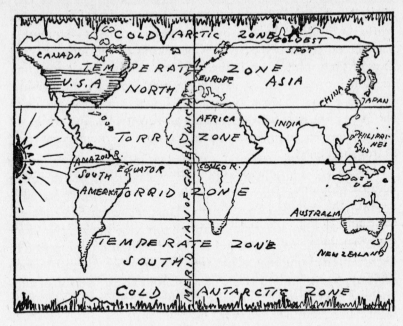

The Zones

deal more complicated than if we had to deal with a perfect circle.

The axis of the earth does not stand at right angles to the plane which we could draw through the sun and our own planet, but at an angle of 66½°.

But on its course around the sun the axis of the earth always remains at the same angle which is directly responsible for the variations in the seasons in different parts of the world.

On March 21st, the position of the earth in relation to the sun is such that the light of the sun illuminates exactly one-half of the surface of our planet. As a result, on that particular day, day and night are of equal length in every part of the world. Three months later, when the earth has finished one-fourth of her voyage around the sun, the North Pole is turned towards the sun and the South Pole is turned away from the sun. As a result, the North Pole is celebrating its yearly day of six months, while the South Pole is enjoying its yearly night of six months; and the northern hemisphere is partaking of the long, shining days of the summer, while the southern hemisphere is spending the long winter evenings reading a good book by the fireside. Remember that when we go skating at Christmas, the people in the Argentine and Chile are dying of sun-stroke, and while we suffer from our annual heat-wave, it is time for them to get their skates sharpened.

The next day of seasonal importance is the 23d of September, because then once more the days and nights are of equal length all over the world. Then we reach the 21st of December when the South Pole has turned its face towards the sun and the North Pole has turned its back upon our source of heat. Then the northern hemisphere is cold and the southern hemisphere is warm.

But the peculiar slant of the axis of the earth, together with the earth's rotation, is not alone responsible for the change in seasons. That 66½° angle also gives us our five zones. On both sides of the equator we have the tropical zone, where the rays of the sun hit the surface of the earth either vertically or almost vertically. The northern and southern temperate zones are those regions between the tropics and the polar regions where the sun's rays hit the earth a little less vertically and therefore have to warm a greater surface of soil or water than they do in the tropics. Until finally the two polar regions receive the rays of the sun at such an angle that even in summer each sixty-nine miles of sunlight is obliged to heat almost double that amount of land.

It is not easy to make these things clear on paper. There are planetariums where you can see all this and understand it too in much less time than you need to read this. But only very few of our cities have thought it necessary to establish such a plane-tarium. Go to the Board of Aldermen and tell them that you want one for a Christmas present. While they are looking this difficult word up in the dictionary (it may take them twenty or

Wind

thirty years) you had better try your luck with oranges or apples and a candle and a little black ink to mark off the zones. A match will do for the North Pole and South Pole. And don't indulge in comparisons when a fly descends upon your little home-made planet. Don't say to yourself, "Suppose—just suppose—that we too should be only some sort of fly, crawling aimlessly across the surface of a gigantic orange, a gigantic orange illuminated by a gigantic candle—both of them little playthings in the hands of some colossus who wanted an afternoon's entertainment!"

Imagination is a good thing.

But not in the realm of astronomy.

VI

CONCERNING THE LITTLE SPOTS OF DRY LAND ON THIS PLANET AND WHY SOME OF THEM ARE CALLED CONTINENTS WHILE OTHERS ARE NOT

ALL of us, without exception, live on islands. But some of these islands on our planet are so much larger than the others that we have decided to let them belong to a class of their own and have called them "continents". A continent therefore is an island which "contains" or "holds together" more territory than just an ordinary island like England or Madagascar or Manhattan.

But there are no hard and fast rules. America and Asia and Africa, being the biggest continuous pieces of land, are continents by right of their enormous size. Europe, which to the astronomers of the planet Mars undoubtedly looks like a peninsula of Asia (a little larger perhaps than India, but not very much) has always insisted on being a continent by itself. The Australians would undoubtedly go to war if any one dared to suggest that their beloved island was not really big enough and did not have enough inhabitants to be ranked among the continents. The Greenlanders on the other hand seem quite contented to remain plain, ordinary Eskimos, although the country of their birth is twice as large as the combined area of New Guinea and Borneo, the two biggest islands on our planet. While the penguins of the South Pole, if they were not such humble and amiable creatures, might easily claim to be living on a continent, for the Antarctic region is surely as vast as all the land between the Arctic Sea and the Mediterranean.

I don't know how all this confusion arose. But the science of geography passed through many centuries of absolute neglect.

72

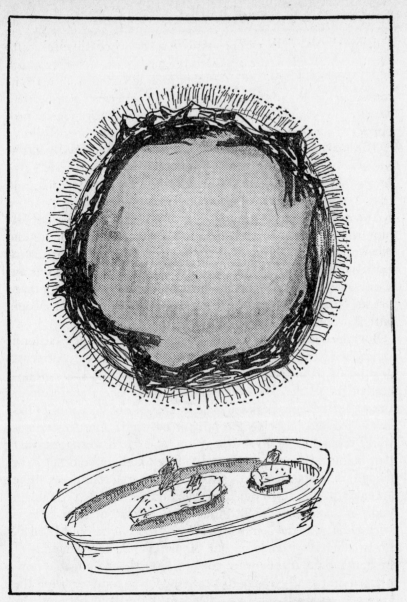

Are our proud continents perhaps islands of some lighter
material which float on the heavier substance of
the earth's interior as pieces of cork will
float on the water in a basin?

During that period, erroneous notions attached themselves to the body of our geographical information as barnacles attach themselves to the keel of a ship that lies neglected in port. In the course of time (and the dark ages of our ignorance lasted about 1400 years) some of those barnacles assumed such gigantic proportions that they were finally mistaken for parts of the ship.

But rather than add to the existing confusion, I will stick to the generally accepted divisions and I will say that there are five continents: Asia, America, Africa, Europe and Australia, and that Asia is four and a half times as large as Europe, America four times as large, Africa three times, while Australia is a few hundred thousand square miles smaller. Asia and America and Africa therefore ought to come ahead of Europe in a handbook on geography; but if we do not merely pay attention to size but also consider the role any given part of the world has played in the historical development of the entire planet, we must begin with Europe.

Let us first of all look at the map. As a matter of fact, let us

Rockall—the top of a submerged continent in the
Northern Atlantic

look at our maps oftener than we look at the printed page. For you might as well attempt to learn music without an instrument or swimming without water as to try to learn geography without a map. And as soon as you look at a map, or better still, if you can get hold of a globe, you will notice that the European peninsula, bounded by the Arctic Ocean and the Atlantic Ocean and the Mediterranean Sea, is situated right in the heart of that part of the world which contains the greatest amount of land. Just as poor, neglected Australia happens to be situated in the exact center of that other half of our planet which contains the greatest percentage of water. That was advantage number one which Europe enjoyed, but there were others. Asia might be about five times as large as Europe but while one-quarter of all its land was too hot for comfort, another quarter was situated in such close proximity to the North Pole that no one but a reindeer or a polar bear would choose it as a permanent place of residence.

There again Europe scored, for it enjoyed certain advantages which none of the other continents did. The toe of Italy, the southernmost point, although fairly warm, is still some 800 miles removed from the tropical zone. Northern Sweden and Norway run quite a distance beyond the polar circle, but it happens that the Gulf Stream visits their shores and keeps them warm, while Labrador, in an equal latitude, is a frozen wilderness.

Furthermore, Europe has a greater proportion of peninsulas and seas that run way inland than any other continent. Just think of Spain, Italy, Greece, Denmark, Scandinavia, the Baltic, the North Sea, the Mediterranean, the Aegean Sea, the Sea of Marmora, the Gulf of Biscay, the Black Sea, and compare that situation with Africa or with South America, which has the lowest record for that sort of thing. The result of such a large body of water touching almost every part of the mainland is a very moderate climate. That means that the winters are not too cold and the summers are not too hot. Life is neither too easy nor too difficult, so that man becomes neither a loafer (as he does in Africa) nor a beast of burden (as he does in Asia) but is able to mix work and leisure in a more agreeable and useful proportion than anywhere else.

But it was not only the climate that helped the Europeans to make themselves the masters of the greater part of our planet and to maintain themselves as such until they committed suicide during the four years of their unfortunate civil war of 1914–1918. Their geological background was another point in their favor. This, of course, was a mere accident for which they deserve no personal credit. But just the same they plucked the fruit of all those colossal volcanic eruptions and those gigantic glacial invasions and those catastrophic floods which had made their continent what it was, which had placed their mountains where they could most easily be turned into national frontiers and which made their rivers flow in such a way that practically every part of the interior enjoyed direct communication with the sea, a most important point for the development of trade and commerce before the invention of the railroad and the automobile.

The Pyrenees cut the Iberian peninsula off from the rest of Europe and became the natural frontier of Spain and Portugal. The Alps performed a similar service for Italy. The great plain of western France lay hidden behind the Cévennes, the Jura and the Vosges Mountains. The Carpathians acted as a bulwark which separated Hungary from the vast plains of Russia. The Austrian Empire, which played such an important part in the history of the last eight hundred years, consisted, roughly speaking, of a circular plain, surrounded by difficult mountain-ranges which protected it against its neighbors. Without those barriers, Austria would never have existed as long as it did. Germany too was no mere political accident. It consisted of a large square of territory which sloped gently from the Alps and the mountains of Bohemia towards the Baltic Sea. And then there were islands, like England and those of the old Greek Aegean Sea, and swamps like Holland and Venice, all of them natural fortresses which Providence herself seemed to have placed there for the development of independent political units.

Even Russia, which we so often hear described as the result

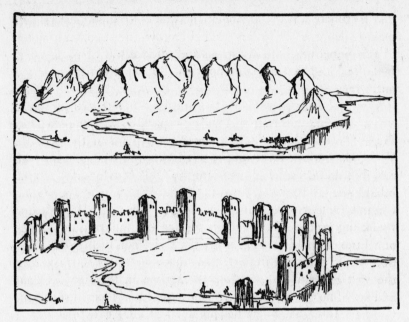

Mountains and seas make excellent natural boundaries

of one man's terrific desire for power (the late Peter the Great of the house of Romanov) was really much more the product of certain natural and inevitable causes than we are sometimes willing to believe. The great Russian plain, situated between the Arctic Ocean, the Ural Mountains, the Caspian Sea, the Black Sea, the Carpathians and the Baltic, was ideally situated for the foundation of a highly centralized empire. The ease with which the United Soviet Republics survived after the downfall of the Romanov dynasty seems to be conclusive proof of this.

But the rivers, too, in Europe, as I have already remarked, ran in such a way that they could play a most important and practical part in the economic development of that continent. Draw a line from Madrid to Moscow and you will notice that all the rivers, without any exception, run either north or south, giving every part of the interior direct access to the sea. Since civilization has always been a product of water rather than land, this fortunate aquatic arrangement was of tremendous help in making Europe the richest and therefore the dominant center of our planet until the disastrous and suicidal war of 1914–1918 made her lose that enviable position. But let the maps bear me out.

Compare Europe with North America. On our own continent two high mountain-ranges run almost parallel with the sea; and the entire middle part, the great central plain of the Middle West, has but one direct outlet to the sea, the Mississippi River and its tributaries, which run into the Gulf of Mexico, a sort of inland sea far removed from both the Atlantic and the Pacific Oceans. Or compare Europe with Asia, where a helter-skelter wrinkling process of the earth's surface and the irregular slopes of all the mountain-ranges make the rivers run in any old direction, while the most important of those water-ways, traversing the vast Siberian steppes, lose themselves in the Arctic Ocean and are of no earthly use to any one except a few local fishermen. Or with Australia, which has no rivers at all. Or with Africa, a vast central plateau which forces the rivers to break through the high fringe of mountains near the coast and prevents sea traffic from using the natural waterways to reach the interior. Then you will begin to understand why Europe, with its convenient mountain-ranges and its even more convenient river systems, with nine times as much coast-line as it would have if it were rounded off as neatly as Africa or Australia, with its moderate climate and its convenient location right in the heart of the land masses of this earth, was predestined to play the role of the leading continent.

But those natural advantages alone would not have been enough to allow this tiny corner of the world to lord it over all its neighbors. Man's ingenuity had to lend a hand. That was easy. For the climate of northern Europe was an ideal climate to stimulate men's brains into activity. It was neither too cold for absolute comfort nor too hot for a regular daily task, but just right to make one feel like doing something. As a result, the inhabitants of northern Europe, as soon as their respective coun-

We can only live on the land between the high
mountains and the submerged valleys called oceans
and seas

tries had duly settled down and were able to guarantee their citizens that indispensable minimum of law and order without which no mental life is possible, began to devote themselves to those scientific pursuits which in the end were to make them the owners and exploiters of the four other continents.

Their mathematics and their astronomy and trigonometry taught them how to sail the Seven Seas with a reasonable assurance of being able to return whence they had come. Their interest in chemistry provided them with an internal combustion machine (that queer motor called a "gun") by means of which they could kill other human beings and animals faster and more accurately than any other nation or tribe had ever been able to do. Their pursuit of medicine taught them how to make themselves comparatively immune against a variety of diseases which hitherto had kept whole regions of the earth in a state of chronic depopulation. And finally the comparative poverty of their own soil (poor when compared to the plains of the Ganges or the mountain-ranges of Java) and the everlasting necessity of living rather "carefully" had gradually developed such deep-seated habits of thrift and greed that Europeans would go to any extreme in order to acquire the wealth without which their neighbors regarded and scorned them as regrettable failures.

As soon as the introduction of that mysterious Indian instrument known as the compass had made them independent of the church-tower and the familiar coast-line and allowed them to roam at will, and as soon as the rudder of the ship had been moved from the side to the stern (an improvement which seems to have occurred during the first half of the fourteenth century and which was one of the most important inventions of all time, since it gave man such command over the course of his vessel as he had never enjoyed before) the people of Europe were able to leave their little inland seas, the Mediterranean and the North Sea and the Baltic, and to make the gigantic Atlantic the high-road for their further exploits of a commercial and military character. Then at last they were able to make the fullest possible use of the fortunate incident which had placed their continent right in the heart of the greatest amount of land on our planet.

They maintained this advantage for more than five hundred years. The steamer succeeded the sailing vessel, but since trade has always been a matter of cheap modes of communication, Europe was able to continue at the head of the procession. And those military authors have been right who maintained that the nation with the biggest navy was also the nation that could dictate its will to the rest of the world. In obedience to this law, the Norsemen had been succeeded by Venice and Genoa, and Venice and Genoa had been succeeded by Portugal, and Portugal as a world-power had been succeeded by Spain, and Spain by Holland, and Holland by England, because each country in turn had had the largest number of battle-ships. Today, however, the sea is rapidly losing its former importance. The ocean as a highroad for commerce is being succeeded by the air. And perhaps it is not so much the Great War which has reduced Europe to the rank of a second-rate continent as the invention of the heavier-than-air flying-machine.

The son of a Genoese wool-merchant changed the course of history by discovering the unlimited possibilities of the ocean.

The owners of a simple bicycle-repair-shop in the outskirts of Dayton, Ohio, did the same for the air. As a result, the children of a thousand years hence may never have heard the name of Christopher Columbus, but they will be familiar with Wilbur and Orville Wright.

For it was a product of their patient and ingenious brains more than anything else which is gradually moving the center of civilization from the Old World to the New.

VII

OF THE DISCOVERY OF EUROPE AND THE SORT OF PEOPLE WHO LIVE IN THAT PART OF THE WORLD

THERE are twice as many people in Europe as there are in North and South America together. There are more people within the confines of that small continent than in America, Africa and Australia together. Only Asia has a greater number of inhabitants than Europe, 950,000,000 against Europe's 550,-000,000. These figures are more or less accurate for they were gathered by the International Statistical Institution connected with the League of Nations, a gathering of learned men who are able to consider such matters with a cool and detached eye and who are under no obligation to doctor the returns to please the local pride of any particular country.

According to that same erudite body, the average net increase in population on this planet is 30,000,000 per year. And that is a very serious matter. For at that rate of speed, the population of the world will double itself in about six decades. And as we still have millions and millions of years to go, I hate to think what conditions will be later on, in the year 19320 or 193200 or 1932000. "Standing room only" in the subway is bad enough. "Standing room only" on our planet would be absolutely unbearable.

And yet that is the prospect before us unless we are willing to face facts and take certain measures before it is too late.

All that however belongs in a handbook on political economy. The question that faces us here is the following: Where did these early settlers of the European continent, who were to play such a great role in history, come from, and were they the first to arrive upon the scene? The answer, I regret to say, must be exceedingly vague. Those people probably came from Asia and they probably entered Europe through the gap between the Ural Mountains and the Caspian Sea and they probably found that earlier races of immigrants and older forms of civilization had preceded them. But until the anthropologists shall have gathered many more data than are now at their disposal, the story of those pre-pre-historic invaders is still too vague to be incorporated in a popular handbook of geography and we must stick to the later arrivals.

Why did they come? For the same reason that made over a hundred million people move from the Old to the New World during the last hundred years—because they were hungry and the lands toward the west offered them a better chance to survive.

These immigrants scrambled all over Europe, as the immigrants of a later day were to scatter all over the great American plains. And in the mad rush for land and for lakes (in those early days, a lake was even more valuable than a piece of land) all traces of "pure racial stock" were speedily lost. Here and there along the more inaccessible parts of the Atlantic sea-shore or in the hidden depths of some obscure mountain valley, a few of the weaker tribes continued to vegetate, proud of their purity of race, but having little else to console them for the loss of touch with the outside world. And therefore when we speak of "race" today, we have given up all idea of absolute ethnological purity.

We use the expression for the sake of convenience to describe certain large groups of people who happen to speak the same language (more or less); who have a common historical origin (more or less); and who during the last two thousand years of written history have developed certain traits of character and certain modes of thought and social behavior which have made them conscious of belonging to what, for lack of a better word, we continue to call a "racial group".

According to this notion of race (the x of the algebraic equation, invented solely for the sake of cutting through a thousand

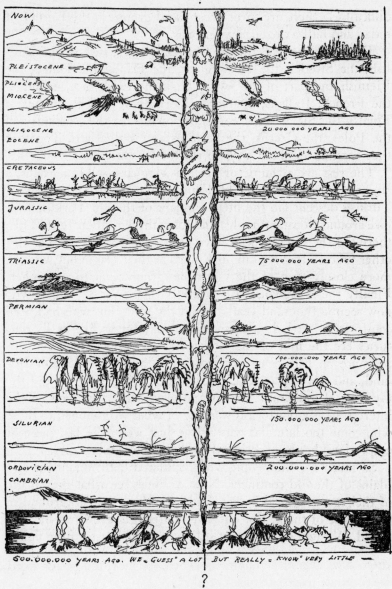

From Animal to Man

difficulties) there are three great racial groups in the Europe of today and half a dozen smaller ones.

There are, first of all, the Germanic races, such as the English, the Swedes, the Norwegians, the Danes, the Dutch, the Flemish and part of the Swiss. Then the Latin race, including the French, Italians, Spaniards, Portuguese and Roumanians. Finally the Slavic races, consisting mainly of the Russians and the Poles, the Czechs, the Serbians and Bulgarians. Together they account for about 93% of the total population.

The rest are a couple of million Magyars or Hungarians, a slightly smaller number of Finns, about a million people of Turkish descent (in the little remnant of the old Turkish Empire around Constantinople) and some three million Jews. Then there are the Greeks, who have been so hopelessly mixed with other "races" that we can only guess at their origin but who are more closely akin to the Germanic group than to any other. Finally the Albanians, also probably of Germanic origin, who now seem a thousand years behind the times but who had been comfortably settled on their present day farms five or six centuries ere the first of the Romans and Greeks made their appearance on European territory. And finally the Celts of Ireland, and the Letts and Lithuanians of the Baltic Sea, and the Gypsies, of indefinite number and hazy origin, who are chiefly interesting as an historical warning of what will happen to those who come too late and who arrive just when the last piece of empty land has been occupied by some one else.

So much for the people who populated both mountains and plains of the old continent. Now we must see what they made of their geographical background and what that background in turn made of them. For out of that struggle grew our modern world. Without it, we would still be like the beasts of the fields.

JUST A MOMENT BEFORE WE GO ANY FURTHER WHILE I TELL YOU HOW TO USE THIS BOOK

This book should be read with an atlas. There are a large number of excellent atlases and almost any one will do. For atlases are like dictionaries. Even a bad one is better than none at all.

As you will soon discover, there are quite a number of maps in this volume but these are not meant as a substitute for a regular atlas. I drew them merely to show you the many ways of approach to the subject under discussion and (if I must tell the truth) to get you personally interested in drawing maps according to your own notion of the geographical right and wrong. You see, flat maps, however ingeniously conceived, must be somewhat out of gear. The only approximately correct maps are those pasted on globes but even our globes are not entirely above suspicion for they should really be spheroids. We make them spheres merely for the sake of convenience. The earth, of course, is slightly flattened near the poles but it would take a gigantic globe to show the difference, and so we need not worry about that minor irregularity. Get yourself a globe (I wrote this book with the help of a ten-cent-store globe which was really a pencil-sharpener) and use it to your heart's content, but remember that it is an "approximation" and not an "established fact". The "established facts" will only enter into your life if you should try to qualify for a master mariner's certificate. But in that case, you would have to spend many years mastering an exceedingly difficult branch of science; and this book was not writ for specialists but for the average reader who wants to get some general ideas about the planet upon which he happens to live.

Now let me tell you one thing. The best and most convenient way to learn geography is to revaluate everything into pictures.

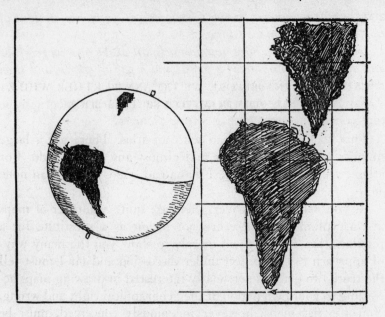

Compare the proportions of Greenland and South America on a globe and on a flat map and notice what a difference that makes!

Don't copy me or anybody else. Look at my pictures if you care to do so, but regard them merely as a sort of geographical appetizer, as polite suggestions for the meal you intend to prepare yourself by and by.

I have tried to give you quite a number of samples according to the geographical notions of the author himself. I have drawn you two-dimensional maps and three-dimensional maps. It will take you some time to get accustomed to these three-dimensional contraptions but, once you see them, you will no longer like the two-dimensional variety. I have given you maps as seen from mountain tops and according to the different angles from which you are able to contemplate a landscape. And I have given you maps as seen from aeroplanes and Zeppelins and the sort of maps we might expect to see if the oceans should run dry. I have given you a few maps which are merely pretty and ornamental and others which resemble geometrical patterns. Take your choice, and then *draw your own maps according to your own notions of how the thing should be done.*

Draw maps. . . . Get yourself a small globe or a large globe and an atlas. Buy yourself a pencil and a pad of paper, and then draw your own pictures.

For there is only one way in which you can learn geography so that you will never forget it—*draw pictures.*

VIII

GREECE, THE ROCKY PROMONTORY OF THE EASTERN MEDITERRANEAN WHICH ACTED AS THE CONNECTING LINK BETWEEN THE OLD ASIA AND THE NEW EUROPE

THE Greek peninsula is the southernmost point of the much larger Balkan peninsula. This is bounded on the north by the Danube, on the west by the Adriatic, which separates it from Italy, on the east by the Black Sea, the Sea of Marmora, the Bosporus and the Aegean Sea, which separate it from Asia, and on the south by the Mediterranean, which separates it from Africa.

I have never seen the Balkan peninsula from the air but it seems to me that from a high distance it must look like a hand, reaching out from Europe to Asia and Africa. Greece is the thumb. Thrace the little finger. Constantinople the nail on the little finger. The other fingers are the mountain-ranges that run from Macedonia and Thessaly to Asia Minor. Only the tops of these mountain-ranges are visible. The lower parts are covered by the waves of the Aegean, but from a great height one would undoubtedly be able to follow them as closely as the fingers of a hand partly submerged by the water in a wash-bowl.

The skin of this hand is stretched across a skeleton of sturdy mountain-ranges. In the main, these run from north-west to south-east, I might almost say, diagonal-wise. They have Bulgarian, Montenegrin, Serbian, Turkish, Albanian and Greek names but there are only a few important enough for you to remember.

These are the Dinaric Alps, stretching from the Alps of Switzerland to the Gulf of Corinth, the wide bay which separates the northern half of Greece from the southern half, the triangle which the early Greeks mistook for an island (small wonder, since the isthmus of Corinth which connects it with the mainland is only about three and a half miles wide) and which they called the Peloponnesus or the Island of Pelops, who, according to Greek tradition, was the son of Tantalus and a grandson of Zeus, and who at Olympia was honored as the father of all good sportsmen.

The Venetians who conquered Greece during the Middle Ages were prosaic merchants with no interest in a young man who once upon a time in his career had been served up as a roast at his father's dinner table. They found that a map of the Peloponnesus looked very much like the leaf of a mulberry-tree. And so they called it the Morea, and that is the name you will find on all modern atlases.

There are two mountain-ranges in this part of the world which have a separate existence of their own. In the north there are the Balkans which have given their name to the entire peninsula. The Balkans are merely the southern end of a half circle of hills of which the northern part is known as the Carpathians. They are cut off from the rest of the Carpathians by the so-called "Iron Gate"—the narrow ravine through which the Danube has dug itself a path on its way to the sea; and they act as a barrier which forces the Danube to run straight from west to east and to lose itself finally in the Black Sea instead of the Aegean Sea, towards which that river seems bound when it leaves the plains of Hungary.

Unfortunately, this wall separating the peninsula from Roumania is not as high as the Alps and so does not succeed in protecting the Balkan region from the chilly blasts that come blowing down from the great Russian plain. The northern part of the peninsula therefore is quite familiar with snow and ice, but ere the clouds can reach Greece they are stopped by a second wall, the Rhodope Mountains which, by their very name of the "rose-covered hills" (the same word as you will find in rhododendron, the rose-tree, and in Rhodes, the "rose-covered island" of the Aegean), indicate a milder climate.

The Rhodope Mountains reach a height of almost 9000 feet. The highest top in the Balkans, situated near the famous Shipka pass which the Russian armies forced in September of 1877 amidst a great deal of discomfort, is only 8000 feet. The Rhodope Mountains therefore play a very important part in deciding the climate of the rest of the peninsula, and for good measure there is snow-covered Olympus, 10,000 feet high,

Greece

which stands sentinel over the plains of Thessaly, where the real Greece begins.

This fertile plain of Thessaly was once upon a time an inland sea. But the river Peneus (the Salambria of the modern map) cut itself a road-bed through the famous valley of Tempe, and the vast Thessalian lake emptied itself into the Gulf of Saloniki and became dry land. As for Thessaly, the granary of ancient Greece, the Turks neglected it, as they neglected everything, not so much through wickedness of heart as that hopeless Mohammedan inertia which answers all questions of immediate practical importance with a shrug of the shoulder and a brief "What is the use?" And as soon as the Turks had been driven out, the Greek money-lenders got hold of the peasants and continued where the others had left off. Today Thessaly is raising tobacco. It has one harbor, Volo, from which the Argonauts set forth on their quest of the Golden Fleece, a story that was already hoary with age long before the heroes of Troy were born. It also has one industrial town and railroad center, Larissa.

As a matter of curiosity and in order to show how strangely people got scrambled in the olden days, I might mention that this city in the heart of the Greek land of Thessaly has a negro quarter of its own. The Turks, who did not care who got killed fighting their battles for them, had imported several regiments of Sudanese natives from their Egyptian possessions to help them suppress the great Greek uprising of 1821–1829. Larissa was their headquarters during that war and after the war the poor Sudanese were forgotten. They remained stranded and they are still there.

But you will meet with stranger things than that ere we get through. You will hear of Red Indians in northern Africa and Jews in eastern China and horses on an uninhabited island in the Atlantic Ocean. This much for the benefit of the "pure race" enthusiasts.

From Thessaly we cross the Pindus Mountains into the Epirus. This mountain-range, as high as the Balkans, has always been a barrier between the Epirus and the rest of Greece.

Why Aristotle should have identified this part of the world with the original home of the human race will ever remain a mystery, for it is a poverty-stricken country of high hills and wandering herds of cattle, without harbors or decent roads. Of its early population little remained when the Romans on one of their campaigns sold 150,000 Epirotes into slavery (the famous Roman way of establishing law and order). But two parts of the Epirus, separated from the mainland by narrow stretches of water from the Ionian Sea, are interesting. One is Ithaca, the legendary home of long-suffering Odysseus, and the other is Corfu, the early home of the Phaeacians, whose king, Alcinous, was the father of Nausicaa, loveliest of all women in ancient literature and an example of gracious hospitality until the end of time. Today the island (one of the Ionian islands, occupied first by Venice, later by the French, then by the English until ceded by them to Greece in 1869) is chiefly famous as the place of retreat for the defeated Serbian armies in the year 1916 and as a target for some very loose and useless shooting on the part of the Fascist navy only a few years ago. It has however a great future as a winter resort, but is undoubtedly situated on one of the great European earthquake belts.

The Dinaric Alps have a bad record as earthquake producers, while the neighboring island of Zante suffered most severely from an earthquake as recently as 1893. But earthquakes have never yet prevented people from going where it was pleasant to be and we can discount the element of danger. We shall meet with a great many volcanoes on our trip around the world and still find their gentle slopes more densely populated than the less energetic parts of the world's brittle surface. Explain this who may. I proceed from the Epirus further towards the south, and behold, Boeotia!

I mention this region, which lies like a vast, empty soup-plate between the hills of Attica towards the south and Thessaly and the mountains of the Epirus towards the north, most particularly because it is a classical example of that influence of Nature upon Man which I mentioned in the beginning of this book.

To the average Greek of the good classical days, a Boeotian, although he came from the land of Mount Parnassus, the home of the Muses, on the slopes of which the Delphic Oracle had established its shrine, was a clod-hopper, a heavy-witted rustic, a clown, an oaf, a lout, a gawk, a thick-skulled dunderpate, pre-destined for all the cheap slap-stick humor of the early stage.

And yet, the Boeotians by nature were no less intelligent than the rest of the Greeks. Epaminondas, the strategian, and Plutarch, the biographer, were Boeotians but they had left their native haunts at an early age. Those who remained behind suffered

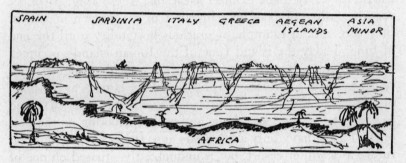

The Mediterranean

from the poisonous vapors that arose from the swamp-ridden borders of Lake Copais. In plain, modern medical terms, they probably were victims of malaria, a disease which does not tend to make people brilliant-minded.

The French Crusaders, who set up as rulers of Athens during the entire thirteenth century, began to drain these quagmires, and conditions among the Boeotians improved. The Turks, of course, allowed the mosquitoes to breed to their hearts' content and the Boeotians grew worse. Finally under the new kingdom, a French and afterwards an English company let the muddy waters of Lake Copais flow into the Euboic Sea and turned the bottom of this inland sea into fertile pasture-land.

Today the Boeotian is no more Boeotian than an Athenian or Brooklyn bootblack and, Heaven knows, they are quick-witted enough to get an extra nickel out of a Scotchman or Armenian. The marshes are gone, the vapors are gone, the malaria mosquitoes are gone. And an entire country-side that had been derided for centuries as Exhibit A of rustic numskullery and ignoble imbecility was restored to normal behavior by the draining of a few miasmic swamps.

And then we come to Attica, most interesting of the Greek lands. Nowadays we take the train that goes from Larissa to Athens and that connects with the trunk-lines to Europe. But in the olden days, those who wanted to get from Thessaly in the north to Attica in the south had only one route at their disposal, the route of the famous pass of Thermopylae. It was not really a pass in the modern sense of the word—a narrow gap between two high mountains. It was a narrow track, about 45 feet wide, between the rocks of Mount Oeta and the Gulf of Halae, which was part of the Euboic Sea. It was here that Leonidas and three hundred Spartans sacrificed themselves to the last man to save Europe from Asia, when they tried to halt the advancing hordes of Xerxes in the year 480 B. C. Two hundred years later it was here that the barbarous Gauls were prevented from invading Greece. Even as late as the years 1821 and 1822 the pass played an important military role in the war between Turks and Greeks. Today the pass is no longer visible. The sea has retreated almost three miles from the mainland and all that remains is a fifth-rate bathing establishment where people afflicted with rheumatism and sciatica try to find relief in those hot springs ("thermos" is Greek for "hot", as you will know from "thermometer" and "thermos bottle") which gave their name to a battle-field which shall be remembered as long as mankind continues to honor those who died in defending a lost cause.

As for Attica itself, it is a small triangle—a rocky promontory bordered by the blue waters of the Aegean Sea. Between its many hills lie numerous small valleys, all of them having direct access to the sea and kept fresh and pure by the breezes that come in from the water-front. The ancient Athenians declared that their sharpness of wit and clearness of vision were due to the delightful air they breathed. They may have been right. There were no stagnant Boeotian pools to encourage the thrifty malaria mosquito. As a result, the Athenians were healthy and kept healthy. They were the first people to recognize that man is not divided into two equal parts, body and soul, but that body and soul are one, that a healthy body is necessary to encourage a healthy soul, that a healthy soul is an indispensable part of a healthy body.

In that air it was possible to look all the way from the Acropolis to the Pentelian Mountains that dominated the plain of Marathon and provided the city with marble. But it was not only the climate that made the Athenians what they were, and for that matter are to this very day.

There was the sea that gave the people of Attica direct access to every part of the inhabited and uninhabited world. And there was that geological freak of Nature which had dumped a steep but flat-topped miniature mountain, a sort of mesa more than 500 feet high, 870 feet long and 435 feet wide, right in the heart of the plain surrounded by Mt. Hymettus (home of the best Athenian honey), by Mt. Pentelicus and by that Aegaleus from the slopes of which the unhappy fugitives from Athens watched the annihilation of the Persian fleet in the straits of Salamis a few days after the troops of Xerxes had set their city on fire. This flat-topped, steeply sloped hill had first of all attracted the immigrants from the north, for there they found what we all need—food and safety.

It is a curious fact that both Athens and Rome (or modern London or Amsterdam), the most important settlements of ancient Europe, were situated not immediately on the sea but several miles away from it. The example of Cnossos, the Cretan center of the Mediterranean world hundreds of years before either of them had been founded, may have acted as a warning of that dreadful thing that may happen when one is forever exposed to a surprise attack by pirates. Athens, however, was more conveniently near to the sea than Rome. A short time after he had landed in the Piraeus, then as now the harbor of Athens, the Greek sailor could be with his family. The Roman merchant needed three days for the trip. That was a little too long. He lost the habit of going back to his home city, settled down in the port at the mouth of the Tiber, and Rome gradually lost that intimate touch with the high seas which is of such tremendous benefit to all nations aspiring to world domination.

But gradually these mesa people, these inhabitants of the "top city" (for that is what *acro-polis* meant) moved into the plain, built houses around the foot of their hill, surrounded them with walls, finally connected these fortifications and those of the Piraeus and settled down to a glorious life of trade and robbery which ere long made their impregnable fortress the richest metropolis of the entire Mediterranean Sea. Then their Acropolis was given up as a place of abode and became a shrine—a shrine which lifted its white marble temples proudly against the violet-tinted sky of Attica—a shrine which even today, when an explosion in a Turkish powder-magazine has destroyed some of its more important buildings (during the siege of Athens in 1645), remains unique and sublime among those show-places where the genius of man is revealed in its highest forms of perfection.

When Greece regained her liberty in 1829, Athens had dwindled down to a mere village of 2000 inhabitants. In 1870 it had a population of 45,000. Today it has 700,000, a growth that is only paralleled by some of our own western cities. If the Greeks had not gambled with fate immediately after the Great War and had not foolishly thrown away all those immensely valuable possessions they had acquired in Asia Minor, Athens today would be the center of a mighty Aegean power. But all that may still happen in the near future. The mills of the Gods grind slowly but they continue day and night. And the city called after the shrewdest and wisest daughter of Zeus, born out of her father's brain, has shown itself to have a tremendous power of recuperation.

This brings us to the last and most distant part of the great

Greek peninsula and there, alas, our confident and prophetic words of hope are of no further avail. The curse that rested upon Pelops on account of his father's great wickedness has never been lifted from the land upon which that unfortunate prince bestowed his name. Here, hidden from the sea by mighty mountain-ranges, lay the idyllic land of Arcadia, praised by all poets as the home of simple but honest and lovable shepherds and shepherdesses. Poets are apt to wax most enthusiastic about that of which they know least. For the Arcadians were not more honest than the rest of the Greeks. If they did not practice the shabby tricks of their more sophisticated fellow-Hellenes, it was not because they disapproved of them. It was simply because they had never heard of them. It is true they did not steal, but there was nothing worth the taking in a country of dates and goats. They did not lie, but their hamlets were so small that everybody knew everything about everybody anyway. And if they kept away from the refined and decadent luxuries of those Gods worshipped in Eleusis and other Athenian centers of mysteries, they had a deity of their own, the great God Pan, who could give cards and spades to all the other Olympians when it came to coarse jokes and the low wit of barn-yard yokels.

It is true, then as now the Arcadians could fight, but it did them little good, for like most peasants they loathed discipline and could never agree who would be their commander-in-chief.

Southward of mountainous Arcadia stretched the plain of Laconia, a fertile plain, infinitely more fertile than the valleys of Attica, but sterile as to independence of thought and barren of all ideas that stretched beyond the mere necessities of life. In this plain the most curious city of antiquity was situated. Its name was Sparta and it stood for everything the northern Greeks held in abhorrence. Athens said "yea" unto life and Sparta said "nay". Athens believed in inspired brilliancy, while Sparta worked towards efficiency and service. Athens proudly preached the divine right of her exceptional individuals. Sparta reduced all men to the dreary monotony of the mediocre. Athens opened its doors

wide to foreigners. Sparta kept them out of the country or murdered them. The Athenians were born traders, but no Spartan
was allowed to soil his hands with business. If we are to judge
by the final success of these two policies, the town of Sparta did
not do so well. The spirit of Athens has penetrated the whole
world. The spirit of Sparta has gone the way of the city that
gave it birth—it has disappeared.

You will find a place called Sparta on the modern maps of
Greece. It is a village composed of small scale farmers and humble keepers of silk-worms. It was built in 1839 on the spot where
ancient Sparta was supposed to have stood. English enthusiasm
provided the money, a German architect drew the plans. But no
one wanted to go and live there. Today after almost a century
of effort, it has 4000 inhabitants. The old curse of Pelops! A
curse that makes itself felt even more distinctly in another part
of the peninsula—a curse that comes to full fruition in the prehistoric fortress of Mycenae.

The ruins of Mycenae are not far away from Nauplia, the
best-known harbor of the Peloponnesus, situated on the gulf of
that name. The town was destroyed five centuries before the
birth of Christ. But to us people of the modern world it is of
more direct importance than even Athens or Rome. For it was
here that long before the beginning of written history, civilization for the first time touched the shores of savage Europe.

In order to understand how this came about, look at the three
half-submerged ridges of the great Balkan hand that reaches
from Europe to Asia. These fingers are composed of islands.
Those islands nowadays belong to Greece except for a few in the
eastern part of the Aegean which Italy has occupied and continues to occupy for the reason that no other nation wants to go
to war on account of a few worthless rocks in a distant sea. For
convenience' sake we divide those islands into two groups, the
Cyclades near the Grecian coast and the Sporades near the coast
of Asia Minor. Those islands, as St. Paul already knew, are
within short sailing distance of each other. And they formed the

bridge across which the civilization of Egypt and Babylonia and Assyria moved westward until it reached the shores of Europe. Meanwhile that civilization, under the influence of those early immigrants of Asiatic origin who had settled down on the Aegean islands, had already been very distinctly "easternized" and it was in that form that finally it reached Mycenae which should have become what Athens afterwards became, the center of the classical Greek world.

Why didn't this happen? We do not know. No more than we know why Marseilles, the logical successor to Athens as the dominating power of the Mediterranean, should have been forced to surrender that honor to a very modern and very up-start village called Rome. The short-lived glory of Mycenae and its abrupt decline will ever remain a mystery.

But, you will object, all that is history and this is supposed to be a book on geography. But in Greece, as in many ancient lands, history and geography have become so interwoven that the two cannot be discussed separately. And from a modern point of view there are only a few geographical items really worth men-tioning.

The isthmus of Corinth has been pierced by a canal about three miles long but too shallow and too narrow for large ves-sels. Greece, as a result of a series of wars with Turkey (alone and together with Bulgaria, Serbia and Montenegro), almost doubled its territory, then lost one-half of all those new acquisi-tions because in her dreams of grandeur she underestimated the fighting qualities of the Turks. The Greeks today, as in ancient times, take readily to the sea, and the blue and white flag of the republic (the ancient Bavarian colors imported by the first king of the country after it had regained its independence in 1829) is to be seen in every part of the Mediterranean. Also occasionally in the North Sea and the Baltic, where such Grecian vessels, un-like the Grecian urn of Keats, are famous for their slovenliness and dirt. And for the rest, there are the figs and the olives and currants that are exported to all countries that care for such delicacies.

Will Greece ever return to her ancient glories as so many of her people hope and fervently expect? Perhaps.

But a nation overrun in turn by Macedonians, by Romans, by Goths and Vandals and Herulians and Slavs, conquered and turned into a colony by Normans, Byzantines, Venetians and the unspeakable riff-raff of the Crusades, then almost completely depopulated and repopulated by Albanians, forced to live under Turkish domination for almost four entire centuries and used as a base of supply and a battlefield by the forces of the Allies in the Great War—such a nation has suffered certain hardships from which it will find it extremely difficult to recuperate. As long as there is life, there is hope. But it is a mighty slender one.

IX

ITALY, THE COUNTRY WHICH DUE TO ITS GEOGRAPHICAL
SITUATION COULD PLAY THE ROLE OF A SEA-
POWER OR A LAND-POWER, AS THE
OCCASION DEMANDED

GEOLOGICALLY speaking, Italy is a ruin—all that is left of a
vast mountain complex which formed a square like modern
Spain but which withered away (as even the hardest rock will
do in the course of a few million years) and finally disappeared
beneath the waters of the Mediterranean. Only the easternmost
part of that ancient mountain-range is visible today, the Apennines, which reach from the valley of the Po to Calabria in the
toe of the boot.

Corsica, Elba and Sardinia are visible remnants of that high
prehistoric plateau. Sicily was of course another part of it. Here
and there in the Tyrrhenian Sea small islands betray the presence of ancient pinnacles. It must have been a terrific tragedy
when all that land was captured by the sea. But as it happened
some 20,000,000 years ago, when the earth suffered from the
last of its great volcanic epidemics, there was no one present to
tell the tale. And in the end it proved to be of enormous benefit
to those who afterwards were to occupy the Apennine peninsula,
for it gave them a country enjoying such sublime natural advantages of climate, soil and geographical location that it seemed almost predestined to become the dominating power of antiquity
and one of the most important factors of the development and
dissemination of art and knowledge.

Greece was the hand that reached out to Asia, caught hold of
the ancient civilization of the valleys of the Nile and the Euphrates, and re-exported this article to the rest of Europe. But
all that time the Greeks themselves remained something apart

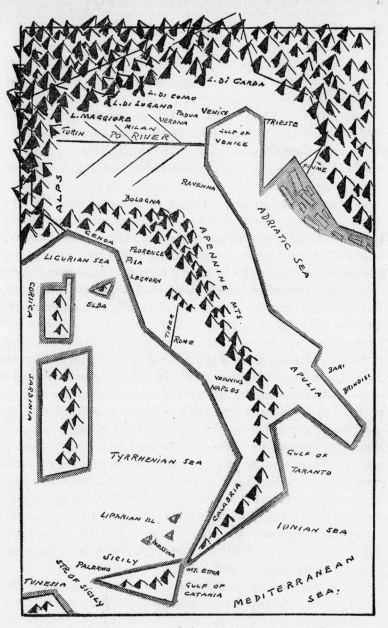

Italy

from the continent upon which they bestowed their manifold blessings. Their country might just as well have been an island. The fact that it was a peninsula did not do it any good, for rows and rows of mountains, indeed, the whole of the Balkan range, cut it off from the rest of European humanity.

Italy, on the other hand, enjoyed the advantages of being both a sort of island, surrounded on three sides by the sea, while at the same time being very distinctly a part of the land-mass of northern Europe. We often overlook that fact and talk of Spain and Greece and Italy as if they more or less resembled each other. Spain and Greece had much in common. The Pyrenees and the Balkan mountain-ranges were impassable barriers between north and south. But the great plain of the Po was a salient that reached well up into the heart of Europe. The northernmost cities of Italy enjoy a higher latitude than Geneva or Lyons. Even Milan and Venice are of a higher latitude than Bordeaux and Grenoble, while Florence, which we unconsciously associate with the very heart of Italy, is almost on a line with Marseilles.

And furthermore, the Alps, although much higher than the Pyrenees and the mountains of the Balkans, had been formed in such a way as to offer comparatively easy access from south to north. The Rhine and the Rhône, running parallel with the northern frontier of Italy, divided the Alps into two halves; and therefore the valleys of the little brooks and streams running into the Rhine and Rhône, making an angle of ninety degrees with the mother river, offered convenient short-cuts into the plain of the Po—as Hannibal, with a whole circus of elephants, was the first to prove, to the great detriment of the unsuspecting Romans.

Italy therefore was able to play a dual role, that of a maritime nation, dominating the Mediterranean, and that of a continental power, conquering and exploiting the rest of Europe.

When the Mediterranean ceased to be a world sea and the discovery of America made the Atlantic Ocean the center of commerce and civilization, Italy lost its former advantages. Without coal and iron she could not hope to compete with the industrial countries of the west. But for almost twelve hundred years, from the founding of Rome in 753 B. C. till the fourth century of our era, Italy dominated and administered every part of Europe south of the Elbe and the Danube.

Unto the wild Germanic tribes that had just arrived from Asia and were now quarreling violently for the possession of this desirable "far west" Italy gave their first conception of law and order and the superior advantages of a semi-civilized life over the uncertainties and filth of a merely nomadic existence. Of course she enriched herself incredibly at the expense of every one else. But while taking a heavy toll of taxes, she delivered certain "goods" that were to shape the destinies of all those different regions for all times to come. And even today, the more than casual observer, visiting Paris or Bucharest, Madrid or Treves, will at once be struck by a certain similarity of look and outlook on the part of the inhabitants. He will be surprised that he can read the signs on the shops, no matter whether they are in French or Spanish or Roumanian or Portuguese. And then he will realize: "I am in an old Roman colony here. All this land once upon a time belonged to Italy just as the Philippines today belong to us. The first houses were built by Italian architects, the first streets were laid out by Italian generals, the first traffic and commercial regulations were written in the tongue of central Italy", and he will begin to appreciate what tremendous natural advantages were enjoyed by this country that was at once an island and part of the mainland.

At the same time the fortunate geological accident which had enabled Italy to conquer the whole of the known world carried with it certain very decided drawbacks. A country born out of volcanic upheavals was forever threatened to be killed by the very mother that had given it birth. For Italy is not only the classical land of moonlit ruins, orange trees, mandolin concerts and picturesque peasants. It is also the classical land of volcanic eruptions.

Every Italian who reaches the normal threescore and ten (easy in a country where laughter and gracious manners seem to come as natural as grouchy grins and boorishness do in other less favored parts of the world) is sure to have been an active participant in at least one major earthquake and a couple of minor ones before he is reverently carried to the family lot in the Campo Santo. The seismograph (most reliable of instruments I wish all our instruments were as painstakingly true) reported 300 quakes for the period of 1905–1907 alone. The next year, 1908, Messina was completely destroyed. If you want a few vital statistics (and mere figures are often infinitely more eloquent than pages of print) here is the record for the island of Ischia, situated just opposite Capri.

That island alone suffered from earthquakes in 1228, 1302, 1762, 1796, 1805, 1812, 1827, 1828, 1834, 1841, 1851, 1852, 1863, 1864, 1867, 1874, 1875, 1880, 1881, 1883, etc., etc.

As a result of these millions of years of volcanic eruptions, enormous tracts of Italian land got gradually covered with thick layers of tufa or tuff, a soft sort of rock composed of volcanic ash, thrown up by craters when in a state of violent eruption. These layers of tufa are very porous and they have a very decided influence upon the landscape of the entire peninsula. Some of those tufa fields cover areas of not less than 4000 square miles and the classical seven hills of Rome were really nothing but heaps of hardened volcanic ash.

But there are other geological developments, also the result of prehistoric upheavals, which make the soil of Italy so treacherous. The Apennines, which run the entire length of the peninsula, dividing it nearly into halves, are for a great part composed of limestone, a softish substance which lies on top of the older and harder rock formations. This limestone is apt to slide. The ancient Italians were so thoroughly familiar with this fact that even in the absence of volcanic upheavals they used to inspect the boundary lines of every large country estate once in twenty years to see whether the stone marks, indicating where one man's property ended and another man's began, were still in their correct position. And the modern Italians are made to realize this "sliding process" of their soil (and in a very costly

and painful way) every time a railroad is pushed out of shape
or a road is squashed to pieces or another village is rolled down
the embankment of a lovely green mountain.

When you visit Italy you will be surprised at the large number of towns perched on the tops of high hills. The usual explanation is that the original inhabitants fled to those eagles'
nests for safety's sake. That, however, was only a secondary consideration. When they moved to those uncomfortable pinnacles,
so far removed from the wells of the valley and the main routes
of communication, they did so primarily to avoid the dangers of
sliding to death. Near the top of the mountains the base rocks of
the ancient geological structure usually came to the surface and
offered future residents a permanent place of abode. The sides
of the hills, covered with soapy limestone, were as dependable
as quicksand. Hence those picturesque villages that look so marvellous from a distance and are so incredibly uncomfortable once
one is inside.

And this brings us to a consideration of modern Italy. For
Italy, unlike Greece, does not merely have its future behind it.
It works intelligently and courageously towards a new goal, and
if it keeps long hours, it does so to undo the damage of a thousand years of neglect and once more regain its ancient and honorable status among the ranking nations of the earth.

In the year 1870 Italy once more became a united nation and
as soon as the struggle for independence was over and the foreign
rulers had been driven back across the Alps (where they belonged) the Italians started upon the gigantic and well nigh
hopeless task of putting their long-neglected house in order.

First of all they turned their attention to the valley of the
Po—the larder from which the whole peninsula could be conveniently fed. The Po is not a very long river as rivers go. As
a matter of fact, if you will look at the picture of the comparative
length of rivers, you will notice that the Volga is the only European river that is a fit candidate for such honors. The Po, which
keeps close to 45° N. Lat., is only 420 miles long but its basin
area, the territory from which it draws its tributaries and which

therefore comes under its direct influence, is 27,000 square miles. That is not as much as several other rivers have, but the Po has some other qualities which make it unique.

It is navigable for fully five-sixths of its entire length and it is one of the fastest delta-builders of the world. Every year it adds almost three-quarters of a square mile to its delta and pushes it 200 feet further outward. If it continues to do this for another ten centuries, it will have reached the opposite coast of the Istrian peninsula and Venice will be situated on a lake, separated from the rest of the Adriatic by a dam seven miles wide.

Part of this vast amount of sediment which the Po carries to the sea has of course sunk to the bottom of the river and has filled it up with a layer of solid substance several feet thick. In order to keep the ever-rising river from flooding the surrounding landscape, the people living along its banks had to build dikes. They began to do this in Roman times. They are still doing it. As a result, the surface of the Po is much higher than the plain through which it flows. In several villages the dikes are thirty feet high and the river runs at the same height as the roofs of the houses.

But the Po region is famous for something else. Once upon a time, and not so very long ago, geologically speaking, the entire northern plain of Italy was part of the Adriatic Sea. Those lovely Alpine gorges which are now so popular with the summer tourists were narrow bays, like the fjords, the submerged valleys of the modern Norwegian mountains. These valleys were the outlet for the water that descended from the glaciers which then covered the greater part of Europe and of course a great deal more of the Alps than they do today. Glaciers get thickly covered with stones that roll down on them from the mountain slopes between which they pass on their way downwards. Such fringes of rocks are called moraines. When two glaciers meet, two moraines are bound to combine into a moraine double as high as the original ones, which is then called a "median moraine", and when the glacier finally melts, it drops this rocky ballast, which is called the "terminal moraine".

Erosion

These terminal moraines are a sort of geological beaver-dam, for they close the uppermost part of the valley off from the lower. As long as the glacier period lasts, there will be enough water to make the terminal moraines a negligible hindrance for the water on its downward course. But gradually, as the glaciers disappear and there is less and less water, the terminal moraine rises higher than the water and we get a lake.

All the north Italian lakes, the Lago Maggiore, the Lago di Como and the Lago di Garda, are moraine lakes. When man appeared upon the scene and began his works of irrigation, those moraine lakes acted as handy reservoirs. For in the spring, when the snow began to melt, they caught the surplus water which, if it had descended upon the valley in one solid body, would have caused the most destructive inundations. The Lago di Garda can rise twelve feet and the Lago Maggiore as much as fifteen feet and still take care of the extra water. A simple system of locks will then do the rest and tap those lakes according to the necessities of the day.

At a very early date the inhabitants of the great Po plain began to make use of this fortunate circumstance. They connected with canals the hundreds of little streams that feed the Po. They built dams and dikes and today thousands of cubic feet of water pass through these canals every few minutes.

It was an ideal region for the growing of rice. In the year 1468 the first rice plants were introduced by a Pisa merchant and today the rice-terraces are a common sight of the central plain of the Po. Other crops, corn and hemp and beet-root, were added and the vast plain, although it has less rainfall than the rest of the Italian peninsula, is the most fertile region of the entire country.

But not only did it provide man with food. It also looked after his wife's garments. Early during the ninth century, the mulberry tree, which is the basic necessity for the cultivation of the silk-worm, made its entrance, brought hither from China by way of Byzantium, the eastern half of the Roman Empire, which survived until 1453 when the Turks took its chief city, Constantinople, and turned it into the capital of their own empire.

The mulberry tree needs a great deal of heat. It found ideal living conditions in Lombardy, the plain of the Po, so-called after the Lombards or Long Beards, a Teutonic tribe from the mouth of the Elbe who lived here for a long time. Today almost half a million people are engaged in the silk industry and their product ranks much higher than that of China and Japan, the original home of Bombyx Mori, that inconspicuous little insect who provides us with the most luxurious of our wearing apparel.

No wonder that the whole of the plain is densely populated. The original town builders, however, kept at a safe distance from the river. Their engineering technique had not yet far enough advanced to provide them with reliable dikes and furthermore they feared the marshes which were an annual occurrence after the spring floods. Turin, the old residence of the house of Savoy, which now rules over the whole of Italy, and the connecting point for the passes that lead into France and Switzerland (the pass of the Mont Cenis going to France and the St. Bernard pass, famous for its dogs and monastery, giving access to the valley of the Rhône) is the only city of any importance directly situated on the Po. But it is so high that it needed have no fear of drowning. As for the other cities, Milan, the capital of that region, meeting-point for five important trade-routes (the St. Gothard road, the Simplon, the small St. Bernard, the Maloja and the Splügen pass), lies half way between the river and the Alps. Verona, the end station of the Brenner pass, one of the oldest connections between Germany and Italy, lies at the foot of the Alps themselves. Cremona, famous as the home of Stradivarius, Guarnerius and the Amati family, the fiddle-making dynasties, lies on the Po, but Padua and Modena, Ferrara and Bologna (the home of one of the oldest universities of Europe) are all at a safe distance from that main artery upon which they depend for their prosperity.

The same is true of two of the most romantic cities of the ancient world, Venice and Ravenna. Venice, the town in which 157 canals, 28 miles in length, serve the purpose of streets, was originally a place of shelter for those who no longer considered them-

Northern and Southern exposure

selves safe on the mainland and who preferred the discomforts
of the mud banks thrown up by the Po and several smaller
rivers to the dangers that followed in the wake of the Great
Migrations. Once there, these fugitives discovered that they had
a gold mine in the salt which lay there, so to speak, for the pick-
ing. Their salt monopoly started them on the road to riches.
Their straw-covered huts became marble palaces. Their fishing
boats assumed the size of warships. For almost three entire centuries they were the leading colonial power of the entire civilized
world and high-hatted Pope, Emperor and Sultan with a most
haughty and at the same time a most elegant air. When news of
the safe return of Columbus and the discovery (the supposed
discovery, of course) of the road to India reached the Rialto,
their business quarter, there was a panic. All stocks and bonds
dropped fifty points. For once the brokers were prophets, for
Venice never recovered from this blow. Her well-protected
trade-routes became a useless investment. Lisbon and Seville
succeeded her as the international store-house towards which all
of Europe turned for its spices and other Asiatic and American
products. Venice, gorged with gold, became the Paris of the
eighteenth century. All the rich young men who cared for a genteel education and some rather less genteel entertainment went
to Venice. When the carnival began to last the greater part of the
year, the end had come. Napoleon conquered the city with a cor-
poral's squad. The canals are still there for you to admire. Another twenty years and the motor-boat will have destroyed them.

The other city, also a product of Po mud, was Ravenna. Today it is an inland city removed from the Adriatic by six miles of
mud. A dull hole, a city that must have driven such famous
guests as Dante and Byron to drink and distraction. During the
fifth century of our era it was more important than the New
York of today, for it was the capital of the Roman Empire—it
harbored an enormous garrison and was the main naval base of
that time, with the largest wharves and timber supplies.

In the year 404 the Emperor decided that Rome was no
longer safe. The barbarians were getting too powerful. And so

he moved to the "city in the sea" where he had a much better chance to protect himself against surprise attacks. Here he and his descendants lived and ruled and loved, as you may see to this very day when you stand speechless before those incredible mosaics of that dark-eyed woman who started life as a dancing girl in the circus of Constantinople and died in an odor of sanctity as Theodora, the beloved wife of the famous Emperor Justinian.

Then the town was conquered by the Goths and turned into the capital of their newly founded empire. Then the lagoons began to fill up. Then Venice and the Pope fought for it. Then for a while it became the home of that pathetic exile, whose services to his native city of Florence had been rewarded by a threat of being burned at the stake. He spent silent hours among those famous pine forests that surrounded the city. Then he descended into his grave. And soon afterwards the famous old imperial residence followed his example.

One more word about northern Italy. The kingdom has no coal but it has an almost unlimited supply of water-power. This water-power was just being harnessed when the war broke out. The next twenty years will see a tremendous development of this cheap form of electricity. The lack of raw materials will always remain a difficult problem. But with the proverbial industry of the average Italian citizen, his very sober mode of living and his moderate needs, Italy will be a dangerous rival for other countries which are rich in raw material but poor in man-power.

On the western side, the great plain of the Po is cut off from the Mediterranean by the Ligurian Alps, the connecting link between the Alps proper and the Apennines. The southern slopes of the Ligurian Alps, completely protected against the cold breezes from the north, form part of the famous Riviera, the winter playground of all Europe, or rather of that part of Europe which can afford a lengthy railroad trip and fairly expensive hotels. Its chief city is Genoa, the chief port of the modern kingdom and a city of the most imposing marble palaces, relics of the day when Genoa was the most dangerous rival of Venice for the colonial spoils of the Near East.

Toward the south of Genoa lies another small plain, that of the river Arno. The Arno takes its origin among the mountains about twenty-five miles north-east of Florence. It flows through the heart of that city which during the Middle Ages lay on the highroad that connected Rome, the center of Christianity, with the rest of Europe and which was able to use this favored commercial position so cleverly that ere long it became the most important banking center of the world. One family especially, that of the Medici (they started life as doctors, hence the three pills in their coat of arms, which became the three golden balls of our own pawnshops) showed such brilliant gifts for that sort of work that they finally became hereditary rulers of the whole of Tuscany and were able to make their home town the most marvellous artistic center of the fifteenth and sixteenth centuries.

From 1865 to 1871 Florence was the capital of the new Italian kingdom. Then it dropped slightly back in importance, but it still is one of those places that one ought to have seen to appreciate how beautiful life can be if money and good taste happen to be present in a well-balanced ratio.

The two cities near the mouth of the Arno, which flows through one of the loveliest garden spots to be found anywhere outside of the island of Java, are merely of some slight historical interest. Pisa has a leaning tower which leans because the architects were not very careful in laying their foundations, but which proved very handy when Galileo wanted to study the habits of falling objects. The other town is Livorno, which the English, for some curious reason, call Leghorn, and which is chiefly remembered as the town near which Shelley was drowned in the year 1822.

From Livorno southward the old stage-coach road as well as the modern railroad keep close to the seashore. They give the traveller a quick but hazy glimpse of the island of Elba (Napoleon's place of exile until he unexpectedly descended upon France to rush towards the final doom of Waterloo), and then enter the plain of Tiber. This famous river, called the Tevere in Italian, is a sluggish and tawny current, vaguely reminiscent of the Chicago River but not quite so wide, and of the Spree in Berlin, but infinitely less clear. It takes its origin among those Sabine Mountains where the earliest Romans went to steal their wives. In prehistoric times its mouth was only twelve miles west of Rome. Since then it has added two miles to its length, for like the Po, the Tiber is a first-rate mud-carrier. The plain of the Tiber is different from that of the Arno. It is much wider and while the Arno region is healthy and highly fertile, that of the Tiber is barren and a breeder of disease. The very word "malaria" was coined here by those medieval pilgrims who were firmly convinced that the "mal aria"—the "bad air"—was responsible for those dreadful attacks of fever which burned up the body while one was still alive. In consequence of this fear, all the houses in this neighborhood were hermetically sealed as soon as the sun had set. This system of preventive hygiene had one great disadvantage. It kept all the little mosquitoes carefully indoors, but as we only learned about the relationship between malaria and mosquitoes some thirty years ago, we can hardly blame our ancestors for that particular bit of ignorance.

In Roman times this flat territory, the famous Campagna, was decently drained and fairly well populated. But because it lay open and unprotected along the shores of the Tyrrhenian Sea it was an ideal spot for the pirates who infested the whole of the Mediterranean as soon as the Roman policeman had disappeared. The towns were destroyed, the farms deserted, the drainage ditches neglected. Stagnant pools bred malaria mosquitoes and all during the Middle Ages and even as late as thirty years ago, this entire region from the mouth of the Tiber to the Pontine marshes near Monte Circeo was either avoided or passed through as fast as the unfortunate horse could drag the rattling coach.

Arises the question, Why should the most important city of the ancient world have been founded in a plague-spot? Why indeed? Why was St. Petersburg built in a marsh which took hundreds of thousands of lives to drain? Why was Madrid built on a bleak and treeless plateau hundreds of miles removed from everywhere? Why is Paris situated at the bottom of a large saucer, forever dripping with rain? I don't know. Chance mixed with greed—or that famous political foresight which covers such a multitude of blunders! Or chance alone—or greed alone. I don't know. And I am not writing a handbook of philosophy.

Rome was built where it was built, regardless of an unhealthy climate, scorching summers, chilly winters, and an absence of all decent communications. And yet it grew to be the center of a world-wide empire, the holy shrine of a world-wide religion. Under such circumstances, don't look for a single explanation. Look for a thousand different and inter-locking explanations. But don't look for them here, for it would take three volumes like the present one to get to the bottom of the secret.

Nor shall I go into details about the city itself. For I am the last person in the world to do justice to the Eternal City of the eastern hemisphere. It may have been due to those rebellious ancestors of mine who from the year 50 before the birth of Christ until 1650 of our own era felt themselves in the most cordial discord with everything that emanated from Rome. I ought to have wept, standing on the Forum, and I could only see the gangsters and racketeers who under the name of generals and party leaders despoiled all of Europe and a greater part of Africa and Asia, in exchange for those roads which seem to have been their eternal excuse for much that was unspeakably cruel. I ought to have felt a sense of trembling awe before the church devoted to St. Peter's memory and martyrdom, and I could only deplore the waste of so much money upon a building that had not a single claim to either beauty or charm except that it was "bigger" than any other edifice constructed for a similar purpose. And I longed for the harmony of Florence and Venice—for the well-balanced proportions of Genoa. I know of course that I am particularly alone in these feelings. Petrarch, Goethe, everybody that ever amounted to something, has wept tears upon catching his or her first glimpse of Bramante's dome. We will let it go at that, but rather than spoil your taste for a city

you will sometime see yourself, I duly note that Rome since
the year 1871 is the capital of the kingdom of Italy and that it
harbors a city within a city—the so-called Vatican City—which
was surrendered to the Pope in the year 1930 and now gives the
Pontiff that freedom of action which he had not enjoyed since
that fateful day in September of 1870 when the troops of the
Italian Kingdom entered the city and proclaimed a constitution
instead of that absolute sovereignty which had been the form of
Roman government until then.

The modern city of Rome has few industries. It has some
terrible-looking monuments, a main street which reminds one
of Philadelphia and many people in uniforms. The uniforms
are good.

And that brings us to another city, until recently the most
populous of the entire peninsula, which is a strange mixture of
geography and history and which brings us once more face to
face with that irritating puzzle, "Why didn't this city, enjoying
every possible natural advantage, take the predominant place
occupied by Rome, situated in a dead alley on a mean little
river?"

For Naples was right on the sea front at the head of a magnificent bay. It was older than Rome and the territory around
it was originally among the most fertile spots along the western
Italian coast. Originally the Greeks, who founded Naples, had
done their trading with the dangerous Apennine tribes from the
safe distance of the island of Ischia. But Ischia proved too uncertain a proposition. It was forever trembling with volcanic
emotions and the Greeks had moved to the mainland. The usual
and apparently unavoidable quarrels between the colonists
(bored because far away from home and badly administered by
grasping governors) had caused civil strife and three or four
little settlements had been destroyed (it sounds like the beginning of our own country) when a fresh batch of immigrants had
decided to begin from the very beginning and had built themselves a town which they called "New City" or "Neapolis," which
eventually became Napoli, or in plain English, Naples.

It was already a prosperous commercial center when Rome was still a village inhabited by shepherds, and yet those shepherds must have had a veritable genius for administration, for already in the fourth century before our era Naples was an "ally" of Rome, an agreeable-sounding term, much less harsh than the word "subject" but describing the same sort of relationship. And from that moment on, Naples played the second role, was afterwards overrun by whole hordes of barbarians and finally fell into the hands of one of the Spanish branches of the Bourbon family, whose rule became a byword for scandalous mismanagement and suppression of every form of independent thought and action.

Nevertheless, such were the town's natural advantages that it became the most over-crowded city of the European continent. How all those people lived, nobody knew and nobody cared until the cholera epidemic of 1884 forced the modern kingdom to clean house, which it has done with admirable intelligence and severity.

The background of this marvellous spot is most appropriately occupied by the ornamental Vesuvius. Vesuvius is the neatest and most systematic of all the known volcanoes in the way it spreads its ashes. It rises up to a height of about 4000 feet and is entirely surrounded by lovely little villages which grow a particularly fiery wine, the famous Lacrimae Christi. The ancestors of those villages already existed in Roman days. And why not? Vesuvius was extinct. Since the memory of man, almost a thousand years, there had not been an eruption. There had been vague rumblings in the bowels of the earth in the year 63, but that meant nothing in a country like Italy.

The great surprise was sprung sixteen years later. In less than two days time Herculaneum and Pompeii and a third smaller city were so deeply buried beneath deep layers of lava and ashes that they completely disappeared from the face of the earth. Thereafter, at least once every hundred years, Vesuvius gave signs of being far from extinct. The new crater, rising 1500 feet above the ruins of the original one, is forever belching heavy clouds of smoke. And the statistics for the last 300 years—1631, 1712, 1737, 1754, 1779, 1794, 1806, 1831, 1855, 1872, 1906, etc.—show that Naples is by no means sure of not being turned into another Pompeii.

South of Naples we enter the province called Calabria. It suffers from the fact that it is so far away from the center of the country. It has railroad connections with the north but the coastal regions suffer from malaria, the central part is composed of granite, and agriculture is practiced as it was in the days of the first Roman Republic.

A narrow strait, the strait of Messina, separates Calabria from the island of Sicily. The strait, which is only a little over a mile wide, was famous in antiquity for the presence of two whirl-pools, called Scylla and Charybdis, which were said to swallow up whole ships if they ventured so much as half a yard out of their course. The fear those whirlpools aroused gives us an ade-quate idea of the helplessness of such ancient vessels, for a mod-ern motor-boat putt-putts quietly right through the heart of these eddies without noticing that there is any commotion in the water.

As for Sicily, its geographic position had made it the natural center of the ancient world. Furthermore it enjoyed a delightful climate, was densely populated and highly fertile. But like Naples, life here was perhaps a little too good, a little too easy, a little too comfortable, for the Sicilians during more than two thousand long years submitted peacefully to every form of mis-government that foreign potentates wished to bestow upon them. When they were not being plundered or tortured by Phoenicians or Greeks or Carthaginians (they were only about a hundred miles away from the northern coast of Africa) or Vandals or Goths or Arabs or Normans or French or by any of the 120 princes, 82 dukes, 129 marquises, 28 counts and 356 barons who derived their titles from this happy island, they were repairing their houses from the damage done by the local volcano, Mt. Etna. The eruption of the year 1908, which completely destroyed the most important city, Messina, is still in everybody's memory. It killed more than 75,000 people.

The island of Malta is really a sort of aquatic suburb of Sicily and therefore ought to be mentioned here, although politically speaking it does not form part of Italy. It is a very fertile island and lies midway between Sicily and the coast of Africa. It dominates the trade-route from Europe to Asia by way of the Suez Canal. After the failure of the Crusades, it was presented to the knights of St. John who thereupon called themselves the Maltese Order, Knights of Malta. In the year 1798 Napoleon took the island on his way to drive the English out of India via Egypt and Arabia (a most ingenious plan which however failed because the desert was so much larger than he had expected). This was an excuse for the English to occupy it two years later and they have been there ever since, much to the chagrin of the Italians but not of the Maltese, who on the whole are better off than they would be under a government of their own people.

I have paid little attention to the east coast of Italy, but it is not very important. In the first place, the Apennines used to reach almost as far as the water-front, making large settlements very difficult. As the other side of the Adriatic was practically uninhabitable on account of the steepness of its hills, the development of trade was not encouraged. From Rimini in the north to Brindisi in the south (from where the mail leaves for Africa and India) there are no harbors of any importance.

The heel of the boot is called Apulia. Like Calabria it suffers from the fact that it is so far removed from civilization, and like Calabria its agricultural methods are those practiced in the days when Hannibal honored this region with his presence, waiting twelve long years for the help from Carthage that was never to come.

There is a city in Apulia which enjoys one of the finest natural harbors in the world but which, alas, has no customers. It is called Taranto and it gave its name to a particularly venomous sort of spider and to a dance by which the people who had been bitten by that spider were prevented from falling asleep and entering into a deadly coma.

The Great War has made geography very complicated, for no account of modern Italy is perfect without mention of the Istrian peninsula which was given to the Italians in recognition of the fact that they had turned against their own allies and joined with the enemy. The city of Trieste was the principal export harbor of the old Austro-Hungarian Empire. Having lost its natural hinterland, it is not doing so well. And finally, tucked away at the further end of the bay of Guarnero, is Fiume, another former possession of the Habsburgs. It was the natural outlet for the German people who had no other good port along the whole of the Adriatic coast. But fear that it might eventually be a rival of Trieste made the Italians clamor for Fiume. When the statesmen who concluded the treaty of Versailles refused to give it to them, they simply took it, or rather, their poet d'Annunzio, an excellent writer and a great scoundrel, took it for them. Then the Allies turned it into a "free state", but finally, after prolonged negotiations between Italy and Yugoslavia, it was ceded to Italy.

That ends the present chapter, except for the island of Sardinia. This is really a very big island but it is so far away and so few people have ever been there that we sometimes forget that it exists. But it does exist, the sixth biggest island of Europe, covering an area of almost 10,000 square miles. Being the other extreme of that prehistoric mountain-range of which the Apennines were part, it turns its back upon the mother country. The western coast has excellent harbors. The east coast is steep and dangerous and has not a single convenient landing place. During the last two centuries it has played a curious role in the history of Italy. Until the year 1708 it belonged to Spain. Then it went over into Austrian hands. In 1720 the Austrians swapped Sardinia against Sicily, which then belonged to the Dukes of Savoy, whose capital was the city of Turin, situated on the Po. Thereafter the Dukes of Savoy proudly called themselves Kings of Sardinia (from duke to king is a decided step upward) and that is how the modern kingdom of Italy happened to grow out of a kingdom called after an island which not one Italian in a hundred thousand has ever seen.

X

SPAIN, WHERE AFRICA AND EUROPE CLASHED

THE people of the Iberian peninsula are famous for their very pronounced "racial" characteristics. The Spaniard is supposed to be so "racially" different from any other group of people, that one will recognize him anywhere and under all circumstances by his racial haughtiness, his formal courtesy, his pride, his sobriety and his ability to play the guitar and the castanets. For even music has been dragged in to bolster up the "racial theory".

Perhaps so. Perhaps it is as easy to recognize the Spaniard by his haughtiness and pride as by his ability to play the guitar and the castanets. But I have very serious doubts upon the subject. The Spaniards merely took to playing the guitar and the castanets because in their dry and warm climate they were able to use out-of-door instruments. When it comes however to playing them really well, both Americans and Germans are greatly superior to the native talent. If they play them less frequently than the Spaniards do, that is the result of the climate under which they live. You can't very well play the castanets in the pouring rain of a cold Berlin evening nor the guitar when your fingers tremble with frostbite. And as for those qualities of pride and haughtiness and formal courtesy, weren't they all of them the result of centuries of hard military training, and wasn't this military life the direct outcome of the fact that Spain was geologically speaking quite as much a part of Africa as of Europe? Therefore wasn't it bound to be a battlefield for Europeans and Africans until either one side or the other should have won? In the end, the Spaniard was victorious, but the land for which he had been obliged to fight for such a long

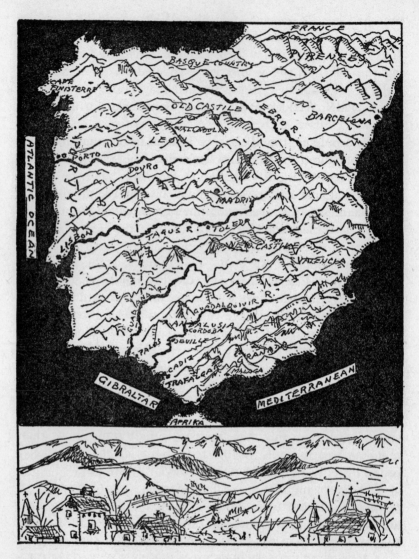

The Iberian Peninsula

time had left its imprint upon him. What would he have developed into if his cradle had stood in Copenhagen or Berne?
Into a perfectly ordinary little Dane or Swiss. Instead of playing the castanets, he would have yodeled, because the steep
walls of a mountain valley with their marvellous echoes invite
one to yodel. And instead of living on a little dry bread and
sour wine, raised with infinite care and patience on his own
neglected soil (neglected again on account of that clash between
Africa and Europe), he would have eaten a lot of butter, necessary to protect his body against the eternal dampness of the
climate, and he would have drunk aquavit, because the abundant
presence of cheap grain would have made gin the almost inevitable national beverage.

And now look at the map. You remember the mountain-
ranges of Greece and Italy. In Greece they ran diagonally across
the country. In Italy they ran in an almost straight line from
north to south, dividing the country into halves but allowing
enough space on both sides for the construction of roads that
coasted the country from one end to the other, while the salient
of the Po plain made the Apennine peninsula an integral part
of the European continent.

In Spain the mountains make horizontal ridges which one
might almost describe as visible degrees of latitude. After a
single glance at the map you will understand how these
mountain-ranges must have acted as barriers to any sort of
orderly progress. They begin with the Pyrenees.

The Pyrenees, 240 miles long, run in a straight and uninterrupted line from the Atlantic to the Mediterranean. They
are not as high as the Alps and therefore it ought to be easier
to cross them by means of mountain passes. But that is not so.
The Alps, although very high, are also very wide and the roads
that run across them, although quite long, rise only very slowly
and offer no special difficulties to either man or pack-horse. The
Pyrenees on the other hand are only 60 miles wide, and as a
result their mountain passes were much too steep for anybody

except a goat or a mule. According to well-seasoned travellers, even the mules experienced difficulties. Trained mountaineers (mostly professional smugglers) were able to get through, but only during a few months of summer. The engineers who built the railroads connecting Spain with the rest of the world real-

A Spanish Canyon

ized this, for they built the two trunk lines from Paris to Madrid and from Paris to Barcelona along the shores of the Atlantic and the Mediterranean. Whereas the Alps have half a dozen railroad lines passing over them or under them, the Pyrenees, between Irun in the west and Figueras in the east, are not pierced by a single tunnel. After all, one can't very well dig a tunnel sixty miles long. Neither can one send trains across a track with an inclination of forty degrees.

There is one fairly easy pass in the west, the famous pass of Roncesvalles, where Roland, Charlemagne's famous Paladin, died loyally serving his master's interests until the moment he succumbed under the last of the Saracens' attacks. Seven hundred years later, another army composed of Frenchmen used this pass as an entrance gate into Spain. They got across the pass itself but were stopped before Pamplona, the city that dominates the road on the southern side. During the siege, one of the Spanish soldiers, a certain Ignatius de Loyola, was desperately wounded through a shot in the leg. While recovering, he had those visions which inspired him to found the Company of Jesus, the famous Society of the Jesuits.

The Jesuits afterwards did more to influence the geographic development of a vast number of countries than any other religious organization, more even than those indefatigable travellers, the Franciscans. It was here that they began, defending the only passage across the center of the Pyrenees.

It was undoubtedly this inaccessibility of the Pyrenees which gave the famous Basque people their chance to maintain themselves from prehistoric times until today and which accounts for the independent Republic of Andorra, very high up in the eastern part of the mountains. The Basques, about 700,000 in number, inhabit a triangle that is bounded by the Gulf of Biscay in the north, by the Spanish province of Navarre in the east, while the western frontier follows a line from the city of Santander to the city of Logroño on the Ebro River. The name Basque means the same as our word Gascon, but it has nothing to do with the cronies of the famous Captain d'Artagnan. The Roman conquerors called them Iberians and called the whole of Spain the Iberian peninsula. As for the Basques themselves, they proudly say that they are Eskualdunak, which sounds very un-European and quite like Eskimo.

Just for good measure, and because your guess is apt to be as sound as mine, here are a few of the current theories about the origin of the Basques. Some of the professors who distil racial theories out of skulls and gutturals, believe them to be connected with those Berbers whom I mentioned several chapters ago as the possible descendants of one of the earliest tribes of prehistoric Europeans, the so-called Cromagnon race. Others claim that they are the survivors who saved themselves on the European continent when the romantic island of Atlantis disappeared beneath the waves of the ocean. Still others hold that they have always been where they are now and don't bother to ask where they came from. Whatever the truth, the Basques have shown remarkable ability in keeping themselves aloof from the rest of the world. They are very industrious. More than a hundred thousand of them have migrated to South America. They are excellent fishermen and sailors and iron workers and they mind their own business and keep off the front page of the newspapers.

The most important city of their country is Vitoria, founded in the sixth century by a Gothic king and scene of that famous battle in which an Irishman by the name of Arthur Wellesley, but better known by his English title of the Duke of Wellington, defeated the armies of a Corsican general by the name of Buonaparte, but better known by his French title of the Emperor Napoleon, and forced the latter to leave Spain for good and all.

As for Andorra, this strange commonwealth numbering fully 5000 inhabitants, connected with the outside world by a bridle-path, is the only surviving specimen of those queer little medieval principalities which retained their independence because, as frontier posts, they might render valuable service to some distant monarch and because afterwards they were too far removed from the busy outside world to attract anybody's attention.

The capital has 600 inhabitants, but the Andorrans, like the Icelanders and the people of San Marino in Italy, were ruling themselves according to their own desires at least eight hundred years before we started our experiment in applied democracy. As a sister republic of great antiquity, Andorra should at least enjoy our sympathetic respect. Eight hundred years is a long time. Where shall we be in the year 2732?

In one other respect, the Pyrenees are quite different from

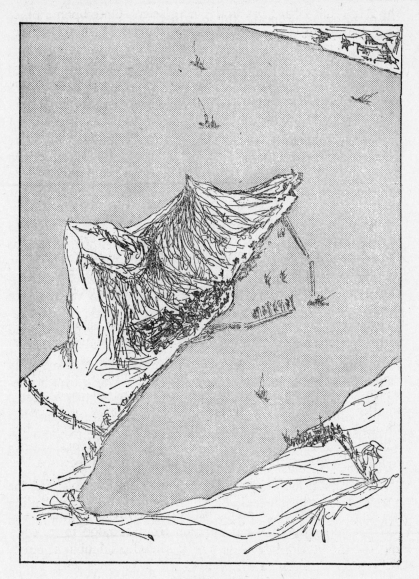

Gibraltar

the Alps. They have practically no glaciers. Once upon a time
they may have been covered more thickly with snow and ice
than the Swiss mountains, but a few square miles of glacier are
all that remain. The same holds true of practically all Spanish
ridges. They are steep and difficult to cross. But even the Sierra
Nevada, the range of southern Andalusia, only shows a few
snow caps from October till March, if that long.

The direction of the mountains was of course of immediate
influence upon the Spanish rivers. They all of them start on or
near the barren high plateau in the center—the remnant of a
terrific prehistoric mountain-range which has worn away in the
course of millions of years, and they hasten to the sea, but at
such terrific speed and with so many waterfalls that none of
them possesses the slightest value as a trade-route. Furthermore,
the long dry summers deprive them of most of their water, as
you may see in Madrid where the sandy bottom of the Man-
zanares provides the children of the capital with a nice imitation
sea-shore for at least five months of the year.

That is why I won't even bother to tell you the names of most
of them. The Tagus on which Lisbon, the Portuguese capital,
is situated is an exception. It is navigable almost as far as the
Spanish-Portuguese frontier. The Ebro too in northern Spain,
which runs through Navarre and Catalonia, can be used by
smaller vessels, but larger ones have to pass most of the way
through a canal which runs parallel with the river itself. The
Guadalquivir (Wadi-el-Kebir or Big River of the Moors) which
connects Seville with the Atlantic Ocean can only be used by
vessels that draw less than fifteen feet. Between Seville and
Cordova, the famous Moorish capital that used to boast of no
less than nine hundred public baths before the Christians captured it and reduced the population from 200,000 to 50,000
and the public baths from 900 to 0, the Guadalquivir is only
available for small vessels. After that it becomes what most
Spanish rivers are, canyon rivers (like our own Colorado) which
are a great hindrance to overland trade while contributing
practically nothing to commerce along the water routes.

Generally speaking, therefore, Nature was not particularly kind to the Spaniards. The great central part of the country consisted of a high plateau, divided into halves by a low mountain ridge. Old Castile is the name of the northern half and New Castile that of the other. The dividing ridge is called the Sierra de Guadarrama.

The name Castile, which merely means "castle", is a very pretty name. But it resembles those boxes of Spanish cigars of which the label is so much more imposing than the quality of the contents. For Castile is as harsh and ill-favored a land as may be found anywhere. When General Sherman, after his march through Georgia, remarked that henceforth a crow wishing to cross the Shenandoah Valley would have to pack his own rations, he was consciously or unconsciously quoting a remark which the Romans made 2000 years before when they said that a nightingale trying to cross Castile would have to take its food and drink with it or it would die of hunger and thirst. For the mountains which surround this plateau are sufficiently high to prevent the clouds that arise from the Atlantic and the Mediterranean from reaching this unfortunate table-land.

As a result, Castile suffers from nine months of inferno and during the other three months of the year it is exposed to the cold and dry winds which sweep across this treeless tract with such a merciless fury that sheep are the only animals that can live here with any degree of comfort, while the only plant that prospers is a variety of grass, the esparto or halfa grass, which is very tough and can therefore be used for basket-work.

But most of this table-land, called the meseta by the Spaniards (a word which you meet again in our own "mesas", familiar to all those who know New Mexico or follow the adventures of Krazy Kat), is something that closely resembles a plain, ordinary desert, and that makes you understand why Spain and Portugal, although much larger than England, have only half the population of the British Isles.

For further particulars about the shabby poverty of these regions, I refer you to the works of a certain Don Miguel de

Cervantes Saavedra. You may remember that the "ingenious hidalgo" who was his hero bore the proud name of Don Quixote de la Mancha. Well, Mancha was one of those inland deserts with which the plateau of Castile was dotted then as it is now, a bleak, inhospitable stretch of waste land near Toledo, the ancient Spanish capital. The name itself was ominous to Spanish ears, for in the original Arabic, *al mansha*, it meant "wilderness" and the poor Don was really the "Lord of the Wilderness".

In a country like that, where Nature is both stingy and obstinate, Man must either settle down to hard labor and force her to yield him the necessities of life, or he can choose to live as the average Spaniard lives, who as a rule can load all the family possessions on the back of one very small donkey. And that brings us to one of the greatest tragedies that ever occurred as a result of a country's unfortunate geographic position.

Eight hundred years ago, the country belonged to the Moors. It was not the first time the Iberian peninsula had been invaded. For the country possessed valuable mineral deposits. Two thousand years ago copper, zinc and silver were what petroleum is today. Wherever copper, zinc and silver were to be found, rival armies would fight for their possession. When the Mediterranean was divided into two great armed camps and when the Semites (of Carthage, a colony of the Phoenicians and ruthless in its exploitation of subject nations) and the Romans (not of Semitic origin but quite as ruthless in their exploitation of subject nations) were throwing loaded dice (one of the chief early uses made of lead was for the purpose of loading dice) for the treasures of the world, Spain could not long escape her fate. Like many a modern land, unfortunately blessed with natural riches, Spain was turned into a battleground for the mercenaries of two large groups of organized brigands.

As soon as they were gone, the country was used as a convenient land bridge for wild tribes from northern Europe, trying to break into Africa.

And then, early during the seventh century, a camel driver in Arabia had a vision and started a number of desert tribes of whom no one had ever heard, on the war-path, bound for world-domination. A century later, they had conquered all of northern Africa and were ready to tackle Europe. In the year 711 Tarik sailed for the famous Monkey Rock (the only spot in Europe where monkeys continued to live in a wild state) and without meeting any opposition landed his troops near Gibraltar, the famous rock (which incidentally does not look like the well-known advertisement because it turns its back upon the land and not upon the sea) which during the last two hundred years has belonged to England.

Thereafter the old Pillars of Hercules, the straits which Hercules had dug by the simple process of pushing the mountains of Europe and Africa aside, belonged to the Mohammedans.

Could the Spaniards have defended themselves successfully against this invasion? They tried to. But the geography of their country prevented any concerted action, for the mountain-ranges which ran a parallel course and the rivers with their deep canyons divided the country into a number of independent little squares. Remember that even today some five thousand Spanish villages have no direct communication with each other or any other part of the world, except by a narrow track which pedestrians, free from dizziness, may use during certain parts of the year.

And then remember one of the few definite facts which history and geography teach us, that such countries are breeding places for clannishness. Now clannishness has undoubtedly certain good qualities. It makes the members of the same clan loyal to each other and loyal to the common or clan interests. But Scotland and the Scandinavian peninsula are there to show us that clannishness is the deadly enemy of all forms of economic coöperation and national organization. Island dwellers are supposed to be "insular" and to care for nothing except the affairs of their own little islet. But they at least can sit themselves down in a boat once in a while and spend an afternoon with their neighbors, or rescue the crew of a ship-wrecked vessel and hear what the big world is doing. The man of the valley, shut off from the rest of humanity by an almost unsurpassable mountain ridge, has no one but himself and his neighbors and they in turn have no one but themselves and their neighbors.

The conquest of Spain by the Mohammedans was possible because the Moors, although a desert people and therefore great worshippers of the restricted "tribal" idea, were for once united under strong leaders who had given them a common national purpose which made them forget their own petty ambitions. While the Spanish clans fought each one for itself and hated their rival clans as cordially (and often more so) than they hated the common enemy who was driving them out of house and home, the Mohammedans obeyed a single head.

The seven centuries during which the great Spanish war of liberation lasted are an endless recital of treachery and rivalry between the little Christian states of the north that survived because the Pyrenees formed a barrier across which they could not hope to retreat without getting into trouble with the French, who, after a few vague gestures on the part of Charlemagne, had left them completely to their own fate.

Meanwhile the Moors had turned southern Spain into a veritable garden. These desert people appreciated the value of water, and they loved the flowers and trees which were so sadly lacking in their own part of the world. They constructed vast irrigation works and imported the orange, the date, the almond tree, sugar-cane and cotton. They set the Guadalquivir to work to turn the valley between Cordova and Seville into one vast "huerta" or garden where the farmer was able to reap as many as four harvests every year. They tapped the Jucar River which flows into the Mediterranean near Valencia and added another 1200 square miles of fertile land to their possessions. They imported engineers, built universities where agriculture was scientifically studied, and constructed about the only roads the country possesses to this very day. What they did for the progress of astronomy and mathematics we have already seen in the first part of this book. And they were the only people in the Europe of that day who paid the slightest attention to medicine and hygiene, carrying their tolerance in such matters so far that they reintroduced the works of the ancient Greeks into the west by means of their own Arabic translations. And they set another force to work which was to be of tremendous value to them. Instead of shutting the Jews up in ghettos or worse, they gave them free rein to develop their great commercial and organizing power for the benefit of the country at large.

And then the inevitable happened. Almost the whole of the country had been conquered, and there was little danger from the side of the Christians. Other Arab and Berber tribes, thirsting in their miserable deserts, heard news of this terrestrial Paradise. And since Mohammedan rule was autocratic, the success or failure of that rule depended upon the ability of a single person. Amidst these luxurious surroundings, dynasties founded by strong-armed plow-boys degenerated and became weak. Other strong-armed plow-boys, still sweating behind their oxen, cast envious eyes upon the joys of the Alhambra of Granada and the Alcazar of Seville. There were civil wars. There was murder. Whole families were wiped out. Others pushed to the front. Meanwhile in the north, the strong man had made his appearance. Clans were being combined into tiny principalities. Tiny principalities were being combined into small states. Men began to hear the names of Castile and Leon and Aragon and Navarre. Finally they forgot their ancient rivalries long enough to marry Ferdinand of Aragon with Isabel of Castile, the land of the castles.

During this great war of liberation over three thousand pitched battles were fought. The Church turned the "racial" struggle into a conflict of religious aspirations. The Spaniard became the soldier of the Cross—a most noble ambition which was to bring ruin to the country for which he so valiantly fought. For in the same year that the last of the Moorish strongholds, Granada, was taken from the Moors, Columbus discovered the road to America. Six years later, Vasco da Gama sailed around the Cape and found the direct route to the Indies. Therefore, just at the moment when the Spaniard should have taken possession of his own home and should have continued to develop those latent natural forces of his country which had been set into motion by the Moors, he came into easy money. His religious feeling of exaltation made it easy for him to imagine himself a holy missionary when in reality he was nothing but an uncommon (because uncommonly brutal and greedy) brigand. In 1519 he conquered Mexico. In 1532 he conquered Peru. After that, he was lost. All further ambitions were drowned in the steady flow of gold which the cumbersome galleons dumped into the storehouses of Seville and Cadiz. No man would disgrace himself working with his hands when he could belong to the "gold collar class" by demanding his share of the Aztec and Inca plunder.

All the painful work of the Moors became undone. The Moors themselves were forced to leave the country. Next the Jews went, thrown wholesale into filthy vessels to carry them, naked and deprived of all their possessions, wherever it pleased the captain of the ship to put them on land. Their hearts filled with revenge but their minds sharpened by their sufferings, they struck back at their tormentors, had a hand in every heretical enterprise that was directed against the hated name of Spain. But even Providence must take a hand and give these unfortunate sufferers of the Golden Illusion a monarch whose view of life did not extend beyond the cloistered cell he erected for himself in the palace of the Escurial, situated on the outskirts of the bleak Castilian plain, to which he had transferred his new capital city of Madrid.

Henceforth the riches of three continents and the man-power of an entire nation were to be used to curb the aggressions of the unbelievers, the Protestants of the north, the Mohammedans of the south. The Spanish people, changed by seven centuries of religious warfare into a race in whose eyes the supernatural had become the natural, willingly obeyed their royal master. And they bled to death in the attempt just as they impoverished themselves by growing too rich.

The Iberian peninsula made the Spanish people what they

are today. Can the Spanish people now turn around and after centuries of neglect change the Iberian peninsula into what they want it to be, regardless of the past and with only an eye to the future?

They are trying and in some cities, like Barcelona, they are trying very hard.

But what a job! What a job!

XI

FRANCE, THE COUNTRY THAT HAS EVERYTHING
IT WANTS

We often hear it said that France does not consider herself a part of the rest of the world, that the French people, who live on a continent, are infinitely more "insular" than their English neighbors who dwell in rainy solitude on an island, in short, that the French, by their persistent and systematic refusal to take any interest, however slight, in the affairs of this planet, are the most selfish and self-centered of all nations and are at the bottom of most of our present troubles.

Well, in order to understand things thoroughly, we must go down to their roots. The roots of any given people are situated deep down in the soil and in the soul. The soil has influenced the soul and the soul has influenced the soil. We cannot understand the one without understanding the other. But when we have grasped the true inner meaning of both, we have a key to the character of almost any nation.

Most of the accusations we hear so often uttered against the French are based upon the truth. But so was that unbounded and unquestioning praise heaped upon them during the days of the Great War, for both their virtues and their defects grew directly out of the geographic position of their country. It had made them self-centered and self-contented, because the land they occupied between the Atlantic Ocean and the Mediterranean was absolutely self-sufficient for their needs. Why go abroad for changes of climate or changes in scenery when you can find all of those in your own backyard? Why travel all over the globe to study differences of language and habits and customs when a few hours in a train will carry you from the twentieth to the twelfth century or from a smiling, verdant country of castles to the magnificent mysteries of a land of sand-dunes and solemn pine trees? Why bother about passports or letters of credit and bad food and sour wine and the dull, stodgy faces of frozen northern peasants when your own food and drink and beds and conversation are about as good as any this vale of tears can provide, when you live in a land where (believe it or not!) they can make spinach a dish fit for human consumption?

Of course a poor Swiss, who has never seen anything except a mountain, or a poor Dutchman, who has never seen anything except a flat piece of green meadow with a few black and white cows, must go abroad once in a while or he would die of bore-dom. A German will sooner or later tire of his exclusive diet of excellent music interspersed with indifferent sausage-sandwiches. An Italian cannot live on spaghetti all his life long. And a Rus-sian must crave an occasional meal without standing six hours in line for half a pound of oleomargarine.

But the Frenchman, lucky devil, lives in an earthly paradise where all things are to be had by all men without a change of cars and therefore he will ask you, "Why should I ever stir from my own country?"

You may answer that this is a hopelessly one-sided point of view and that my Frenchman is all wrong. I wish that I could agree with you but I am forced to admit that France in many respects is a country singularly blessed by Nature and its gen-eral geographical background.

In the first place, France has every sort of a climate. It has a temperate climate. It has a hot climate. It has a medium climate. France is the proud possessor of the highest mountain in Europe. At the same time the French have been able to connect all the industrial centers of their land with canals that run through absolutely flat country. If a Frenchman likes to spend his winter sliding down the slopes of a hill, he moves to a village in the Savoy in the western branch of the Alps. Does he prefer swim-ming to skiing, all he need do is take a ticket for Biarritz on the Atlantic or to Cannes on the Mediterranean. And should he be

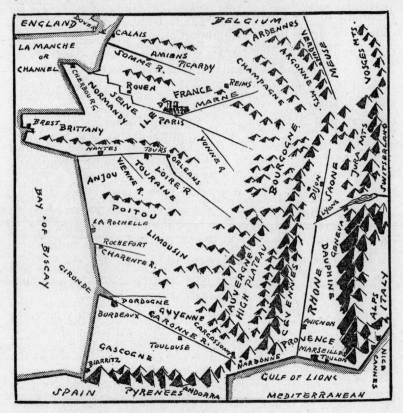

France

of a particular curiosity about men and women, should he interest himself in the outward aspect of monarchs in exile and exiles about to turn monarchs, of actors with a future before them and actresses with a future behind them, of fiddle virtuosos or paragons of the piano, of dancers who have lightly upset a couple of thrones and all the other great little people who are in the limelight, he need merely take a chair in the Café de la Paix, and order himself a glass of coffee and cream, and wait. Sooner or later, every man, woman or child who ever made the front page of the world's news-sheets will pass that corner. And what is more, they will pass that corner without attracting any particular attention, for this procession has been going on for almost fifteen centuries and a king or an emperor or even the highest dignitary of the Church causes about as much commotion as a freshman on a college campus.

Right here we come upon one of the unanswerable mysteries of political geography. Two thousand years ago most of the territory that flies the Republican tricolor (and flies it day and night, for the French, once they have hoisted a flag, never pull it down until time and the weather have reduced it to unrecognizable shreds) was part of the great western European plain and there was no earthly (that is to say, geographic) reason why some day all the land between the Atlantic and the Mediterranean should become one of the most highly centralized nations of the world.

There is a school of geography which holds that climate and geographical background play the decisive part in shaping human destinies. Undoubtedly they do—sometimes. Quite as often it is the other way around. The Moors and the Spaniards lived on the same soil and the sun shone with equal violence upon the valley of the Guadalquivir in the year 1200 as it did in the year 1600. But in the year 1200 it bestowed its blessings upon a paradise of fruit and flowers and in the year 1600 it forced its accursed rays upon a parched wilderness of neglected irrigation ditches and weeds.

The Swiss speak four languages, yet feel themselves to be members of one single nation. The Belgians speak only two and hate each other to the point where the desecration of each other's soldiers' graves has become a regular Sunday afternoon pastime. The Icelanders on their little island maintained their independence and self-government for over a thousand years against all comers, and the Irish on their island hardly ever know a moment of independence. And so it goes. Human nature, regardless of the advance of the machine and of science and of standardization of every sort, will always remain an extremely unstable and undependable factor in the general scheme of things. It has been responsible for the many strange and unexpected developments of which the map of the world is the living evidence; and France is merely one of the object lessons which bears me out on this point.

Politically speaking, France seems to be one country. But if you will kindly look at the map you will notice that France is really composed of two separate parts which actually turn their backs upon each other—the valley of the Rhône in the southeast which looks out upon the Mediterranean and the great inclined plain of the north and the west which faces towards the Atlantic.

Let us begin with the oldest of these two halves. The Rhône takes its origin in Switzerland but it really does not become a river of any importance until it has left the Lake of Geneva and has reached the city of Lyons, the center of the French silk industry, where it combines with the Saône, a river which comes down from the north and which has its source only a few miles from that of the Meuse, a river which is as intimately connected with the history of northern Europe as the Saône (combined with the Rhône) is with that of the south. The Rhône is not a very navigable river. Before it reaches the Gulf of the Lion (no, the name Gulf of Lyons which appears on many maps is an error) it has come down some 6000 feet, which accounts for its rapid currents which have not yet been entirely overcome by the modern steamer.

Nevertheless it offered the ancient Phoenicians and Greeks a convenient entrance way into the heart of Europe, for manpower—slave-power—was cheap. The ships could be dragged upstream by these prehistoric Volga boatmen (their fate cannot have been much happier than that of their Russian colleagues) and downstream was a matter of a few days. And so it happened that the old civilization of the Mediterranean made its first attack upon the European hinterland by way of the Rhône valley. Strangely enough Marseilles, the earliest commercial settlement in that region (and still the most important French port on the Mediterranean) was not situated directly at the mouth of the river but several miles towards the east. (It is now connected with the Rhône by means of a canal.) Nevertheless it proved a very good choice, for Marseilles became such an important center of trade that as early as the third century before Christ Marseillian coins had found their way as far as the Austrian Tyrol and the region around Paris. And soon the whole region immediately to the north of it recognized Marseilles as its capital.

Then, during an ill-fated moment in its history, the citizens of the town, hard pressed by wild tribes from the Alps, asked the Romans to come and help them. The Romans came and, as was their habit, stayed. All the land along the mouth of the Rhône became a Roman "provincia" and the name "Provence", which has played such a great role in history, bears silent testimony to the fact that it was the Romans, rather than the Phoenicians and Greeks, who recognized the importance of this fertile triangle.

But here we find ourselves face to face with one of the most perplexing problems both of geography and history. The Provence with its mixture of Greek and Roman civilization, its ideal climate, its great fertility, its front door opening upon the Mediterranean and its back door leading conveniently to the plain of central and northern Europe, seemed predestined to become the logical successor to Rome. It was given every possible natural advantage and then, with all the trump cards in its hands, it failed to play them. During the quarrels between Caesar and Pompey, the Provence took the side of Pompey and the rival gang destroyed the city of Marseilles. But that was a minor incident, for soon afterwards its citizens were doing business once more at the same old stand, while literature and courtly manners and the arts and sciences, no longer safe in Rome, fled across the Ligurian Sea and turned the Provence into an island of civilization entirely surrounded by barbarians.

When the Popes with all their wealth and power were no longer able to maintain themselves in the city of the Tiber (the Roman mob of the Middle Ages was little better than a pack of

wolves and as relentless as our own gangsters) they too moved
their court to Avignon, the town famous for the first attempt at
bridge-building on a large scale (most of the bridge now lies
on the bottom of the river, but in the twelfth century it was one
of the world's wonders) and where they owned a castle that
could withstand a hundred sieges. Thereupon, for almost an
entire century the Provence was the home of the head of Christendom, its knights took a very prominent part in the Crusades
and one noble Provençal family became the hereditary ruler of
Constantinople.

But somehow or other the Provence was never able to play
the role for which Nature seemed to have predestined her when
she created these delightful and fertile and romantic valleys.
The Provence gave us the Troubadours, but even they, although
recognized as the founders of that form of literature which has
maintained itself ever since in our novels and our plays and our
poetry, were never able to make their soft Provençal dialect, the
langue d'oc, the general tongue of all France. It was the north
with its *langue d'oil* (*oil* and *oc* were merely different forms for
oui or *yes*)—it was the north, which enjoyed none of the natural
advantages of the south, which was to found the French state,
create the French nation and bestow upon the world in general
the manifold blessings of French culture. But sixteen centuries
ago, no one could have foreseen this development. For then
the entire plain which reaches from the Pyrenees in the south to
the Baltic in the north seemed predestined to become part of a
vast Teutonic empire. That would have been the natural development. But man not being very much interested in natural
developments, everything came differently.

To the Romans of Caesar's time, all this part of Europe had
been the Far West. They had called it Gallia because it was inhabited by Gauls, by people belonging to the mysterious race of
fair-haired men and women to whom the Greeks had given the
general name of Keltoi or Celts. And in those days, there were
two kinds of Gaul. One was the region of the Po River, between

the Alps and the Apennines, where the fair-haired savages had made their appearance at a very early date and which was known as Gallia Cisalpina or Gaul-this-side-of-the-mountains. That was the Gaul which Caesar left when he threw his famous dice and boldly crossed the Rubicon. Then there was the Gallia Transalpina, the Gaul-across-the-mountains, and that accounted vaguely for all the rest of Europe. But after Caesar's famous expedition of the years 58–51 B. C., it came to be associated more particularly with the France of today. It was a fertile land which could be made to pay taxes without too much objection on the part of the natives, hence an ideal domain for intensive Roman colonization.

The passes between the Vosges Mountains in the north and the Jura in the south offered no great difficulties to the progress of an army consisting mostly of infantry. Soon the great plain of France was dotted with Roman fortresses and Roman villages, markets, temples, jails, theaters and factories. A small island in the river Seine, where the Celts still lived on houses built on poles, and called Lutetia (or Lutetia Parisiorum after the Parisii who had first taken possession of this natural fortress) became an ideal spot on which to build a temple dedicated to Jupiter. That temple stood where Notre Dame arises today.

As the island had direct water communication with Great Britain (a most profitable Roman colony during the first 400 years of our era) and was an excellent strategic center from which to watch the turbulent regions between the Rhine and the Meuse, it quite naturally developed into the chief center of the vast Roman organization that administered the Far West.

As I told you in the chapter on maps, we sometimes wonder how the Romans were able to find their way across the whole island and mainland world of that day, but there can be no question about it—they had an unerring instinct for the right spot, whether they were building a harbor, a fortress or a trading-post. A casual observer, after passing six dreary weeks amidst the rains and fogs of the Parisian valley, may ask himself, "Why in the name of Mars did the Romans ever select this forlorn

The geology of the Île de France

spot to be their administration headquarters for all their western and northern possessions?" But a geologist with a map of northern France before him could show us.

Millions of years ago, when all this territory was being tortured by incessant earthquakes, and when mountains and valleys were thrown hither and yon as casually as the chips on a gaming table, four heavy layers of rock of different ages were tossed about in such a way that they came to lie on top of each other, like the saucers of one of those Chinese tea-sets which used to delight the hearts of our grandmothers. The lowest and biggest of these saucers stretches from the Vosges Mountains to Brittany, where its western brim lies buried beneath the waters of

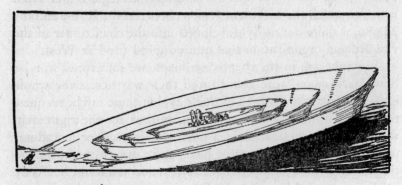

The Île de France expressed in the form of saucers

the British Channel. The second one reaches from Lorraine to the coast of Normandy. The third one, the famous Champagne region, encircles the fourth one, appropriately called the Île de France, or the Island of France. This "island" is a vague circle bounded by the Seine, the Marne, the Thève and the Oise; and Paris is situated right in the heart of it. That meant safety—almost complete safety—because it offered the greatest amount of protection from foreign invasion. For the enemy was obliged to storm the steep outer edges of those saucers while the home troops were not only in an excellent position for defence but in case of defeat could leisurely withdraw to the protection of the next saucer-rim and could repeat that performance four times ere they had reached their little island in the Seine, which, by the burning of the few connecting bridges, could be turned into an impregnable fortress.

It was of course possible for a very determined and well-equipped hostile force to take Paris. But it was exceedingly difficult, as the Great War has shown us only recently. It was not only the valor of the French and English that kept the Germans out of the French capital. It also was that geographical accident of millions of years ago which had put every possible natural barrier in the way of the invaders from the east.

France has been obliged to fight almost ten centuries for her national independence. But whereas most countries have been under the necessity of guarding four separate frontiers, France was able to devote all her energies to the protection of her western boundaries; and this probably accounted for the fact that France could develop into a highly centralized modern state long before any of the other nations of Europe.

The whole of the western part of France, situated between the Cevennes and the Vosges and the Atlantic falls quite naturally into a number of peninsulas and valleys which are separated from each other by low mountain ridges. The most western of these valleys is that of the Seine and Oise which is connected with the plains of Belgium through a natural gateway defended since time immemorial by the city of St. Quentin. In modern times it has become a very important railroad center and as such it was one of the main German objectives during the march on Paris in 1914.

The valley of the Seine and that of the Loire are in easy communication with each other by way of the gap of Orleans. As a result thereof that region was bound to play a very important role in the history of France. The national heroine of the French is known as the Maid of Orleans, and the biggest railroad station in Paris is called the Gare d'Orléans, and it was the geographical position of that city on that pass between the north and the south which was responsible for both names. In the Middle Ages, knights in armor fought for such key positions. Today railroad companies fight for such key positions. The world changes. But often enough, the more it seems to change, the more it really remains the same.

As for the connection between the Loire valley and the valley of the Garonne, it followed the present railroad line via Poitiers, and it was near Poitiers that Charles Martel in the year 732 prevented the Moors from pushing any further into Europe, and it was near Poitiers that the Black Prince in the year 1356 so completely annihilated the French forces that France remained under English domination for almost another hundred years.

As for that wide valley of the Garonne, the southern part of which is that famous land of Gascony whence came the dashing d'Artagnan and the noble King Henry IV, that part of France is in direct communication with the Provence and the Rhône valley by way of a valley that runs from Toulouse on the Garonne River to Narbonne, which used to be on the Mediterranean and which incidentally was the oldest of all Roman settlements in Gaul.

Like all such prehistoric highways (for that route was used thousands of years before the beginning of written history) it has always been a source of revenue to some one. Racketeering and profiteering are as old as the human race. If you doubt this statement, go to any mountain pass in any part of the world and remain in that neighborhood until you have definitely located

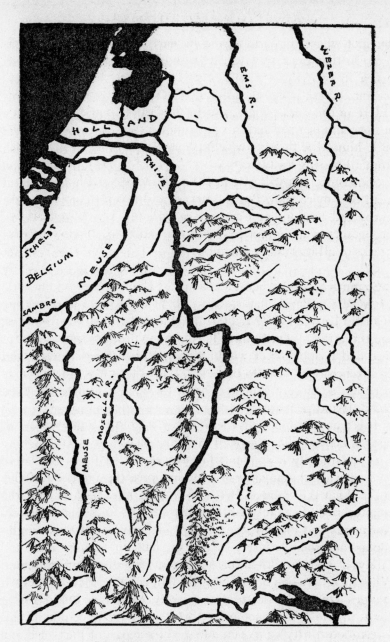

The Rhine, the Meuse and their Delta

the spot where the road was at its narrowest a thousand years ago. On that exact spot you will find the ruins of from half a dozen to two dozen castles and if you know anything about ancient civilizations, the different layers of stone will tell you: "Here in the year 50 B. C. and in the year 600 and in 800 and in 1100 and in 1250 and in 1350 and in 1500 some robber baron built himself a fortress which allowed him to demand tribute from all passing caravans."

Sometimes you will be surprised to find a flourishing city instead of a mere ruin. But the towers and ravelins and counterscarps and bastions of Carcassonne will tell you how terribly strong such a mountain pass fortress had to be to survive the attacks of all its hungry enemies.

So much for the general landscape of France. Now let me add a few very general characteristics about the people who live in this land between the Mediterranean and the Atlantic. There is one thing they seem to have in common, a certain sense of balance and proportion. I would almost feel inclined to say that the French tried hard to be "logical", if that unfortunate word were not so closely connected with the idea of something dry and dull and pedantic.

It is true that France is the home of one of the highest mountains in Europe. The top of Mont Blanc is now French territory, but that is merely an accident. The average Frenchman is as little concerned about that waste of snow and ice as the average American is about the Painted Desert. What he likes best is the harmonious roll of the hills of the Meuse region and Guyenne and Normandy and Picardy, the pleasant little rivers with their high poplars and their leisurely barges, the haze that hangs over the valleys at night and then turns them into paintings by Watteau. What he knows best are those little villages where nothing ever changes (the greatest strength of any country), those small towns in which the people live or at least try to live as their ancestors did fifty or five hundred years ago, and Paris, where the best living and the best thinking have gone hand in hand for more than ten centuries.

For the Frenchman, contrary to the absurd fables foisted upon us during the Great War, is not a sentimental dreamer, but a most intelligent and eager realist. He stands with both feet flatly on this earth. He realizes that he will live but once and that threescore and ten is all he can expect. And so he endeavors to make himself as comfortable as possible while on this planet and wastes no time imagining the world better than it is. *C'est la vie*—such is life—and suppose we make the best of it! Since food is agreeable to civilized man, let us provide even the poorest with the knowledge of good cooking. Since wine, ever since the days of our Savior, has been regarded as a fit drink for true Christians, let us cultivate the best of wines. Since the Lord in

Paris

his wisdom has seen fit to fill this earth with many things agreeable to the eye and the ear and the nose, let us not indulge in a haughty denial of these divine bounties but partake of them as an all-wise Providence has evidently meant us to do. And since Man is stronger when fighting in a group than when acting alone, let us stick closely to the family as the elementary social unit which is responsible for the weal and woe of all its members just as all the individual members are responsible for the weal and woe of the family.

This is the ideal side of French life. There is another side, much less agreeable, which however grows directly out of the very qualities which I have just enumerated. The family quite frequently ceases to be a pleasant dream and becomes a nightmare. The endless grandmothers and grandfathers who rule the clan act as a brake which prevents all progress. The excellent habit of saving for sons and grandsons and great-grandsons degenerates into a hideous habit of scraping and filching and rooking and pinching and economizing on every necessity of life, including that charity towards one's neighbor without which civilized existence becomes a very drab experience indeed.

But by and large the average Frenchman, of however humble rank or station, seems to carry with him a certain practical philosophy of life which provides him with a maximum of content at a minimum of expenditure. For one thing, he is not ambitious in our sense of the word. He knows that all men are born unequal. They tell him that in America every boy may some day hope to become president of the bank for which he works as a clerk. What of it? He does not want to assume all that responsibility! What would become of his three hours for luncheon? It would of course be nice to have all the money that goes with the job, but the sacrifice of comfort and happiness would be too great. And so the Frenchman works and works industriously and his wife works and his daughters and his sons work too, yes, the whole country works and saves and lives the sort of lives it likes to live and does not try to lead the sort of lives other people think they ought to like to live; and that is a bit of wisdom which does not make for great riches, but which is a better guarantee for ultimate happiness than the doctrine of success preached all over the rest of the world.

Whenever we come to the sea in this geography of ours I shall not tell you that the people of the coast indulge in fishing. Of course they do. What else would you expect them to do? Milk cows or dig for coal?

But when we reach the subject connected with agriculture, we shall make a very curious discovery. Whereas in most countries the population during the last hundred years has been attracted to the cities, fully sixty percent of all Frenchmen continue to live in the country; and France today is the only country in Europe which could withstand a prolonged siege without importing grain from abroad. The ancestral methods of working the fields are gradually making way before the improved methods of modern science and when the French peasant shall have ceased to till his soil as his great-great-grandfather did in the days of Charlemagne and Clovis, France will be entirely self-supporting.

What helps to keep the peasant on the land is the fact that as a rule he is his own proprietor. His farm may not be much of a farm but it is his own. In England and in east Prussia, two parts of the Old World where there is a great deal of agriculture, the farms belong to some vague and distant landlord. But the French Revolution did away with the landlord, whether noble or cleric, and divided his property among the small peasantry. That was often very hard on the former proprietors. But their ancestors had acquired those possessions by right of eminent plunder, so what was the difference? And it has proved of tremendous advantage to the country at large. For it gives more than half of the people a direct interest in the welfare of the whole nation. Like everything else, that state of affairs probably has its disadvantages. It may account for the exaggerated feeling of nationalism among the French. It may explain the provincialism which makes every Frenchman stick to the people of his own village even when he moves to Paris, so that Paris is full of little hotels catering to certain groups of regional travellers, a situation which we could only duplicate if New York had hostelries patronized exclusively by Chicagoans or Kalamazooians or Fresnonians or people from Horseheads, New York. It also explains his utter unwillingness to migrate to other parts of the world, but then again, why should any one move to another country when he is perfectly happy at home?

Next to agriculture, the cultivation of the wine-grape keeps vast numbers of Frenchmen attached to the soil. The entire valley of the Garonne is devoted to vine culture. The city of Bordeaux near the mouth of the Garonne and just north of those vast silty plains called the Landes, where the shepherds walk on stilts and the sheep can remain out of doors all the year long, is the center for the export of this wine, as Cette, on the Mediterranean, is the harbor for the famous wines of the piping hot valley of the Rhône. The wines from Burgundy—the so-called Côte d'Or—are gathered together in Dijon, while those of the Champagne are assembled (and multiplied and divided) in the ancient French coronation city of Rheims.

When grain and wine fail to support the population, industry helps out. The ancient French monarchs were something more than haughty imbeciles who oppressed their subjects and wasted useless millions on the pretty ladies of Versailles. They made their courts the center of fashion and civilized living towards which all the world flocked to learn agreeable manners and to be taught the difference between eating and dining. As a result, even today, a century and a half after the last of the ancient rulers was thrown into the quick-lime of a Paris potter's-field, with his head between his feet, Paris dictates unto the rest of the world what to wear and how to wear it. The industries which provide Europe and America with those indispensable luxuries which most people prefer to the sheer necessities, are centered in and around the Île de France and they provide employment to millions of women and girls. The endless flower fields of the Riviera are the original source whence flows most of our perfumery at six and ten dollars a bottle (a very small bottle, too, but that is the result of our wise decision to tax all those things which we ourselves can't make).

Then came the discovery of coal and iron in the soil of France, and Picardy and Artois grew drab and ugly with those vast dump-heaps of cinders and slag which played such a great part during the battle of Mons, where the English tried to stop the Germans in their march upon Paris. Lorraine became the center for the iron industry. The central plateau fabricated steel. When the war was over, the French hastened to annex the Alsace which provided them with more steel and which, during the last fifty years of German domination, had gone in heavily for textiles. As a result of this recent development, one-quarter of the French people are today engaged in industries, and they can proudly boast that their industrial cities are fully as hideous, as unattractive and as inhuman in their outer aspect as those of England or of our own country.

XII

BELGIUM, A COUNTRY CREATED BY SCRAPS OF PAPER AND RICH IN EVERYTHING EXCEPT INTERNAL HARMONY

THE modern kingdom of the Belgians consists of three parts: the plain of Flanders along the shores of the North Sea, the low plateau between Flanders and the mountains of the east, rich in iron and coal, and the Ardennes Mountains of the east, through which the Meuse flows in pleasant curves, bound for the marshes of the Low Countries a short distance further towards the north.

The iron and coal deposits centering around the cities of Liége, Charleroi and Mons (the great war for Democracy had a strange habit of bringing the names of coal and iron cities to the front pages of our newspapers) are so plentiful that Belgium will probably be able to provide the world with those two necessities of modern life long after the coal fields and iron beds of Germany, France and England shall have been exhausted.

But this country, blessed with what the Germans so often call the "heavy industry", has curiously enough no good modern harbors of its own. The coast along the Channel, shallow and protected by a most complicated arrangement of sand banks and shallow places, has no ports worthy of the name. The Belgians have dug artificial harbors in Ostende and Zeebrugge and Nieuwport, but Antwerp, her most important harbor, lies forty miles distant from the North Sea, and the river Scheldt for the last thirty miles of its course runs through Dutch territory, a slightly absurd arrangement and one which might be called "unnatural" from a geographic point of view but unavoidable in a world ruled by scraps of paper signed by the delegates to solemn international conferences. As however Belgium is a country that was the direct outcome of a number of such conferences, we ought to know something about the historical antecedents that faced their Excellencies whenever they settled comfortably around their green tables to decide the fate of the world.

The Gallica Belgica of the Romans had been inhabited by Celts (the same people as the original settlers of Britain and France) and a number of small Germanic tribes. All of these were forced to recognize the suzerainty of the Romans who pushed forward in a northern direction across the plains of Flanders and over the hills of the Ardennes until they reached the almost impassable marshes which were to give birth to the modern kingdom of the Netherlands. Next it was a minor province of the empire of Charlemagne. Next, by the disastrous treaty of Verdun of 843 it was made part of the central kingdom of Lothair. Next it was divided into a large number of semi-independent duchies and counties and bishoprics. Next, the Habsburgs, the most competent real estate manipulators of the Middle Ages, got hold of it. But the Habsburgs were not looking for coal and iron. They were looking for safe returns on farm land and for quick returns on trade. Hence the eastern part of the country (and by far the most important) was regarded as a semi-wilderness. But Flanders was given every opportunity to develop its latent forces and did so, until during the fourteenth and fifteenth centuries of our era it was by far the richest part of northern Europe.

This was due to a fortunate geographic position which allowed medieval ships of moderate size to penetrate far inland and to the fact that the early rulers of Flanders were men and women of quite exceptional ability who encouraged the development of industrialism while all other feudal chieftains stuck closely to agriculture and despised capitalism as heartily as the Church despised the idea of taking interest on loans.

In consequence of this very wise policy, Bruges and Ghent and Ypres and Cambrai waved fat and rich and opulent, doing the work that other countries should have performed for themselves if their sovereigns had allowed them to grasp their opportunities. The subsequent downfall of these early centers of capitalistic industries was brought about by a combination of geography and human—all too human—characteristics.

Geography did its share by changing certain currents in the North Sea which filled the harbors of Bruges and Ghent with such vast and unexpected masses of sand that those cities became completely landlocked. While the labor unions (the guilds) which in the beginning had been a source of tremendous strength, rapidly degenerated into tyrannical and short-sighted organizations, founded for no other purpose than to slow up and impede every known form of industrial activity.

From Man to Mole

As the old native dynasties had died out and Flanders had been temporarily annexed by the French, there was no one to intervene and the tides and the walking-delegates between them reduced Flanders to a somnolent region of pleasant little white-washed farms and beautiful ruins which inspire old English ladies to some of their most atrocious water-colors but where the grass has never ceased to grow between the well polished cobble-stones of the ancient tenement quarters.

The Reformation did the rest. For Flanders after a short and very sharp upheaval in favor of the Lutheran doctrines remained faithful to the Mother Church. And when their northern neighbors gained their independence, Holland hastened to close the last remaining port of their old rival, and with Antwerp cut off from the rest of Europe, the whole of Belgium went into a prolonged period of hibernation, out of which it did not arise until the needs of James Watt's hungry machines drew the world's attention to her immense riches in natural materials.

Then foreign capital hastened to the valley of the Meuse and in less than twenty years Belgium had become one of the leading industrial nations of Europe. It was then that the Walloon or French speaking part of the country (everything west of Brussels) came fully into its own, for although it contained only 42% of the total population it soon became by far the richest part of the whole country and the Flemings were reduced to a race of semi-conquered peasants whose language might be tolerated in the kitchen and in the stable but which should never be spoken in the parlor of a civilized household.

To make matters still a little more complicated, the Congress of Vienna of 1815 which was supposed to settle the peace of the world for all time (a sort of Versailles of a century ago) had seen fit to make Belgium and Holland into a single kingdom, so as to have a powerful northern balance against the French.

The end of this strange political marriage came in the year 1830 when the Belgians arose against the Dutch, and the French (as was to be expected) rushed to their assistance. The Great Nations (a little late as usual) interfered. A prince of the house of Coburg, uncle of Queen Victoria (Uncle Leopold was a very serious gentleman who exercised a very *profound influence* upon his dear little niece) was made King of the Belgians. He had just refused a similar offer from the side of the Greeks and never had any reason to regret his choice. For the new kingdom proved to be a success. The mouth of the Scheldt remained in Dutch hands, but Antwerp became once more one of the most important harbors of western Europe.

The Great European Powers had officially proclaimed Belgium a "neutral power". But King Leopold (the son of the founder of the dynasty) was much too shrewd to have any confidence in such paper keep-off-the-grass signs. He worked hard to make his country something more than a third-rate little nation, existing merely by the grace of its richer neighbors. When a certain gentleman by the name of Henry Stanley returned from the heart of Africa, Leopold prevailed upon him to come to Brussels and out of this interview grew the International Association of the Congo, which in due course of time was to make Belgium one of the largest colonial powers of the modern world.

Today the main problem before Belgium, with its magnificent geographic situation right in the heart of the most prosperous part of northern Europe, is no longer an economic one. It is a racial one. The Flemish majority is rapidly catching up with the French minority in the matter of general education and scientific and cultural development. It is clamoring for a share in the administration of the country from which it has been kept separated ever since the founding of the independent kingdom. It insists upon absolute equality for both languages, for Flemish as well as for French.

But I had better leave this subject alone. It puzzles me and I fail to see why it should be that way. The Flemings and the Walloons have a common racial origin and share almost twenty centuries of common history. Yet they live like cats and dogs. In the next chapter we shall meet the Swiss who speak four different languages, German, French, Italian and Romonsch (a

Coal in the making

strange Roman tongue surviving among the mountains of the Engadine) and they get along with each other without any real basic friction. There must be a reason for this but I for one am willing to confess that it surpasses my own understanding.

Heat

XIII

LUXEMBURG, THE HISTORICAL CURIOSITY

But ere I talk of Switzerland I ought to mention a curious little independent principality, the name of which would hardly be known if it had not played quite an important role during the first days of the World War. Luxemburg (the "lützel" or "little" burg) counts only one quarter of a million inhabitants, whose ancestors lived in this neighborhood when it was still part of the Roman province of Belgium. It was however of considerable importance during the Middle Ages on account of the strength of the capital, which was supposed to be one of the "impregnable" fortresses of the world.

That same fact and the jealousy between France and Prussia as to who should own it made the Congress of Vienna of 1815 give the tiny country an independent status as a duchy of which the kings of the Netherlands should be the personal rulers to compensate them for the loss of their ancestral territories in Germany.

Twice during the nineteenth century the small duchy almost caused a war between Germany and France. In order to prevent further difficulties of that sort, the fortifications were finally dismantled and Luxemburg was officially declared to be "neutral territory"—like Belgium.

When the war broke out, the Germans violated this act of neutrality, basing their decision to do so upon the geographical necessity of invading France by way of the flat plains of the north and east without trying the hopeless expedient of forcing the steep tea-cup barriers of the west. (See France.) Luxemburg remained in German hands until 1918. Even now the small duchy is not actually out of danger, for the soil contains a considerable amount of iron ore.

SWITZERLAND, THE COUNTRY OF HIGH MOUNTAINS, EX-
CELLENT SCHOOLS AND A UNIFIED PEOPLE WHO
SPEAK FOUR DIFFERENT LANGUAGES

THE Swiss are apt to call their country the Helvetian Con-
federation, and a rather dowdy lady, called Helvetia, is apt to
appear upon the coins and stamps of the twenty-two independent
little republics whose representatives gather together at the capital city of Berne to discuss the affairs of the common fatherland.

Since the war, when the greater part of the country (70% of
the people speak German, 20% speak French, 6% speak Italian
and 2% speak Romonsch) was more or less on the side of the
Germans (although maintaining a most scrupulous neutrality),
the image of a slightly idealized young hero by the name of
William Tell has somewhat tended to replace the Helvetian
goddess who, I am sorry to say, was beginning to look more and
more like Britannia as she was depicted by the eminent artists
of the mid-Victorian period in England. This conflict of coin and
stamp deities (they are not restricted to Switzerland; almost any
country has one of these queer problems) clearly shows the dual
nature of the Swiss Republic. To the outside world, all this is of
very little importance. Switzerland, to those of us who are not
of Swiss origin, is merely the country of the picturesque
mountain-ranges and it is of these that I shall speak in the present chapter.

The Alps, which stretch from the Mediterranean to the Adriatic, are almost twice as long as Great Britain and contain about
the same amount of territory. Sixteen thousand square miles of
this land belong to Switzerland (Denmark is just about as large)
and of these 16,000 square miles, 12,000 are productive in some

way because they are covered with forests or vineyards or small bits of pasture. Four thousand square miles are of no use to anybody because they are either covered by the water of the big lakes or form part of some picturesque precipice; and 700 square miles are covered by glaciers. As a result, Switzerland has only 250 inhabitants per square mile, while Belgium has 655, and Germany 347. But Norway has only 22 per square mile, and Sweden has 35, and the idea therefore that Switzerland is merely a sort of gigantic mountain resort, inhabited exclusively by hotel-keepers and their guests is slightly erroneous. For Switzerland, aside from its dairy products, has turned the wide northern plateau between the Alps and the Tura into one of the most prosperous industrial countries of Europe, and it has been able to do so without the help of any raw materials. It has of course a superabundance of waterpower, and furthermore it enjoys a very favorable position right in the heart of Europe, which makes it possible for the finished products of the Helvetian Republic to slide quietly but continuously into at least a dozen surrounding countries.

In a previous chapter I tried to give you an idea of the origin of all such complicated masses of mountain-ridges as are represented by the Alps and the Pyrenees. I told you to take half a dozen clean handkerchiefs, unfold them and put them on top of each other and push them together and then watch the wrinkles and the creases and double-jointed circles and crumples that are the result of such a forcible concentration. The table on which you performed this geological operation was the original base or core of granite (countless millions of years old) across which the younger layers folded themselves during subsequent millions of years, to become those queerly shaped pinnacles which were given their present form and aspect by still other millions of years of incessant wind and rain and snow and ice.

These enormous folds, from ten to twelve thousand feet above the plains, have gradually crumbled into a series of parallel ranges. But in the center of the country (the village of Andermatt on the Gothard pass is the geographical center of the country) they meet in a vast complex of mountains (the so-called St. Gothard range) which send the Rhine on its course towards the North Sea, the Rhône on its way to the Mediterranean, and which also give birth to those mountain rivers which feed the lakes of Thun, of Lucerne and Zürich in the north, and the famous Italian lakes in the south. And it is precisely in this neighborhood of glaciers and precipices and valleys, so deep that they hardly ever see the rays of the sun, in this region of avalanches and impassable mountain streams, green with the chilly waters of a dozen glaciers, that the Swiss Republic took its origin.

As usual it was a combination of practical politics with certain geographical peculiarities of the land which gave the Swiss their first chance to make a bid for independence. For almost a thousand years the half-savage peasants of these inaccessible valleys had been left alone by all their more powerful neighbors. What was the use of hoisting the proud standard of empire when there

Switzerland

was no plunder? At best one could deprive these wild men of a couple of cow-hides. But they were dangerous barbarians with their aptitude for guerrilla warfare and those uncomfortable boulders that came crashing down from the hillsides and that would squash a suit of armor as if it were a piece of parchment, and so the Swiss were treated as the original settlers of the Atlantic coast treated the Indians that lived behind the Alleghenies —they were ignored.

But with the rising importance of the Papacy and the tremendous upward sweep of Italian commerce during and immediately after the Crusades, northern Europe felt a very sincere need of a more direct and convenient route from Germany to Italy than those provided by the St. Bernard Pass (which necessitated a long detour by way of Lyons and the entire Rhône valley, via the lake of Geneva) or the Brenner Pass, which meant

The Mountain Pass

that one had to cross the Habsburg domains with their almost unbearable tariff rates.

It was then that the peasants of the Cantons (the name for the independent little Swiss republics or districts) of Unterwalden, Uri and Schwyz decided to combine and each spend a little money (Heaven knows, they did not have much) upon the road that led from the valley of the Rhine to the valley of the Ticino River. They cut down certain parts of the rock. Whenever the rocks were too hard to be removed by means of pick-axes (try and make a mountain road without dynamite!) they made narrow wooden contraptions which they hung from the side of the mountain walls to circumnavigate difficult corners; and they built some primitive stone bridges across the Rhine, which hitherto had been impassable except by pedestrians during the height of the summer. Part of the way they followed the road that had been traced by the engineers of Charlemagne, four centuries before, but had never been completed; and by the end of the thirteenth century a merchant with a caravan of pack-mules could travel from Basel to Milan by way of the St. Gothard Pass with a fair assurance that he would not lose more than two or three of his animals on account of broken legs and falling stones.

As early as the year 1331 we hear of the existence of a hospice on top of the pass and although it was not opened to carriages until 1820 it was soon one of the most popular routes for commerce between the south and the north.

Of course the good people of Unterwalden, Uri and Schwyz allowed themselves to be paid a slight remuneration for all the trouble they had taken. This steady revenue, together with the impetus this international traffic gave to such cities as Lucerne and Zürich, gave these small peasant communities a new feeling of independence which no doubt had a great deal to do with their open defiance of the Habsburg family. The latter, curiously enough, was also originally of Swiss peasant stock, although they did not mention this fact in any of the genealogies which were preserved in their home castle of Habichtsburg (or Hawk's

Nest) that stood near the spot where the river Aar flows into the Rhine.

I am sorry to be quite so prosaic but it was the tangible revenue derived from a busily patronized Alpine trade-route rather than the bravery of a non-existent William Tell which was responsible for the foundation of what afterwards developed into the modern Swiss Republic. That modern Swiss Republic is a highly interesting political experiment built firmly upon one of the most efficient public-school systems of the world. The governmental machine runs so smoothly and so effectively that even Swiss citizens have to think for a moment when you ask them suddenly who happens to be their President. For their country is run by a Bundesrat—a sort of Board of Managers—composed of seven members, and every year they appoint a new President (usually the Vice-President of the previous year) and custom, though not law, provides that one year he shall belong to the German-speaking part of the country, the next year to the French-speaking part, and the third year to the Italian-speaking sub-division.

This President, however, bears no resemblance whatsoever to the President of the United States of America. He is merely the temporary chairman of a Federal Executive which expresses its will through the mouths of seven individual members. The President, apart from presiding over the meetings of the federal council, is minister of foreign affairs, but his position is so inconspicuous that he has no official residence. There is no Swiss "White House". When distinguished strangers have to be entertained, the party is given in the rooms of the foreign office, and even those parties bear more resemblance to a simple bierfest in a little mountain village than to the semi-royal receptions of the French presidents or their American colleagues.

The main details of the administration are too complicated to be mentioned here but the visitor to this part of the Alps is constantly being reminded that somewhere or other an intelligent and honest person is constantly on the watch to see that things

The Conquest of the Barriers

are being done and are being done both honestly and intelligently.

Take the matter of railroading, which is of course connected
with innumerable difficulties. The two main arteries that connect
Italy with northern Europe run straight through the heart of
the Swiss Alps. The Mount Cenis tunnel connects Paris with
Turin (the ancient capital of the kingdom of Savoy) by way of
Dijon and Lyons. And the Brenner line provides a direct communication between southern Germany and Vienna, but although
it crosses the Alps it does not pass through any tunnel. The
Simplon line and the St. Gothard lines however are not only
tunnel-borers but veritable mountain-climbers. The Gothard is
the older of the two. It was begun in 1872 and finished ten years
later. It took eight years to dig the tunnel which is nine and a
half miles long and reaches a height of almost 4000 feet. Even
more interesting than the tunnel itself are the spiral tunnels between Wassen and Goeschenen. Since the valleys were so narrow that they offered no room for even a single track, the railroad had to do its climbing through the heart of the mountains
themselves. Outside of these special tunnels there are fifty-nine
other tunnels (several of them almost a mile long), nine large
viaducts and forty-eight bridges.

The second most important transalpine road, that of the Simplon, offers us a direct route between Paris and Milan by way
of Dijon, Lausanne and the valley of the Rhône as far as Brieg.
It was opened for traffic in the year 1906, exactly a century after
Napoleon had finished his famous Simplon Pass road with its
250 big and 350 small bridges and its ten long tunnels, the greatest piece of road-building the world had ever seen. The Simplon
road, which was much easier to construct than that of the St.
Gothard, follows the slowly ascending valley of the Rhône until
it reaches a spot about 2000 feet high where the tunnel begins.
This tunnel is twelve and a half miles long and provided with
double tracks. So is the Lötschberg tunnel (nine miles long)
which connects northern Switzerland with the Simplon road and
western Italy.

Although one of the narrowest of all mountain-ranges, the so-called Pennine Alps, through which the Simplon road runs, have a climate all their own. There are no fewer than twenty-one peaks of 12,000 feet or more within this small quadrangle and 140 glaciers feed the turbulent streams, which have a most annoying habit of washing away railroad bridges just a few minutes before the arrival of one of the big international express trains. That there never have been any wrecks on account of these aquatic surprise parties speaks highly for the efficiency of the Swiss railroad men. But as I have said before, in this somewhat stiff and rather bureaucratic republic, nothing much is left to chance. Life is too difficult and too dangerous to encourage the amiable philosophy of "muddling through". Somewhere, somehow, some one is forever watching, observing, paying attention.

That such a general tendency towards a rather schoolmasterish punctuality and efficiency does not make for artistic success is a well-known fact. In the line of literature and the arts—painting, sculpture or music—the Swiss have never produced anything that has travelled far beyond their own narrow confines. But then, the world is full of "artistic" nations while only a few can boast of centuries of uninterrupted political and economic growth and development. And the system suits the average Swiss and his wife. What more can we ask?

XV

GERMANY, THE NATION THAT WAS FOUNDED TOO LATE

MERELY for the sake of convenience I have divided the different countries of Europe into racial or cultural groups, and I have started my general discussion with those nations which still showed unmistakable evidences of having been Roman colonies ere they began an independent political existence of their own.

It is true that Rome had also conquered the Balkans and that in one country at least (Roumania) the Latin language has survived as the national tongue. But the great Mongolian, Slavic and Turkish invasions of the Middle Ages have so completely destroyed all evidence of Roman civilization in that part of the world that it would be decidedly erroneous to include the Balkan monarchies in the present discussion, wherefore I shall now bid farewell to the Mediterranean range-of-influence and proceed to that other form of civilization which was of Teutonic origin and which came to be centered around the North Sea and the Atlantic Ocean.

There is (I have already told you that when I spoke of France) a vast semicircular plain which stretches all the way from the eastern Russian hills, where the Dnieper and the Dvina and the Neva and the Volga take their origin, to the Pyrenees. The southern part of that semi-circle was brought under Roman control a very short time after the Germanic tribes began their mysterious migrations towards the west. The eastern part, even then, seems to have been occupied by those nomadic Slavic masses which replenished themselves just as rapidly as they were killed off and which therefore, like the rabbits of Australia, were invincible. Thus the only part that was still available when the hungry Teutonic invaders appeared upon the scene was that big square which stretched from the Vistula on the east to the Rhine delta on the west. The Baltic was its northern limit and in the south a long line of Roman block-houses reminded all newcomers that they were entering upon a "forbidden territory".

The western part of this region was mountainous. First there were the Ardennes and the Vosges, on the western bank of the river Rhine. Then, running due east and west, came the Black Forest, the Tyrolean Mountains, the Erz (or Iron Ore) Mountains (present day Bohemia), the Riesengebirge, and finally the Carpathians which stretched almost as far as the Black Sea.

The rivers in this territory were forced to flow due north. In order of their appearance from west to east there was first of all the Rhine, the most literary of rivers, over which people have fought and wept more copiously than over any other little mountain stream. For the Rhine is really a very modest little rivulet. The Amazon is over five times as long. The Mississippi and Missouri are six times its length, and even the Ohio, which we do not consider much of a river as rivers go in our part of the world, is five hundred miles longer. Then comes the Weser river, with the modern city of Bremen near its mouth. Then the Elbe, which has made Hamburg what it is today. Then the Oder, which gave rise to the city of Stettin, the export harbor for the products of the town of Berlin and its industrial hinterland. Finally there is the Weichsel or Vistula, with the city of Danzig which is now a free state, ruled by a commissioner appointed by the League of Nations.

Millions of years ago all this territory was covered with glaciers. When they retreated they left behind them a large, sandy waste which towards the North Sea and the Baltic degenerated into a trackless morass. Gradually these northern marshes developed a fringe of sand dunes, and these dunes reach almost all the way from the Flemish coast to Königsberg, the old Prussian capital near the Russian frontier. As soon as these dunes had developed, the marshes began to enjoy a certain protection from the tides of the ocean. That meant the beginning of vegetation and as soon as the soil had been prepared for timber, the forests appeared, those same forests which, converted into peat fields, provided our ancestors with an unlimited supply of fairly good fuel.

Both the North Sea and the Baltic, which are the northern and western frontiers of this plain, bear the name of "sea" as a courtesy title. They are really shallow ponds. The average depth of the North Sea is only sixty fathoms (a fathom is six feet) and its greatest depth is not more than 400 fathoms. The average depth of the Baltic is about thirty-six fathoms. The average depth of the Atlantic, on the other hand, is 2170 fathoms while that of the Pacific is 2240 fathoms. These figures show you that you had better think of the North Sea and the Baltic as submerged valleys. A slight elevation of the surface of the earth would once more turn them into dry land.

And now let us look at a map of the dry land of Germany. I mean the map as it is today and as it must have been more or less when human beings followed the retreating glaciers and settled down permanently in this part of the old continent.

These early immigrants were savages. They lived by catching wild animals and by raising a little grain. But they were savages with a very decided sense of beauty, and as their own territory was poor in those metals which could be used for ornaments, they had to send abroad for their gold and silver.

The following statement may come as a mild shock to many of my readers but all original trade-routes are luxury routes. All early contests between the races that inhabited different parts of the world were luxury contests. The Romans learned the main outlines of the geography of northern Europe from traders who had penetrated as far as the mysterious Baltic in search of amber —a sort of petrified resin which Roman matrons used to color their hair. The desire for that hard, concrete lump of limestone, which is sometimes found inside the body of an oyster and with which women delight to attract attention to the pretty curves of their ears or the slenderness of their fingers, has been responsible for more voyages of discovery in the Pacific and in the Indian Ocean than any other cause, including the desire of many honest people to carry the Gospel unto the heathen.

The quest for ambergris, a substance found in the intestinal canals of sperm whales, and the result of what in plain English we would call a bilious attack on the part of the unfortunate whale, has driven more ships to the coasts of Brazil and Madagascar and the Moluccas than the search for herring or sardines or other forms of useful food. For ambergris could be used as a base for many perfumes that smelled deliciously of flowers and distant lands, whereas food was merely food and not half as interesting.

A change in fashions which made the women of the seventeenth century wear their corsets underneath their gowns and out of sight (twelve-course dinners were bad for the figure) was directly responsible for most of our knowledge of the Arctic. As soon as Paris had decided that hats should be adorned with aigrets, those hunters who went after the white herons to deprive them of their head plumes (regardless of the fact that this meant the extinction of one of the loveliest and noblest birds of all creation) penetrated further into the lagoons of our southern states than they had ever done before when they were merely in quest of their daily bread and butter.

I might continue the list for almost a dozen more pages. Whatever was rare and therefore expensive has always been an object of veneration to those who, by a wasteful demonstration of their riches, hoped to impress their less fortunate neighbors. Ever since the beginning of history, luxury rather than necessity has been the real pioneer of progress along the lines of exploration. And when we study the map of prehistoric Germany carefully we can still trace the old luxury routes, for in the main they are the same as those of medieval and modern times.

Take the conditions some three thousand years ago. The mountain-ridges of the south, the Harz, the Erz Mountains and the Riesengebirge were situated hundreds of miles away from the sea. The plain that stretched northwards towards the North Sea and the Baltic had long since changed from marshland into dry land and was now thickly covered with forests. And Man, following in the wake of the glaciers, which had now retreated in the general direction of Scandinavia and Finland, had claimed this entire wilderness as his own. Among the hills of the south, the tribes which inhabited the valleys had found that it paid them to cut down their trees and sell them to the Romans who had occupied strategic positions along the Rhine and the Danube. For the rest, few of these early Teuton nomads and farmers had ever seen a Roman. One Roman expedition had tried to penetrate to the heart of their country, had been ambushed in a dark and water-logged valley and slaughtered off so completely that the experiment had never been tried again. That did not mean however that northern Germany was completely cut off from all contact with the rest of the world.

The great prehistoric trade-route from west to east, from the Iberian peninsula to the plains of Russia, followed the line from the Pyrenees to Paris, through the gaps of Poitiers and Tours, which I described in the chapter on France. It then skirted the Ardennes and from there followed the outskirts of the central European highlands until it reached the northern lowlands now occupied by the United Soviet Republics of Russia. On its course eastward this road was of course obliged to cross a great many rivers and it did this wherever it could find a convenient shallow place. Just as the city of Rome grew out of a ford across the Tiber, so a number of the earliest cities of northern Germany were but the continuation of prehistoric and early historic settlements which were located on the exact spot where today we would find a filling station and a general store. Hanover and Berlin and Magdeburg and Breslau had all of them got their start that way. Leipzig, although originally it was a village in the heart of Slavic lands, was also of commercial origin, for it was there that the mineral products from the Saxon mountains, such as silver and lead and copper and iron, were assembled before they were sent down the rivers and sold to the merchants patronizing the great European highway from east to west.

Of course, once this road reached the Rhine, water traffic began

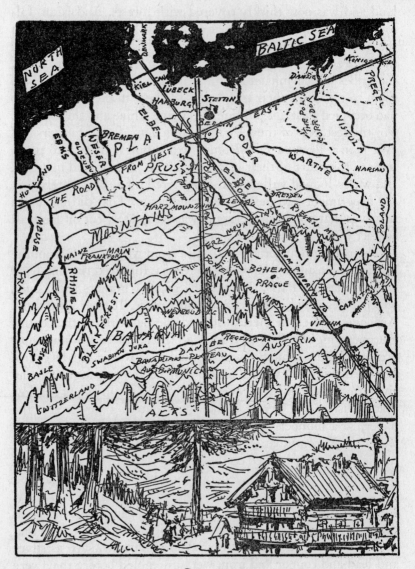

Germany

to compete seriously with the caravans used for the long overland haul. Water traffic has always been much cheaper and much
more convenient than land traffic, and long before Caesar caught
his first glimpse of the Rhine there must have been rafts used to
carry merchandise from Strassburg (where the Rhine connected
with the hinterland of Franconia, Bavaria and Württemberg)
to Cologne and thence to the marshes of the Low Countries and
eventually to Britain.

It is a far cry from Berlin to Jerusalem, but both cities obeyed
the same geographical rule which insists that cities must arise
wherever important trade-routes cross each other. Jerusalem was
situated on the caravan route from Babylonia to Phoenicia and
from Damascus to Egypt and was an important trade center long
before the Jews had heard of its existence. Berlin, situated on a
river where the routes from west to east and from north-west to
south-east (from Paris to Petrograd and from Hamburg to Constantinople in modern terms) happened to meet, was bound to
become a second Jerusalem.

All during the Middle Ages Germany consisted of a large
number of semi-independent states but until 300 years ago there
was nothing to indicate that some day this western part of the
great European plain would develop into the leading nation of
the world. Curiously enough the modern Germany grew almost
directly out of the failure of the Crusading Movement. When
it became certain that no new territory was to be conquered in
western Asia (the Mohammedans had proved more than a match
for the Christians) the disinherited classes of Europe began to
look for other sources of agricultural wealth. Quite naturally
they thought at once of the opportunities offered by the Slavic
lands situated just across the Oder and the Vistula, which were
inhabited by the wild and heathenish Prussians. One of the old
crusading orders moved, lock, stock and barrel, from Palestine
to east Prussia and transferred its business center from Acre in
Galilea to Marienburg, thirty miles south of Danzig. For two
hundred years these knights fought the Slavs and settled the

farms of their victims with imported nobles and peasants from the west. In the year 1410 they suffered a terrific defeat at the hands of the Poles in the battle of Tannenberg, the same place where in 1914 Hindenburg annihilated the Russian armies. But somehow or other the order survived even this blow and when the Reformation occurred, they were still a body of considerable importance.

It so happened that at that time the order was ruled by a member of the Hohenzollern family. This particular Grand Master not only joined the Protestant cause but on the advice of Martin Luther he declared himself hereditary Duke of Prussia with Königsberg on the Gulf of Danzig as his capital. Early in the seventeenth century this duchy was acquired by another branch of the industrious and shrewd Hohenzollern tribe which ever since the middle of the fifteenth century had been administering the sandy wastes of Brandenburg. A hundred years afterwards (in 1701, to be precise) these Brandenburg upstarts felt themselves strong enough to aspire to something better than the rank of a mere "prince elector" and they began an agitation to get themselves recognized as kings.

The emperor of the Holy Roman Empire was willing. Dog as a rule does not eat dog and the Habsburgs were glad to render some small service to their good friends the Hohenzollerns. Weren't they both members of the same club? In 1871, the seventh Hohenzollern King of Prussia became the first Emperor of a United Germany. Forty-seven years later, the ninth King of Prussia and the third Emperor of modern Germany was forced to leave his throne and his country and that was the end of a vast holding company which began as a bankrupt remnant of crusading orders and finished as the strongest and most efficient power of the great age of industrialism and capitalism.

But now that it is all over and the last of the Hohenzollerns is chopping wood in Holland, we might as well be honest about it and confess that those ex-Tyrolean mountaineers were an astonishingly capable sort of men, or at least were clever enough to surround themselves with servants of extraordinary ability.

For remember that their original territories had possessed no natural wealth of any sort. Prussia had ever been a land of farms and forests and sand and marshes. It did not produce a single article that was fit for export, the only means for any country to get a favorable balance of trade.

There was a slight change for the better when a German discovered a way by which sugar could be extracted from beets. But since cane sugar was still infinitely cheaper than beet-sugar and could be imported by the ship-load from the West Indies, all this meant very little money in the pockets of either Prussians or Brandenburgians. But when the Emperor Napoleon, after having lost his navy in the battle of Trafalgar, decided to destroy England by means of an "inverted blockade" there arose a sudden but very steady demand for the Prussian beet-sugar. At about the same time, German chemists established the value of potash and since Prussia had large potash deposits, the country could at last begin to work a little for the foreign market.

The Hohenzollerns, however, were always lucky. After the defeat of Napoleon, Prussia acquired the Rhine region. It was of no particular value until the industrial revolution put a premium upon the possession of coal and iron. Quite unexpectedly Prussia found herself possessed of some of the richest ore and coal fields of the entire world. And then at last the hard school of poverty of the previous five hundred years began to bear fruit. Poverty had already taught the Germans to be thorough and thrifty. It now showed them how to over-manufacture and under-sell all other nations. And when there was no longer room enough on land for the rapidly increasing number of little Teutons, they took to the sea and within less than half a century they were among the leaders of the countries which derive their revenue from the carrying trade.

Hamburg and Bremen, which had been of considerable importance when the North Sea was the center of civilization (a position it held until the discovery of America made the Atlantic the main road of commerce) were called back to life and seriously threatened the claim to exclusive eminence of London and the other British ports. A large ship canal was dug from the Baltic to the North Sea, the so-called Kiel Canal, which was opened in the year 1895. Canals also connected the Rhine and the Weser and the Oder and the Vistula and the Main and the Danube (only partly finished), providing a direct aquatic route between the North Sea and the Black Sea, and Berlin was given access to the Baltic by means of a canal that ran from the capital to Stettin.

Whatever human ingenuity could do to assure the majority of the people a fairly decent living wage was done, and before the Great War, the average German peasant and working man, while by no means rich, and accustomed to very strict discipline, was probably better housed and better fed and in a general way better protected against accidents and old age than any other group of people belonging to the same class anywhere else.

How all this was sacrificed by the unfortunate outcome of the Great War is a very sad story but it does not belong in the present volume. But as a result of her defeat, Germany lost the rich industrial districts of Alsace and Lorraine. She lost all her colonies, her commercial navy and part of the province of Schleswig-Holstein, which she herself had taken away from the Danes after the war of 1864. Several thousand miles of former Polish territory (but thoroughly Germanized by then) were once again separated from Prussia and returned to Poland, while a broad strip of land, following the course of the Vistula and running from Thorn to Gdynia and the Baltic, was put under Polish suzerainty, that this country might enjoy direct access to the open sea. Part of Silesia, which Frederick the Great had taken away from Austria in the eighteenth century, remained in German hands. But the more valuable mineral deposits were given to Poland, although the textile interests stayed under German control.

For the rest, Germany was stripped of everything it had acquired during the previous fifty years and its colonies in Asia and Africa were divided among other nations which had already more than their share and no surplus population with which to settle them.

Politically speaking, the Treaty of Versailles may have been an excellent document. From the point of view of applied geography, it makes one despair of the future of Europe. I am afraid that those sceptical neutrals who wanted to present Lloyd George and the late Monsieur Clemenceau with a handbook on elementary geography were not so very far wrong.

XVI

AUSTRIA, THE COUNTRY THAT NOBODY APPRECIATED
UNTIL IT NO LONGER EXISTED

THE present Republic of Austria has 6,000,000 inhabitants and 2,000,000 of these live in the capital city of Vienna. As a result of this extraordinary arrangement, the country is top-heavy and the marvellous old town on the Danube (which is a muddy gray and not at all as blue as the famous waltz might make you expect) is slowly degenerating into a dead city where disheartened old men and women wander aimlessly among the ruins of their former glory, while the younger generation has fled abroad to start a new existence amidst happier surroundings or has committed suicide because life at home had become in-tolerable. Within another hundred years the gay city of Vienna (one of the few cities where the people seemed to be really happy, if often in a sort of childish and careless way), that old, important center of science and medicine and the arts, will have become a second Venice. From being a capital of an empire containing more than 50,000,000 people it has become a mere village de-pendent upon the tourist traffic and what little importance it re-tains as a port of call for the boats that carry the products of Bohemia and Bavaria to Roumania and to the Black Sea.

At present the geography of the ancient Danube monarchy (this name, by which Austria was formerly known, expressed the true nature of the country about as well as anything could do) is extremely complicated, for it has been hacked to pieces in such an arbitrary fashion as to be almost unrecognizable. But the former dual monarchy of Austria-Hungary was a perfect example of how natural conditions will influence the formation of strong centralized states. Forget all about frontiers for a moment and look at the map of this region, which was situated almost in the very heart of the European continent, as far away from the toe of Italy's foot as from the nose of the Danish peninsula. It was really an immense circle of flat lands and rolling territory, entirely surrounded by high mountain-ranges. On the west there were the Alps of Switzerland and the Tyrol. In the north were the Erz Mountains and the Riesengebirge (the Giant Mountains) of Bohemia, and the Carpathians, which formed a semi-circle sheltering the Hungarian Puszta (or steppes) against invasions from the side of the Slavic plains. The Danube separated the Carpathians and their southern part, the so-called Transylvanian Alps, from the Balkan Mountains, and the Dinaric Alps were the barrier that protected the plains from the raw winds of the Adriatic Sea.

The people who founded this state had very imperfect maps and their theoretical knowledge of geography was quite negligible. But just as our pioneers who conquered the West followed certain definite tracks and routes without ever having consciously studied an outline of the road that carried them to their final destination, so did those medieval conquerors accumulate their vast holdings by merely doing what was "immediately practicable" without bothering themselves about the theoretical side of the problem. Such things took care of themselves. Nature provided them with certain unavoidable "consequences" and Man, whenever he is wise, quietly obeys her commands.

During the first thousand years of our era, the great Hungarian plain was a veritable no-man's-land, invaded by all the tribes who followed the course of the Danube on their way from the Black Sea to the west and were without any settled form of government. Charlemagne, during his life-long warfare upon the Slavic people from the east, founded a small "mark" or frontier post, as we would call it, which being the eastern mark or "Oester Reich" (the same word as our Austria) gave birth to the principality that eventually was to dominate that entire part of the world. Although at times overrun by the Hungarians and the Turks (the last siege of Vienna by the Turks took place long after Harvard University had been founded) the little mark, firmly handled and efficiently administered, first of all by the Babenberg family and afterwards by the Habsburgs, our Swiss friends whom I mentioned a few pages ago, always came out on top. Eventually these rulers of a petty frontier state even managed to get themselves elected as Emperors of that Holy Roman Empire, which was neither Roman nor Holy nor an Empire, but merely a loose federation of all the different German-speaking races. They held this title until the year 1806 when Napoleon threw it on the scrap-heap because he intended to put an imperial crown on his own proletarian brow.

But even thereafter these not over-brilliant but tenacious Habsburgs managed to keep a finger—and a most important finger—in the German pie until finally in 1866 Prussia pushed them back across their own mountains and bade them stay where they belonged.

Today the old Eastern Mark, reduced to the rank of a seventh-rate nation, torn by internal strife and without any hope for a better future, consists, for the greater part, of that mountainous region which is but a continuation of the Swiss Alps and which contains the remnants of those famous Tyrolean mountains which were handed over to Italy by the treaty of Versailles on the ground that once upon a time they had been part of the ancient Roman Empire. This mountainous region contains two towns of some importance, Innsbruck, where the ancient route to Italy via the Brenner Pass crosses the River Inn, and where everything reminds one of the Middle Ages, and Salzburg, the birthplace of Mozart, which is one of the most beautiful cities of Europe and which tries to keep alive today by providing the world with a few musical and theatrical performances.

Neither these mountains nor those of the Bohemian plateau in the north produce anything of any value. The same can be said of the so-called Viennese basin where the Romans founded an armed camp called Vindobona (or Vienna), a small settlement which gained some notoriety when the famous philosopher-emperor, Marcus Aurelius, died there in the year 180 after one of his many campaigns against the barbarians of the northern Germanic plains. The town, however, did not come into its own until ten centuries later, when the great migrations of the Middle Ages, also called the Crusades, made it the point of departure for all those who tried to reach the Promised Land by following the Danube rather than by entrusting themselves to the racketeering ship-owners of Genoa and Venice.

In the year 1276 it became the residence of the Habsburg family and the center of their vast domains, which eventually included all the land between the mountain-ranges enumerated a few pages back. In the year 1485 the Hungarians captured the city. In 1529 and again in 1683 the Turks laid siege to it. But the town survived all these misadventures until the beginning of the eighteenth century, when it began to disintegrate as a result of a mistaken policy which entrusted every position of any importance in the monarchy to noblemen of strictly Germanic origin. Too much power is a hard thing for all people, and the amiable Austrian knights were no exception. They ceased to be merely amiable and became feeble and weak.

In the old dual monarchy, 47% of the people were of Slavic origin and only 25% (or one-quarter) were Germans, while the rest consisted of Hungarians (19%) and Roumanians (7%) with about 600,000 Italians (1.5%) and about 100,000 Gypsies who stuck pretty closely to Hungary where they were treated more or less like respectable citizens.

The German "masters" apparently were never able to learn the lessons which the rest of Europe was slowly beginning to take to heart. Monarchies and an aristocracy can only survive as long as they are willing to assume leadership. The moment they begin to talk about "service" instead of "leadership", they are doomed. After the endless defeats of the Austrian armies during the Napoleonic wars, the people of Vienna got into such a state of irritation in regard to their princely and grand-ducal and baronial rulers that they practically forced them to leave the town and retire to their country estates, where they vegetated and got completely out of touch with the rest of the land.

It was then that geography came to the assistance of the city. With the nobility out of the way, the merchants and the manufacturers could at last come into their own. Vienna, freed from its ancient fortifications (they were so enormous that the sale of the land they covered paid for the different extensions of the town), rapidly developed into the most important commercial, scientific and artistic center of eastern Europe.

The World War made a sudden end to both riches and glory. The country now called Austria bears practically no resemblance to the empire of which it was the head until only a few years ago. Its future is entirely behind it. It is a state in name only. The refusal of the French to let it join the German Republic was the last straw.

It might just as well be put up for public sale. But who would want to buy it?

XVII

DENMARK, AN OBJECT LESSON IN CERTAIN ADVANTAGES
OF SMALL COUNTRIES OVER LARGE ONES

DENMARK is such a tiny country, as modern nations go (it has only about three and a half million inhabitants of which 750,000 live in the capital) that we might well pass it by, if quantity rather than quality were of any real importance in the affairs of men. But as an example of what can be made out of indifferent material by the application of intelligence combined with a sensible ideal of life (that "moderation in all things" which the Greeks had proclaimed as the highest form of wisdom) Denmark, as well as the other Scandinavian countries, deserves special and most honorable mention.

For that country with its 16,000 square miles and its total lack of natural resources, armies, navies, mines or mountains (at no point does the country rise above 600 feet, which is less than half the height of the Empire State Building) is worth a dozen other countries of infinitely greater size and more pretentions and militaristic ambitions which I could mention if I felt so inclined. The Danish people, entirely through their own efforts, nave lowered the illiteracy percentage to zero, they have made themselves the second richest country per capita of all Europe and they have practically abolished both riches and poverty as they are known in the rest of the world, establishing instead a balance of average, moderate well-to-do-ness which is without an equal anywhere else.

Denmark, as one glance at the map will show you, is composed of a peninusla and a number of islands separated from each other by wide open sounds across which the railroad trains are carried on ferries. Its climate is exceedingly unpleasant. All winter long a strong eastern wind is apt to blow across her flat fields, bringing cold showers of rain and forcing the Danes, like the Dutch with whom they have so much in common, to spend a great deal of their time indoors, a circumstance which has contributed greatly to making them a heavy book-reading nation. In consequence thereof they are a singularly well-informed group of people who own more books per capita than any other nation.

But the rain and the wind keep the pastures moist, and the grass grows and makes the cows fat, and as a result of all this Denmark alone is able to provide the world with 30% of its butter. But whereas in most other countries the soil would be owned by rich and absentee landlords, the Danes, who are essentially democratic (in the social and economic rather than the political sense of the word) have never encouraged the development of those vast holdings which we have encountered in most other countries.

There are today 150,000 independent farmers in Denmark who operate small farms, ranging from ten to a hundred acres, and there are only 20,000 farms larger than one hundred acres. The dairy products which are sent abroad are raised and prepared according to the most modern and scientific methods, as taught by the rural agricultural schools which are merely a continuation of the free High School system spread all over the country. The buttermilk that is left over as a by-product of the butter manufacturing is used to feed the hogs which in turn provide the entire British market with its bacon.

As this trade in butter and bacon is much more profitable than the raising of grain, the Danes are obliged to import their grain. They can do this however quite easily and cheaply, as Copenhagen is only two days by steamer from Danzig, and Danzig is the old export-harbor for the vast granaries of Poland and Lithuania. Part of this grain is used for poultry-raising and millions of eggs are sent each year to those same British Isles, which for some mysterious reason have never been able to grow anything more palatable than Brussels sprouts.

Denmark in relation to Norway and Sweden

In order to maintain what almost amounts to a monopoly in farm products, the Danes submit to a most rigorous state control of everything that leaves their country, thereby establishing for themselves such a reputation of absolute integrity that their trademark has come to be accepted as a guarantee of absolute purity.

Like all races of Teutonic origin, the Danes are incurable gamblers, and during the last few years their ventures in banking and in stock-market speculation have cost them a tidy sum of money. But the children and the cows and the hogs remained when the banks closed their doors and now they are at work once more. The only difficulties they have got to fear have to do with the rapidly increasing state of bankruptcy of most of their neighbors, making such a simple dish as ham and eggs a luxury beyond the reach of the average man.

The towns on the mainland are of no importance. On the west coast of Jutland (the name of the old peninsula from which so many of the original settlers of England came) lies Esbjerg, which is the main export harbor for all these many agricultural products, and on the east coast lies Aarhus (the double A is pronounced OA in Danish) which is one of the oldest centers of Christianity in this part of the world where the people continued to worship their heroic Pagan Gods (their Odins and Thors and Baldurs) until only four centuries before the discovery of America.

The Little Belt (I believe there are plans now to build a bridge across it) separates Jutland from Fyen, the first of the big Baltic islands. In the center of Fyen (cows, hogs and children) lies the city of Odense (the place sacred to Odin) where Hans Christian Andersen was born, the son of a poor and sickly shoe-maker, but one of the greatest benefactors of mankind.

Then we cross the Great Belt and reach the island of Zealand, the heart of the old Danish Empire. Here at a wide bay, protected from the violence of the Baltic by the small island of Amager, the vegetable garden of the capital, lies the charming city of Copenhagen, the "Merchants' Harbor" of the Middle Ages.

During the ninth and tenth centuries, when the Danes ruled an empire which included England and Norway and parts of Sweden, Copenhagen was merely a fishing village, and Roskilde, about fifteen miles inland, was the royal residence from which those distant domains were administered; but today Roskilde is of no importance, while Copenhagen has gone on increasing in size and importance until now it provides entertainment for one-fifth of the entire population of the country.

Copenhagen is a royal residence, and a few guards in very handsome uniforms present arms when the King goes swimming or fishing or strolls forth to buy himself a package of cigarettes. But you will look in vain for any other manifestations of military grandeur. This small country, which has done some of the hardest and bitterest fighting in the days gone by, and which even as recently as the year 1864 was able to hold its own against Prussia for quite a long time, voluntarily abolished its army and navy and has replaced them by a small corps of state police to enforce whatever neutrality will survive the next outbreak of a general European conflict.

That is about all there is to say about Denmark. The country peacefully goes its own way. The royal family keeps off the front page of the more sensational newspapers and while few people have three overcoats, none go without, and while only a small percentage has an automobile, every man, woman and child possesses at least a couple of bicycles, as you will know for yourself if you have ever tried to cross a street in a Danish city just before the luncheon hour.

In a world devoted to the idea of bigness, Denmark hardly plays a role. In a world devoted to the ideal of greatness, it would occupy quite a considerable position. For if the greatest happiness of the greatest number of people is the ultimate goal to which all governments should aspire, Denmark has done more than enough to justify her continued existence as an independent nation.

XVIII

ICELAND, AN INTERESTING POLITICAL LABORATORY IN
THE ARCTIC OCEAN

FROM the days of her ancient imperial glory, Denmark has
retained a few scraps of land, including that sixth continent,
Greenland, which seems to contain valuable mineral treasures
(iron, zinc and graphite) but which is so completely covered with
glaciers (only about one-thirtieth of the whole of Greenland is
free from ice) that it may never be of any value to any one unless
the axis of the earth shifts just a tiny little bit and allows Greenland once more to enjoy that tropical climate which must have
prevailed there millions of years ago, as we are able to deduce
from the presence of several large coal fields.

Her other colonies are the Faroe Islands (literally the
Sheep Islands) which lie 200 miles north of the Shetlands
and have a population of about 20,000 people and a capital
city called Thorshavn, from where Hudson commenced his
dash across the ocean which carried him to Manhattan. And
then there is Iceland. The latter is a country of particular interest. Not only on account of its volcanic nature, which makes it
a veritable store-house for all those queer phenomena we usually
connect with the mysterious fires from old Vulcan's furnace, but
also on account of its political development. It is the oldest republic of our planet with a record of self-government which
began some eight centuries before our own and which with only
a few short interruptions has lasted until today.

The first settlers of the island were fugitives from Norway
who found their way to this distant spot in the ninth century.

Although 5000 square miles out of the total of Iceland's 40,-
000 are perpetually covered with glaciers and snowfields, and

What lies underneath

only one-fourteenth of the island is really fit for purposes of agriculture, living conditions there were so much more favorable than in the mother country that already by the beginning of the ninth century there were over 4000 homesteads inhabited by free and independent farmers. And these, continuing the habits of practically all early Germanic tribes, at once established a loose form of self-government. It consisted of an "Althing"— a gathering of the different local "Things" or "moots" (which is really the same word as our "meeting"). This Althing met once a year during midsummer on a huge volcanic plain, called the Thingvellir and situated about seven miles distant from Reykjavik, the present capital, which is only a hundred years old.

During the first two centuries of their independent existence, the Icelanders developed enormous energy, composed some of the best sagas that have ever been written, discovered Greenland and America (five centuries before Columbus), and made this northern island, where in the winter the days are only four hours long, a more important center of civilization than the mother country itself.

But the curse of all Germanic races—an all-too-pronounced individualism which makes political or economic cooperation almost an impossibility—had accompanied the natives on their flight towards the west. During the thirteenth century, Iceland was conquered by the Norwegians, and when Norway became part of Denmark, Iceland followed suit. The Danes completely neglected the island, which henceforth was at the mercy of French and even Algerian pirates until all the old prosperity had disappeared, while the literature and architecture of the heathenish period lay forgotten and the ancient wooden buildings of nobles and freedmen were being replaced by huts made out of peat.

Since the middle of the last century, however, there has been a return of some of the old prosperity and with it a renewed demand for complete independence. Today Iceland once more rules itself as it did eleven centuries ago, although outwardly still recognizing the King of Denmark as its sovereign. The biggest city on the island, Reykjavik, has still fewer than 10,000 inhabitants but is the seat of a university. The total number of inhabitants does not surpass the hundred thousand but they have an excellent literature of their own. There are no villages but only isolated farms where the children are taught and taught well by itinerant schoolmasters.

Iceland

Altogether this is a most interesting little corner of the world. Like so many other small countries, it shows what can be done when intelligence is pitted against unfavorable outward circumstances. For Iceland surely is no earthly paradise. While the winters are not very cold, due to the presence of a branch of the Gulf Stream, the summers are much too short to allow the raising of grain or fruit. And then, it is forever raining!

The twenty-nine volcanoes of which the most famous, the Hekla, has been responsible for twenty-eight outbreaks during the period of which we have any historical record, have covered the island with vast tracts of lava, some of which are over a thousand square miles large. Earthquakes have upon occasion destroyed hundreds of farms and enormous fissures or clefts, running often for miles across the solid sheet of lava, and sulphur springs and lakes of boiling mud make travel from one part of the island to the next a somewhat complicated affair. The geysers or hot-water gushers for which Iceland is so famous are interesting rather than dangerous, for although one of these, the famous Big Geyser, sometimes spouts its boiling water as high as a hundred feet, their activity is steadily decreasing.

And yet people not only live on Iceland but want to go on living there. During the last sixty years more than 20,000 of them have moved to America, chiefly to Manitoba. But many of them have returned whence they came. It rains. And it is uncomfortable. But it is home.

XIX

THE SCANDINAVIAN PENINSULA, THE TERRITORY OCCU-
PIED BY THE KINGDOMS OF SWEDEN AND NORWAY

THE people of the Middle Ages, who lived in a happy world of fairy stories, knew exactly how the Scandinavian peninsula happened to have got its queer shape. After the good Lord had finished the work of creation, the Devil came along to see what He had been doing those seven long days He had been away from Heaven. When the Devil saw our planet in the first flush of its young loveliness, he lost his temper and got so terribly angry that he heaved a large rock at Mankind's new home. That rock landed in the Arctic Sea and became the Scandinavian peninsula. It was so barren and bleak that it seemed entirely unfit for life. But the good Lord remembered that a little bit of rich earth had been left behind when he got through fashioning the other continents. These remnants he then sprinkled across the mountains of Norway and Sweden. But of course there was not enough to go around and that explains why the greater part of these two countries has always remained a home for trolls and gnomes and werewolves, because no human being could ever hope to make a living from such a poor soil.

Modern man has a fairy story of his own, but it is a scientific one based upon certain facts which he has been able to observe with his own eyes. According to the geologists, the Scandinavian peninsula is merely the remnant of a very old and very large continent which long before the era of the coal forests had stretched from Europe all the way across the Arctic Ocean to America.

We know of course that the present arrangement of our continents is of very recent origin—that the continents seem to be constantly on the move, like leaves floating on a pond, and that several continents, now separated from each other by oceans and seas, were once upon a time a solid mass of land. When the continent of which Norway and Sweden had formed a part disappeared from view, only the eastern-most ridge—the mountain-ranges of Scandinavia—remained above water. So did Iceland and the Faroe Islands and the Shetland Islands and Scotland. The rest now lies at the bottom of the Arctic Ocean. Some day the roles may be reversed. Then the Arctic Ocean will become dry land and Sweden and Norway will be turned over to the whales and the little fishes.

The Norwegians do not seem to lose any sleep on account of this threat to their homeland. They have other things to worry them. The problem, for example, of keeping alive, which is by no means a simple one when you remember that in Norway less than four percent of the total area (only 4000 square miles) can be used for purposes of agriculture. Sweden is a little better off with ten percent, but even that is not so very much.

There are of course certain compensations. One-half of Sweden is covered with woods and one-quarter of Norway is covered with pine and fir forests. These forests are slowly being cut down, but lumbering is not the devastating business it is with us. It is done in the most scientific way imaginable, for both the Swedes and the Norwegians know that their country will never be any good for ordinary agricultural pursuits. That is the fault of the glaciers which once upon a time covered the whole of the peninsula, from the North Cape down to Lindesnaes. These glaciers scraped the soil from the rocky hillsides as completely and efficiently as a hound dog licking a plate. Not only did they deprive the mountains of their hard earned soil (it takes millions of years to make enough soil to cover such a vast stretch of land) but they carried it away with them and deposited it all over that great northern plain of Europe of which I told you in the chapter about Germany.

The scouts who went ahead of the great Asiatic invasion of Europe of forty centuries ago must have known this. When at

The barren soil of the mountains

last they crossed the Baltic, they found Scandinavia inhabited by a few nomads of Finnish origin. It was easy enough to drive them back into the fastnesses of northern Lapland. But when that had been done, how could the new settlers hope to make a living?

There were several ways. In the first place, they could go out and fish. The endless bays and fjords, which were really nothing but deep grooves dug into the rocks by the glaciers trying to reach the ocean, gave the country a coast-line almost six times as long as it would have been if the Norwegian coast had formed a straight line, as it does in Holland or Denmark. The Norwegians are still fishing. The Gulf Stream sees to it that all the harbors, even as far north as Hammerfest, remain open the whole year around. The nooks and crannies of the Lofoten Islands, on the brink of those cool, clean Arctic waters which the cod seems to prefer for breeding purposes, provide work for more than a hundred thousand fishermen and to an equal number of people engaged in the business of canning whatever the trawlers bring on shore.

In the second place, if they did not care to fish, they could turn pirates. All along the Norwegian coast there lies a row of islands and islets which account for seven percent of the country's surface and which are separated from each other by such a complicated system of narrows and sands and bights and straits that a steamer going from Stavanger to Vardö has got to carry two pilots who succeed each other every six hours.

During the Middle Ages when there were no beacons and buoys and lighthouses (Lindesnaes is the oldest lighthouse on the Norwegian coast and even that is of comparatively recent date) no outsiders would come within a dozen miles of this

Norway

dangerous coast. Although the story of the famous Maelstrom between two of the Lofoten Islands has been greatly exaggerated, no inexperienced skipper would venture into this watery labyrinth without at least half a dozen natives to show him the way. Those pirates therefore who made their own familiar fjord their base of operations knew that they had little to fear as soon as they were within sight of the home range of mountains and they made very good use of this natural advantage. They improved their ships and their fighting technique until they could venture forth as far as England and Ireland and Holland. Once they had discovered the road to these comparatively nearby places, they gradually lengthened their voyages until the people of France and of Spain and of Italy and of far off Constantinople began to feel uncomfortable whenever some returning merchantman reported that he had seen the dragon of a Viking ship somewhere in the neighborhood.

During the early part of the ninth century they plundered Paris not less than three times. They sailed up the river Rhine and got as far as Cologne and Mayence. As for England, different tribes of Norsemen fought each other for the possession of that country as the nations of Europe of today will make war upon each other for a particularly desirable piece of oil land.

About the same time that Iceland was discovered, Norsemen had founded the first Russian state, of which they themselves were to be the rulers for almost seven entire centuries. Still later, a plundering expedition of two hundred boats (small boats which could be carried overland whenever necessary) had travelled from the Baltic to the Black Sea and had caused such consternation in Constantinople that the emperor of the eastern Roman Empire had hastened to take these wild men into his service, as a special sort of body-guard.

Entering the Mediterranean from the west, they had established themselves in Sicily and on the coasts of Spain and Italy and Africa and had repeatedly rendered the most valuable services to the Papacy in its wars upon the rest of the world.

What has become of all this glory of the ancient Norse nation?

All that remains today is a highly respectable little kingdom which catches and exports a lot of fish and engages in the carrying trade and fights bitter political quarrels about the language the people should speak—quarrels of which the world at large would never notice anything if the Norwegian authorities did not have the fatal habit of changing the names of their most important cities and railroad stations about once every two or three years.

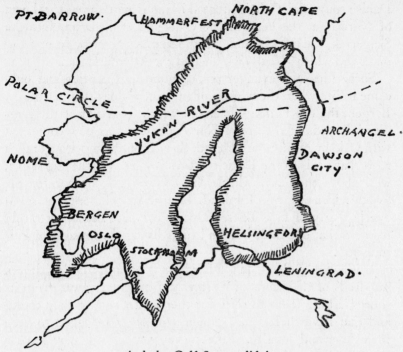

And the Gulf Stream did it

Alaska has 590,000 sq. miles of territory and a population
of 60,000. Norway, Sweden and Finland with only
430,000 sq. miles have a population of 12,000,000

As for those cities of Norway, most of them are merely over-
grown villages where everybody's dog knows everybody else's
dog. Trondheim (formerly Nidaros and then Trondhjem) was
the capital of the old Norwegian kingdom. It has an excellent
harbor and as soon as the Baltic is covered with ice, Trondheim
becomes the port from which a great deal of Swedish wood is
shipped to the rest of the world.

The present capital, Oslo, is built near the ruins of a very old
Norwegian settlement which had burned down. It was built by
the Danish King Christian IV and therefore called Christiania
until the Norwegians decided to purge their language of all

Danish souvenirs. Oslo is situated in the richest agricultural part of Norway at the head of the Oslofjord, which runs into the Skagerrak, the broad sound which separates Norway from Denmark and which is really a branch of the Atlantic Ocean.

Such cities as Stavanger or Aalesund or Christiansand only come to life when the whistle of the nine o'clock steamer blows. Bergen, the old Hansa settlement which looked after the commercial needs of the entire Norwegian coast, is now connected with Oslo by means of a railroad. So is Trondheim with a branch road that leads to the Baltic coast of Sweden. Further up north, well above the Arctic Circle, lies Narvik, the harbor for the Swedish iron ore from Lapland. Tromsö and Hammerfest smell everlastingly of fish. These names occur here because it rarely happens that one finds human beings living comfortably at latitude 70°.

It is a strange land. It is a hard land—a land that has driven hundreds of thousands of its sons and daughters away from its shores, asking them to shift for themselves as best they could, and that nevertheless has somehow or other managed to keep their love and loyalty. Take a boat sometime if you have a chance and travel northward. Everywhere it is the same. Some Godforsaken little village, clinging to a bit of grass, just enough for a single goat, and five or six houses and a few ramshackle boats and one steamer a week and people weeping because they see it again—because it is home—because it is their home—because it is part of their flesh and blood.

The International Brotherhood of Man is a noble dream.

It takes on queer aspects in Bodö or in Vardö, ten days away by steamer from nowhere.

Sweden, the other side of the mountain-range that remained after the great Arctic plateau had disappeared beneath the waves of the Atlantic, is a very different country from Norway. People often wonder why these two nations do not decide to form a single nation. It would mean a great saving in the cost of administration. On paper such an arrangement looks eminently practicable. But their geographical background makes it impossible. For whereas Norway on account of the Gulf Stream enjoys a mild climate with lots of rain and little snow (in Bergen the horses shy whenever they meet a man without an umbrella or a raincoat) Sweden has a continental climate, with long, cold winters and a heavy snowfall. Whereas Norway has deep fjords that penetrate for miles into the interior, Sweden has a low coast with few natural harbors none of which have achieved the importance of Gothenburg on the Cattegat. And whereas Norway has no raw materials of its own, Sweden is possessed of some of the most valuable ore deposits of the whole world. The

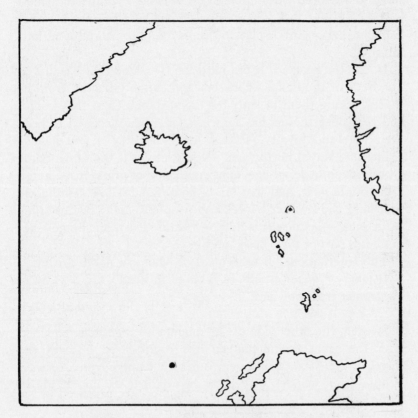

Look at a map of the Arctic and this is all you see

unfortunate absence of coal still forces Sweden to export a great deal of these ores to Germany and France, but during the last twenty years the taming of many important waterfalls has made Sweden increasingly independent of coal while the forests that cover such a great part of the kingdom account for the enormously rich Swedish match trust and the far-famed Swedish paper factories.

The Swedes, like the Norwegians and the Danes (one might say like all nations of Germanic origin except perhaps the English) have unbounded trust in the potentialities of the human intellect. Her scientists are therefore given free scope and as a result her chemists have discovered and developed a large number of by-products which are derived from the wood industry and which otherwise would have gone to waste, such as celluloid and artificial silk. But her agriculture, although much higher developed than that of Norway, suffers from the unfavorable climatic conditions which are the result of being situated on the cold and exposed side of that high mountain-range which divides the Scandinavian peninsula so sharply into two halves. Perhaps that is one of the reasons why the people are so fond of flowers. The winters are so very long and dark. Every Swedish home therefore tries to keep bright with flowers and evergreen shrubs.

In a great many other respects also Sweden is different from Norway. In Norway the feudal system of ancient times died out with the Black Death—that terrible plague of the late Middle Ages which abruptly called a halt to all further Viking ambitions and activities. In Sweden, on the other hand, the continued existence of large land-holding interests has allowed the country nobility to maintain itself up to the present time. And although the country is now being ruled by a socialistic government (like the vast majority of all other European countries) Stockholm is still a city with an aristocratic background, in sharp contrast to Oslo and Copenhagen, where the utmost democratic simplicity is as rigidly maintained as courtly manners are practiced in the Swedish capital.

Perhaps this development too is a direct result of Sweden's

curious geographical position. For whereas Norway faces the Atlantic, Sweden is essentially a country that looks out upon an inland sea and its entire economic well-being, together with its history, is interwoven with that of the Baltic.

As long as Scandinavia was still a half-settled wilderness, there was little to choose between the Norsemen of the western coast and those of the east. To the outside they were all of them "Norsemen" and the famous old prayer, "from the fury of the Norse, good Lord, deliver us," was chanted without specifying what particular sort of Norsemen the humble supplicants had in mind.

But after the tenth century there was a change. Then there arose a great and bitter civil warfare between the Swedes of the north, of Svealand, whose capital was situated on the Mālar lake on which the modern capital of Stockholm is situated, and the Goths of the south or Götaland. They were closely related, these two tribes, and worshipped their Gods near the same shrine, the City of the Gods, which was built on the spot where the town of Upsala rises today, the oldest and most important university town of northern Europe. These quarrels, which lasted more than two centuries, greatly strengthened the position of the nobility while at the same time weakening that of the kings. During this period too Christianity had made its entrance into the Scandinavian peninsula, and the clergy and the monasteries happened to take the side of the nobles (in most countries it was the other way around) until finally the Swedish monarchs became so weak that for a century and a half Sweden had to recognize the sovereignty of Denmark.

Europe had almost forgotten that Sweden existed when in the year 1520 the western world was shocked by the tale of one of the most ghastly and inexcusable murders that has ever disgraced the history of man. In that year King Christian II of Denmark had invited all the heads of the Swedish nobility to a great banquet—a sort of love-feast which once and for all would settle all further difficulties between the King and his beloved Swedish subjects. At the end of the festivities all the guests were taken prisoner and were either beheaded or drowned. Only one man of any importance escaped. That was Gustavus, the son of a certain Erik Vasa, who a few years previously had been beheaded by order of that same King Christian. Gustavus had then escaped to Germany. When he received news of the massacre he returned to his native land and by starting a revolution among the ancient yeomen he finally forced the Danes to return to their own country, whereupon he himself was crowned King of Sweden.

That was the beginning of that extraordinary era of national and international adventure which not only made this small and poverty-stricken land the champion of the Protestant cause in Europe but which turned Sweden into the last bulwark against the ever-increasing threat of a Slavic invasion. For the Russians, after centuries of oblivion, had at last gone on the war-path and had commenced that famous march to the sea which has not yet come to an end today.

Sweden apparently was the only country which recognized the menace. During two whole centuries all her energies were concentrated upon one single purpose—to keep Russia within bounds and away from the Baltic. In the end, of course, Sweden was bound to lose. The struggle completely exhausted her exchequer and it merely retarded the progress of the Russian steam-roller by a few decades. When it was all over, Sweden, which had owned the greater part of the Baltic Sea coast, which had ruled Finland and Ingermanland (where Leningrad is today), Estonia, Livland and Pomerania, had been reduced to a kingdom of the second rank, with an area of 173,000 square miles (something between Arizona and Texas) and a population slightly smaller than that of New York City. (Sweden has 6,141,671 and New York City has 6,930,446.)

Half of this territory is still covered with forests, which in turn supply the timber needs of almost one-half of the European continent. These trees are cut down in the winter and allowed to lie around until after the beginning of spring. They are then dragged across the snow to the nearest river and are dumped into the gorge. When summer comes and the ice of the inland mountains begins to thaw, the rivers, turned into torrents, pick up the logs and carry them down into the valleys.

The same river which has thus far played the role of the railroad now becomes the source of power for the saw-mills, which pick up the logs and turn them into anything desired, from a match-stick to a four inch plank. By this time the Baltic has become free from ice, vessels can once more reach the different parts of the eastern coast, and the finished wood products, which thus far have cost very little, except for the wages of the lumberjacks and the mill-hands, are now entrusted to the steam-boats, which have continued to provide us with the cheapest form of transportation whenever time is not of primary importance.

These vessels serve a twofold purpose. They would be obliged to go home empty unless they could pick up some sort of return cargo. Of course they cannot charge much for these return cargoes and as a result, Sweden gets most of its imports at a very reasonable rate.

The same system is followed in handling the iron ore which is of such excellent quality that it is in high demand even in countries which have ore deposits of their own. As the country is nowhere wider than 250 miles, it is always comparatively easy to reach the coast. In northern Sweden, in Lapland near Kiruna and Gällivara, there are immense deposits of iron which Nature for some mysterious reason has plunked down there right on the surface of the earth in the form of a couple of low mountains. In the summer the ore is taken to Luleå on the Gulf of Bothnia (the northern part of the Baltic) and in the winter, when Luleå is frozen fast, to Narvik in Norway, which, due to the Gulf Stream, remains open all the year round.

Not far from these iron deposits lies Sweden's highest mountain, Kebnekaise (almost 7000 feet high) and there also stands one of the most important power houses of Europe. It is situated well within the Polar Circle but since electricity seems to be indifferent about geographical latitudes, this station is able to run both the railroads and the machinery of the surface mines at a very small cost.

The southern part of Sweden, which got a little of that soil scraped off by the glaciers of the north, is of course the most fertile part of the entire Scandinavian peninsula and therefore the most densely populated. It has a great many lakes. As a matter of fact, Sweden, next to Finland, is the "lakiest" country in the world; 14,000 square miles of it are covered with water. By connecting these lakes with canals, the Swedes have provided that whole part of their country with cheap means of communication, which greatly benefits not only the industrial centers like Norrköping but also the harbors, of which Gothenburg and Malmö are the most important.

There are countries in which Man has submitted to the dictates of Nature until he has become her abject slave, and there are countries where Man has destroyed Nature so completely that he has lost all touch with that great living mother who forever must remain the beginning and the end of all things. And finally there are those where Man and Nature have learned to understand and appreciate each other and have agreed to compromise for their mutual benefit. If you want an example of the latter, go north, young man, and visit the three Scandinavian nations.

XX

THE NETHERLANDS, THE SWAMP ON THE BANKS OF THE NORTH SEA THAT BECAME AN EMPIRE

THE word "Netherlands", which is only used on very official occasions, means exactly what it implies, a combination of "low" localities situated from two to sixteen feet below the level of the sea. A single good flood of prehistoric dimensions, and Amsterdam and Rotterdam and all the most important cities would disappear from the face of the earth.

But this apparent natural weakness of the country has also been the source of its greatest strength. For among these marshes along the banks of the North Sea it was not sufficient for Man to take hold of the country. Ere he could do that, he was obliged to create it, and in that uneven conquest between human ingenuity and the relentless forces of Nature, the Dutch people were triumphant. It taught them to be hard and watchful. In the sort of world in which we happen to live, those qualities are not without merit.

When the Romans visited this distant and lonely part of Europe (which they did about fifty years before the beginning of our era), the entire region consisted of bogs and marshes protected against the ravages of the North Sea by that slender row of sand dunes which stretched all the way from Belgium to Denmark. These dunes were interrupted at irregular intervals by a large number of rivers and rivulets. Most important among the rivers were the Rhine, the Meuse and the Scheldt. Left entirely to their own devices and not hindered by any dikes, these three rivers did exactly what they pleased, and every spring they altered their course and created islands where no islands

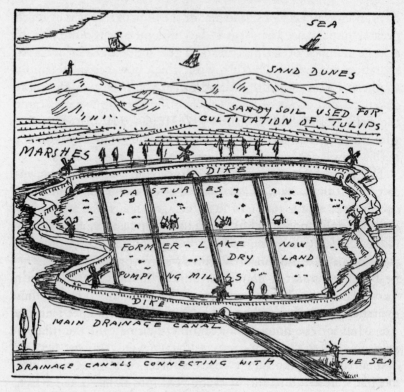

A Polder

had ever been before and swept away vast tracts of land that had seemed as solid as the island of Manhattan. I am not exaggerating. Upon one memorable occasion in the thirteenth century, seventy villages and almost a hundred thousand people disappeared from view in the course of a single night.

Compared to their Flemish neighbors who lived on solid ground, these early Hollanders lived a very miserable existence; but a mysterious change, either in the temperature of the water or the salt percentage of the Baltic, gave them their chance. One day absolutely unexpectedly, the fish known as the herring moved from the Baltic into the North Sea. In an age when all the people of Europe were obliged to eat fish on Fridays and when fish as a staple diet of the human race was of much greater importance than it is today, this meant absolute ruin to a large number of Baltic cities and the sudden rise of a corresponding number of Dutch towns, which now began to supply southern Europe with that dried fish which then took the place of our canned goods of today. Out of the herring fisheries came the grain trade, and out of the grain trade grew the commerce with the spice islands of India. There was nothing extraordinary in this. It was the normal development of a commercial state.

But when fate, regardless of all practical considerations, incorporated the Low Countries into the empire of the Habsburgs and decreed that a nation of lusty peasants and fishermen, without any of the graces of life, but tough-fisted and very practical-minded, should be administered by sour officials trained at the court of an absolute monarch who dwelled somewhere in dignified loneliness among the bleak hills of his windswept Spanish Castle-land, then there was bound to be trouble. That trouble expressed itself in a struggle for liberty which lasted eighty years and which ended with a complete victory for the inhabitants of the Low Countries.

The rulers of the newly-founded state, being practical men of affairs, believed sincerely in the principle of live and let live, especially when it meant a profit to them. They therefore offered their hospitality and their protection to all those who in less fortunate countries were being persecuted for their beliefs, religious or otherwise. Most of these refugees (with the exception of a small group of obscure English dissenters, who however did not stay very long) became loyal subjects of the country that had given them the chance to start upon a new and happier career. As a rule their former masters had deprived them of all their liquid assets and had confiscated their savings. But they carried their old ability with them wherever they went, and they contributed most generously to the commercial and intellectual development of their adopted fatherland. And when the war of independence was over, a million people, living in little cities built on the bottom of some old lake or inland sea, boldly assumed the leadership of Europe and Asia and maintained that position for three generations.

Then they invested their money—bought themselves large country estates, foreign pictures (which are of course always so much better than those painted by the talent at home) and spent their days being respectable. They did their best to make their neighbors forget where the money had come from, and very soon the money forgot to come too. For nothing in this world can afford to stand still, least of all our human energy. And those who won't make an effort to hold what they have got will soon lose all, and that goes for ideas as well as for ducats.

The end came during the beginning of the nineteenth century. Napoleon, who knew only as much geography as he needed to win his battles, claimed that since the Low Countries were merely a delta formed by three French rivers, the Rhine, the Meuse and the Scheldt, the country belonged by right of geological descent to the empire of the French. A large N scrawled at the bottom of a piece of paper undid the work of three entire centuries. Holland disappeared from the map and became a French province.

In 1815 however the country regained its independence and went back to work. The colonial heritage, sixty-two times as large as the mother country, has allowed towns like Amsterdam and Rotterdam to maintain themselves quite successfully as centers for the distribution of Indian products. Holland has never been an industrial country. It has no raw materials except a little coal of very indifferent quality in the extreme south. It is therefore not able to provide its own colonies with more than six percent of all their imports. But the development of the tea and coffee and rubber and quinine plantations in Java and Sumatra and the Moluccas and Borneo and the Celebes demands vast amounts of capital. This fact is responsible for the leading position of the Amsterdam stock-exchange, and the importance of Amsterdam as a place where people and nations go to borrow money, while the necessity of carrying all this merchandise to and from Europe made it possible for the Netherlands to remain fifth on the list of national tonnage.

The tonnage of the vessels used for the trade at home is higher than that of any other country. The country is honeycombed with convenient waterways and the canal-boat is the most dangerous rival of the railroad as it can be operated at a minimum of cost in a country where, until recently, the time element did not play a very important role in the daily affairs of men, women, cows, horses and dogs.

A great many of those canals are really drainage ditches, for one-quarter of the kingdom's territory is no land at all, in the usual sense of the word, but merely a piece of the bottom of the sea reclaimed from the fishes and the seals by endless labor and kept dry by artificial means and perpetual watchfulness. Since the year 1450 thousands of square miles of land have been added to the country by the draining of marshes and by turning lakes into "polders". To make such a polder is really very easy if you know how. First of all, you build a dike around the piece of water you have doomed for destruction and on the outside of that dike you dig a wide and deep canal, which is connected with the nearest river into which it can pour its daily surplus by means of a complicated system of locks. When that has been done, you construct a few dozen windmills on the top of that big dike and furnish them with a pumping machine. The wind or a small gasoline engine will then do the rest. When all the water has been pumped out of the lake and has been pumped into the canal, you dig a number of parallel ditches across your new "polder" and, provided you keep your pumping-mills and pumping-stations working all of the time, these canals will then take care of the necessary drainage.

Some of these polders are quite large and are inhabited by as many as twenty thousand people. If the Zuyder Zee ever gets dried up (the affair may prove a little too costly, now that every nation is on the verge of bankruptcy) there will be room for at least a hundred thousand more. As fully one-quarter of the country consists of such polders, you will easily understand how it happens that the Dutch Department of Rivers, Canals and Dikes disposes of more money every year than any of the other sub-divisions of the government.

Locks

In strange contrast with the high fertility of this low part of the country, the higher regions of the east, where the central European plain met the sea before the formation of the big, marshy delta of the Rhine and the Meuse and the Scheldt, is of very little use to anybody. For thousands of years it was an unloading station for the boulders and the pebbles of the northern European glaciers. In some ways the soil resembles that of New England, only it is much more sandy and it gives the statistics of the Kingdom of the Netherlands that queer twist which allows a country with a density of population of 625 per square

The dike

mile (France has only 191, Russia 17) to carry a ballast of more than 25% of its total area as "territory which is essentially unproductive". (In France the percentage is less than fifteen and in Germany less than nine.)

And this curiously sharp line of demarcation between east and west and fertile and infertile also accounts for the presence of the more important towns in a single small triangle right in the heart of the polder-land. Amsterdam, Haarlem, Leyden, the Hague, Delft and Rotterdam are so close to each other as to form practically one large city and all of them lie close to the protecting bulwark of those famous sand dunes, at the foot of which the Dutch of three centuries ago began to raise and to perfect the pretty little bulbs of a flower called "Tulipa" which their merchants had brought back from Persia and Armenia.

The city of Athens was only as large as eight New York City blocks. Any wheezy old flivver will carry you from one end of Holland to the other in a few hours. And yet, next to the territory of Attica, this narrow strip of land between the Rhine, the North Sea and the Zuyder Zee has probably contributed more to the sum total of our arts and sciences than any other region of similar diminutive proportions. Athens was a barren rock and Holland was a water-logged swamp. But they had two things in common when they suddenly leaped into fame—an excellent geographic location from the point of view of international commerce, and a superabundance of animal spirits and spiritual curiosity, left over from the days when they had been obliged to fight or perish. And out of these their glory was born.

XXI

GREAT BRITAIN, AN ISLAND OFF THE DUTCH COAST WHICH
IS RESPONSIBLE FOR THE HAPPINESS OF FULLY
ONE-QUARTER OF THE HUMAN RACE

UNTIL a few years ago this chapter would have been entitled "Great Britain and Ireland". Then Man improved upon the handiwork of Nature and turned a geographical unit into two separate entities. And all the obedient scrivener can do is to follow suit and give each of the two countries a separate chapter. Any other course might lead to far-reaching complications, and I would hate to see the Irish Navy sail up the Hudson River to demand an apology for this "insufferable insult to the national pride of Saorstat Eireann".

Dinosaurs drew no maps, but the rocks remained behind to tell their story. And they are all there—the igneous rocks, volcanic products which got cooled off near the surface of the earth, and the granite, born under pressure, and the sedimentary rocks, slowly settling down along the bottoms of lakes and seas, and the metamorphic rocks, like slate and marble, which were really limestone and clay, changed into more valuable materials by the subtle chemistry of the great depths.

They are all there, lying about in disordered profusion, like the furniture in a house struck by a cyclone. They provide us with a geological laboratory of rare interest. They may account for the fact that England, which usually takes to the shooting of rabbits with greater zeal and interest than to the hunting of scientific facts, has given the world so many first-rate geologists. It may of course be the other way around: because there were a great many excellent geologists, we learned more about the geology of England than of any other country. But that hardly seems likely. Swimming champions are usually found near the water and rarely in the heart of the Kalahari Desert.

And so the geology was there and the geologists were there, and what did they tell each other about the origin of the land of their birth?

Try to forget the map of Europe as you have come to know it today. Imagine a world which has only recently emerged from below the surface of the sea, which is still rocking with the effort

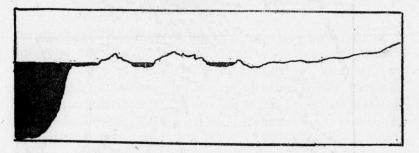

The Atlantic, Ireland, England and Europe

of creation. Picture to yourself vast continents rising high and bleak above the waters, rent asunder by eruptions that crush the rocks as a manhole explosion in New York will split the pavement of the streets. Meanwhile the forces of Nature's laboratory continue their patient labors. Incessantly the winds blow from the ocean carrying billions of tons of moisture on their way from west to east, drenching the land and giving it moisture, covering it with a wide blanket of grass and ferns, arranging for the maintenance of shrubs and trees. Day and night and night and day and year after year after year, the tireless waves beat and pound and grind and file and crunch and rasp until the shores of the land wilt and crumble as the snow melts and crumbles before the rays of the insistent sun. And then suddenly the ice—the slow, merciless wall of death that groaningly hoists itself across the steepest side of the highest mountain-ranges, that rumbles ponderously down the slopes of wide valleys, that fills deep

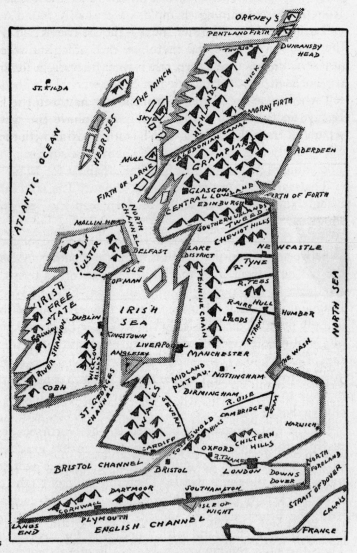

England, Scotland and Ireland

gorges and narrow ravines with frozen water and pieces of rock from the wasted hilltops.

The sun shines—the rain rains—the ice cracks and creeps—the waves gnaw—the seasons follow each other and when Man at last makes his appearance, this is what he finds. A long narrow strip of land, cut off from the rest of the world by a flooded valley which reaches all the way from the Arctic to the Gulf of Biscay, another high plateau rising well above the waves and separated from the narrow strip by an unruly and choppy sea—a few lonely rocks sticking out well above the surface of the sea, a perching place for gulls rather than a habitat for Man.

That vaguely, very vaguely, was the way England came into being. Now let us look at the modern map and see what that shows us.

From the Shetland Islands to Land's End is the same distance as between the middle of Hudson Bay or southern Alaska and the northern frontier of the United States, or, in terms understandable to the average European, from Oslo in Norway to Prague in Bohemia. That means that England, one of the most densely populated countries in the world, with 45,000,000 people, is situated between the same degree of latitude as the peninsula of Kamchatka (opposite Alaska) which also runs from about 50° lat. to 60° lat., and where less than 7000 people just about manage to keep themselves from starving by living on an exclusive diet of fish.

On the east, England is bounded by the North Sea, which is really nothing but an old depression which has gradually run full of water. Again a single glimpse at the map will tell you more than a thousand words. There on the right (the east) is France. Then we get something that looks like a trench across a road, the British Channel and the North Sea. Then the great central plain of England with London in the deepest hollow. Then the high mountains of Wales. Another depression, the Irish Sea, the great central Irish plain, the hills of Ireland, a few lonely rocks further towards the west, rearing their tops above the shallow sea. Finally the rock of St. Kilda (uninhabited since a year ago as it was too hard to reach) and then suddenly down we go, down, down, down, for there the real ocean begins and the last of the vast European and Asiatic continent, both submerged and semi-submerged, here comes to an end.

As for the different seas and bays and channels that surround England, I had better mention them in some detail. I have done my best not to clutter this book with unnecessary names which you would forget as soon as you had turned to the next page. But here we are on classical ground, for this strange little island has influenced the life of every man, woman and child on the whole of the planet for at least four entire centuries. That, however, has not been entirely a matter of chance or racial superiority. That the English have made the best of their opportunities is undoubtedly true. But Nature had given them a tremendous advantage when she placed their lovely island right in the heart of the greatest amount of land in the eastern hemisphere. If you want to realize what that means, think of poor Australia, lost amidst an endless expanse of water, left entirely to its own devices, with no neighbors, with no chance to get new ideas from anywhere; and then compare Australia's position with that of England, which, like a spider in a net, was equally far removed from all the four corners of the world, yet, unlike the spider, was safely protected from the rest of humanity by a convenient moat of salty water.

Of course this peculiar location meant nothing as long as the Mediterranean was still the center of civilization. Up to the end of the fifteenth century, England was just another slightly remote island, holding about the same position in men's minds as Iceland does today. "Have you ever been to Iceland?" "No, but I have an aunt who went there once. Funny place—interesting island—but too far away—means five days of seasickness."

That is exactly what England meant to the people of the first ten centuries of our era—three or four days of seasickness—and remember, a Roman galleon was even less comfortable than a seven hundred ton steamer from Leith to Reykjavik.

Gradually, however, the knowledge about these outskirts of

civilization increased. The painted savages who lived in small round huts, sunk well into the ground and surrounded by a low earthen wall, were tamed by the Romans who, listening to their speech, came to the conclusion that they must belong to the same racial stock as the Celts of northern Gaul and who found them on the whole docile and willing to pay tribute without talking too much about their "rights". It was doubtful anyway whether they had any "rights" to the soil they occupied, for it appeared almost certain that they were newcomers and had taken the land away from an older race of invaders of whom the traces could be found here and there among the less accessible regions of the east and west.

The Roman occupation of England lasted, roughly speaking, four centuries, almost as long as the time during which the white man has been the dominating race in America. Suddenly, almost abruptly, it came to an end. For almost five hundred years the Romans had been able to keep the hungry Teutonic tribes out of their European domains. Then the badly defended barriers gave way, the flood of barbarians swept across southern and western Europe. Rome recalled her foreign garrisons. Temporarily, of course, for no empire ever acknowledges itself beaten until years after it has ceased to exist. A few regiments were left behind to guard the high earthen wall which protected the plains of Britain from the invasions of the savages who dwelled among the impassable mountain-ranges of Scotland. Other castles guarded the boundaries of Wales.

But one day the regular supply ships failed to come from across the water. That meant that Gaul had been lost to the enemy. From that moment on the Romans in England were cut off from the mother country and connections were never reestablished. A little later news appeared from the coastal towns that foreign ships had been seen off the mouth of the Humber and the Thames, and that villages in Durham and York and Norfolk and Suffolk and Essex had been attacked and plundered. The Romans had never dreamed of fortifying their eastern frontier because it had not been necessary. But now some mysterious pressure (whether hunger or wanderlust or an enemy in the rear, we shall never know), which had pushed the advance guard of the Teutons across the Danube and through the mountain passes of the Balkans and the Alps, was carrying raiding parties of Saxon pirates all the way from Denmark and Holstein to the shores of Britain.

The Roman governors, the Roman garrisons, the Roman women and children who must have inhabited those charming villas of which we continue to find the remnants, disappeared from view—disappeared as mysteriously and silently as the earliest white settlers along the coast of Virginia and Maine vanished from the face of the earth. They dissolved into space. Some of them were murdered by their own servants. The women were married by kind-hearted natives—a strange fate for a proud race of conquerors, but one that has overtaken more than one group of "colonials" who have neglected to take the last ship home.

Thereafter chaos—and groups of savage ax-men from Scotland and Caledonia, industriously killing off their Celtic neighbors who had grown soft during the centuries when Rome had acted as the national and international policeman. Then the usual mistake made under such distressing circumstances—the bright idea that invariably spells ultimate disaster: "Let us call in a few strong men from somewhere else and hire them to do our fighting for us." The strong men came from the marshes and the plains between the Eider and the Elbe. They belonged to a tribe called the Saxons, which tells us nothing about their origin, for northern Germany was full of Saxons.

Why they should ever have become identified with the Angles is another problem that will probably never be solved. The term Anglo-Saxon was invented centuries after they had made their first appearance upon the English scene. Anglo-Saxon is now a slogan which makes people fight: the Anglo-Saxon blood—the Anglo-Saxon traditions. Well, one fairy story is as good as the next, and therefore if it makes people happy to think themselves superior to all other people, why not? But the historian must regretfully announce that the Angles as a racial unit are the little brothers of the Lost Tribes of Israel—they have often been mentioned in spurious chronicles of the past but no one has ever been able to find a trace of their whereabouts. As for the Saxons, they were about on a par with the hordes of northern European immigrants one might have seen in the steerage of an ocean liner of thirty years ago. But they were strong. They worked and fought and played and plundered with equal zest. They were given five centuries in which to organize the land over which they now ruled as hereditary masters, and during that period they were able to force their own tongue upon the poor Celtic natives, who rapidly lost all recollection of the few Latin words they had picked up while working in the kitchen of some noble Roman lady. Then they in turn were thrown out of house and home by still another wave of Teuton immigrants.

In the year 1066 England became a Norman dependency, and for a third time the British Isles were forced to acknowledge a sovereign from over the seas. Soon, however, the tail was wagging the dog. The British colony proved to be a more profitable investment than the temporary motherland in France and the Normans left the continent and settled down in England for good.

Their final defeat and the loss of their properties in France were a blessing in disguise for the English. They ceased to be forever looking towards the continent and they became conscious of the existence of the Atlantic Ocean. Even so, England would probably not have started upon her maritime career when she did if Henry VIII had not fallen in love with a lady by the name of Anne Boleyn, who informed him that the road to her heart led through a well-lighted church. This had meant a divorce from His Majesty's lawful spouse, the mother of Bloody Mary, and this had caused a definite break between England and Rome upon the subject of the Pope's supremacy over all Christendom. Since Spain took the side of the Pope, England must then learn how to sail ships and defend herself, or else perish as an independent nation and become a Spanish province. In this curious, roundabout way, a divorce quarrel was the real cause which taught the English how to become expert navigators; and having learned their new trade, the marvellous geographic position of their home country did the rest.

The change, however, did not take place without a very severe domestic struggle. No one can reasonably expect one class of society to commit suicide for the benefit of another, and it was no more than natural that the feudal chiefs who had ruled supreme ever since the Norman conquest should have tried to prevent their country from giving up its agricultural habits and going in for commerce on a world-wide scale. Feudalism and capitalism have always been each other's sworn enemies. The medieval knight looked down upon business as something totally unworthy of free men. A merchant in his eyes was something like a bootlegger. You used him but did not allow him to come in by the front door. Trade therefore was mostly left to foreigners, mainly to Germans, to people who came from the North Sea and the Baltic, the famous "Easterlings" who gave

The Factory conquers the Farm

England its first notion of a coin of an absolute and unquestionable value, the "Easterling's pound"—the pound sterling of today. The Jews were expelled and were so rigorously kept out of the country that even Shakespeare can have known his Shylock merely from hearsay. The coastal towns did a little fishing, but the main occupation of the country was and for centuries to come remained the pursuit of agriculture. Nature had greatly favored the land for this purpose, more especially for stock-breeding, for the soil was often too rocky to raise grain, while offering abundant fodder for cows and sheep.

During two-thirds of the year the winds blew (and continue to blow) from the west, which meant rain, as any one will remember who ever was obliged to spend part of a winter in London. Today agriculture, as I told you when we talked of the northern European states, is no longer as absolutely dependent upon Nature as it used to be a thousand or even a hundred years ago. We can't as yet make rain, but the chemical engineer has taught us how to overcome many difficulties which the con-

Great Britain is a country of Lighthouses

temporaries of Chaucer and Queen Bess accepted as acts of God against which there was neither remedy nor redress. There again the geological structure of the island proved a great boon to the landowners of the east. A cross-section of the British Isles shows that they resemble a soup plate, tilted much higher in the west than in the east. It is a result of the fact, mentioned before, that England is part of a very old continent, that the oldest mountains which used to cover the east have been entirely worn away by water and wind, while the younger rock formations of the west are still standing upright and won't be gone before another ten or fifteen million years. These younger mountains which occupy the territory called Wales (one of the last strongholds of some of the original Celtic tongues) act as a fence to break the force of the Atlantic rainstorms ere they reach the lowlands of the east, and they temper their violence so successfully that the great eastern plain enjoys an almost ideal climate for the purpose of raising grain and cattle.

Since the invention of the steam-boat, which allows us to order our grain from the Argentine or Chicago, and since the introduction of cold storage for the purpose of transporting frozen meats from one end of the world to the other, no nation, able to pay the price, is any longer dependent upon its own farms and fields for the purpose of feeding the home population. But until a hundred years ago, the owners of the food supply were also the masters of the world. Whenever they decided to lock the doors of their larder, millions of people died a slow death of starvation. The wide plain formed by the British Channel in the south, the Severn in the west (the river that divides Wales from England and runs into the British Channel), the Humber and Mersey in the north, and the North Sea in the east was therefore the most important part of the old England, for it produced the greatest amount of food.

Of course, when I speak of a plain, I do not mean a plain in the sense of the word to which we ourselves are accustomed. The great central English plain is no flat pancake like Kansas but consists of a rolling landscape. The river Thames (which is almost as long as our own Hudson, 215 miles against 315) runs through the heart of it. The Thames takes its origin among the Cotteswold Hills, famous for their sheep and for the presence of the city of Bath, where ever since the days of the Romans, the victims of British cookery have come together to partake of the hot calcium and sodium baths and fortify their constitutions by further slabs of underdone beef and half-drowned vegetables.

The Thames then flows between the Chilton Hills and the White Horse Hills, provides the University of Oxford with a convenient water supply for its rowing experiments, and finally enters the lower Thames valley, situated between the low hills of the East Anglian Ridge and the North Downs, which would run all the way to France if the strait of Dover had not eaten its way through this soft chalky substance in its laudable effort to connect the Atlantic with the North Sea.

It is on this river that the world's biggest town is situated. Like Rome and most other cities that go back to obscure and remote dates, the city of London was not an accident or the result of a sovereign's whim. It was located where it stands today as a result of sheer economic necessity. In order to get from southern England to northern England without being dependent upon the proverbially bad good will of the nefarious tribe of ferrymen, it was necessary to construct a bridge. And London arises at the exact spot where the river ceased to be navigable but was not too wide to allow the engineers of twenty centuries ago to build something that would safely carry people and merchandise from one shore to the next without getting their feet wet.

When the Romans left, a great many things were changed in the British Isles, but London remained behind and today, with more than 8,000,000 population, it is still more than an entire million ahead of New York. It covers an area five times as large as ancient Babylon, the biggest city of antiquity, and four times as large as that of Paris. For London is a city of low buildings. The Englishman, with his insistence upon privacy and his desire for being allowed to mind his own business, refuses to live in a bee-hive and as a result, London moves horizontally, whereas our American cities have a tendency to move vertically.

The heart of London, the "city", is now merely a workshop. In the year 1800 it still had 130,000 inhabitants. The number has since shrunk to less than 14,000. But every day almost half a million people come down to the city to administer the billions of capital which England, out of her vast surplus wealth, has invested in foreign enterprises, and to supervise the distribution of those almost incredible quantities of colonial products which lie heaped up in the store-houses stretching all the way from the Tower Bridge to a distance of twenty miles below London Bridge.

As the Thames must remain open to traffic all the time, the only way to handle the shipping was by building docks and warehouses along both sides of the river. Those who want to know what international commerce really means should visit these London docks. It will give them the uncomfortable feeling that New York is after all still some sort of a provincial village, a little too far removed from the main highways of trade to be of any special importance. Eventually this may change. The center of commerce seems to be moving westward. But London still is supreme in her knowledge of the technique of foreign trade, while New York is only beginning to learn the rudiments.

But I am running ahead of my subject. I have got to get back for a moment to the English plain of the year 1500. Its entire southern rim consisted of mountains. In the extreme west lay Cornwall, the geological continuation of Brittany from which it was separated by the British Channel. Cornwall is a curious land where the Celtic tongue maintained itself until two centuries ago and where strange stone monuments, in all respects resembling those of Brittany, bear out the theory that once upon a time all these regions must have been inhabited by people of the same race. Cornwall, by the way, was the first part of England to be discovered by the sailors from the Mediterranean. The Phoenicians in their quest of lead and zinc and copper (re-

England enjoys the enormous advantage of being situated in the heart of the land-masses of our planet

member that they flourished at the beginning of the metal age)
used to come as far north as the Scilly Islands. There they
met the savages from the fog-bound mainland and did their
bartering.

The most important city of this whole region is Plymouth, a
military port without much shipping except an occasional Atlantic steamer. On the other side of Cornwall lies the Bristol
Channel, the "Wrong Channel" of the maps of the seventeenth
century because skippers who returned from America were very
apt to mistake it for the British Channel and were then ship-

wrecked among these treacherous waters where the tide may rise as high as forty feet.

North of the Bristol Channel lie the mountains of Wales. They were of no great importance to anybody until the discovery of their coal and iron beds and of the copper deposits of the nearby island of Anglesey which turned that part of the country into one of the richest industrial units of the entire kingdom. Cardiff, an old Roman fort, is now one of the greatest coal centers of the world. It is connected with London by means of a railroad which dives underneath the river Severn. This tunnel has gained almost as much fame in engineering circles as the bridge which connects the mainland of Wales with the island of Anglesey and the island of Holyhead, from where one starts for Kingston, the port of the city of Dublin in Ireland.

This ancient quadrangle of England, where every city and village is so hoary with age and history that I almost fear to mention their names lest I be tempted to make this a geography of England rather than the whole world, has until this day remained the backbone of the land-owning classes. In France, where large estates are not absolutely unknown but rather rare, there are ten times as many land-owners as in this part of Britain. In Denmark the proportional difference is even greater. That this class of county-squires has lost so much of its former importance and now merely survives as a social institution which teaches the rest of the world the correct way to wear golf-breeches and to kill time by killing what are sometimes called "our dumb friends," is not due to any lack of virtue of their own but rather to that sudden change in our economic life brought about by the invention of a practical and workable steam-engine by James Watt. When that mathematically inclined instrument-maker of the University of Glasgow began to play with his grandmother's tea-kettle, steam was still a plaything used to work a few slow and laborious pumps. When he died, steam ruled supreme and land was no longer the source of riches.

It was then, during the first forty years of the last century, that the center of economic gravity, which ever since the begin-

The North Sea

ning of history had lain in the south, moved northward to Lan-
cashire where the vapor of water set the cotton mills of
Manchester a-spinning, and to Yorkshire, where steam turned
Leeds and Bradford into the woollen centers of the whole
world, and to the so-called Black Country where horse-power
made Birmingham the breeding-place for all those millions of
tons of steel plates and girders which were needed to build the
ships that must carry the finished products of the British Isles
to the ends of the earth.

The upheaval caused by the substitution of steam for human
muscles was the most formidable revolution mankind had ever
experienced. The engines, of course, were not able to think
for themselves, and they needed a certain number of human
attendants to feed them and tend them and tell them when it
was time to begin and to stop. In return for such very simple
services, the farm hands were promised what to them seemed
riches. The country people listened to the lure of the city. The
cities grew by leaps and bounds. The contractors for tenement
houses grew rich. And within a remarkably short space of time
eighty percent of the country population had moved to the
towns. It was then that England accumulated that vast surplus
wealth which will keep her going long after all her other assets
shall have been exhausted.

Many people nowadays are asking themselves whether that
point has actually been reached. Time only will tell—time,
meaning the next ten or twenty years. But it will be very interesting to see what happens. The British Empire up till now
has been the result of a series of accidents. In this it resembled
the Roman Empire. The Roman Empire was the center of the
Mediterranean civilization and it had to conquer its neighbors
in order not to lose its own independence. As soon as England
had become the center of the Atlantic civilization, it was obliged
to follow a similar policy. Now at last the era of world-wide
exploitation seems to have come to an end. Commerce and civilization are beginning to move across the ocean. What only a
few years ago was the heart of a vast empire is rapidly becom-

ing an over-populated island, somewhere off the Dutch coast.

It seems too bad. But that is the way things happen on our planet.

SCOTLAND

The Romans knew of the existence of the Scotch as our own ancestors along the Atlantic seaboard knew about the existence of the Five Nations. Somewhere in the north, beyond the last line of imperial block-houses and the last of the Northumbrian hovels, there lay a land of unhospitable mountains inhabited by rough tribes of shepherds and sheep-owners. They dwelled in almost legendary simplicity, counted descent through the mother instead of the father, as all the rest of the world did, had no roads except a few trails almost too steep for a horse, and had resisted all efforts to civilize them with such ferocious violence that the best policy had seemed to be that of leaving them strictly alone. But as they were also formidable cattle-thieves and had a way of suddenly descending from their mountains to steal the sheep of the Cheviot Hills and the cows of Cumberland, it was considered wise to protect these regions by means of a high wall running all the way from the Tyne to the Solway and bid them stay out on pain of death by means of the sword or crucifixion.

This was done, and during the four centuries of Roman domination in England, the Scots, with the exception of a few punitive expeditions, were rarely exposed to the blessings of civilization. They continued their old commercial relations with their Celtic cousins in Ireland, but their needs were few and they rarely came in contact with the rest of the world. The ancient Roman wall is gone but even today the Scots live very much a life of their own, and they have been able to develop a culture of their own.

The fact that Scotland is such a dreadfully poor land may have helped them to retain their individuality. The greater part of their country is mountainous. Long before the appearance of Man these mountains were as high as the Alps. Erosion (wind and rain) wore them gradually away and great geological upheavals did the rest. Then came the ice, the same ice that covered Scandinavia, and the little bit of soil that had accumulated in the valleys was swept away by it. No wonder that only ten percent of the population of Scotland can maintain themselves in the Highlands. The other ninety percent are gathered together in the Lowlands, a narrow strip of land, often not more than fifty miles wide, which runs from the Clyde in the west to the Firth of Forth in the east. In this valley a wide rift between two mountain-ranges of volcanic origin (most of its castles are built on the necks of extinct volcanoes) lie the two big Scottish cities, Edinburgh, the ancient capital, and Glasgow, the modern city of iron and coal and shipbuilding and manufacturing. These two are connected by a canal. Another canal, running from Loch Linnhe to the Moray Firth, allows small vessels to go directly from the Atlantic to the North Sea without being obliged to navigate the difficult waters between John o' Groats and the Orkneys and Shetlands, remnants of the big continent that reached from Ireland to the North Cape of Norway.

But the sort of prosperity found in Glasgow is not the sort of prosperity that makes a country rich, and the average Scotch peasant spends his days getting just a little too much to eat to die of starvation but never quite enough to feel that he is really alive. This has perhaps made him a little too "careful" in spending his few hard-earned pennies but it has also taught him to depend entirely upon his own efforts, upon his own intellectual courage, regardless of what the rest of the human race may say.

The historical accident which made Queen Elizabeth die bestowing the throne of England on her Scotch cousin James of the house of Stuart, made Scotland a part of the English Kingdom. Thereafter the Scotch could enter England at will, and whenever that island proved too narrow for their ambitions they could roam across the length and the breadth of its Empire.

Their thrift and intelligence and their general lack of emotions made them ideally fit for leadership among the provinces in distant climes.

THE FREE STATE OF IRELAND

And now a different story, one of those inexplicable tragedies of human destiny in which a race possessed of unlimited mental possibilities was seen to turn its back deliberately upon the task in hand and to waste its strength in the futile pursuit of some lost cause; while on a nearby island an implacable enemy was ever on the alert, stolidly relentless in its determination to humiliate and enslave those who had failed to learn that an enlightened self-interest is the primary law of existence.

Who was to blame? I don't know. Nobody knows. Geology? Hardly. Ireland, also a remnant of the great Arctic continent of prehistoric days, would have been much better off if during the period of readjustment the center of the land had not sunk so deep below the mountainous ridges of the seaboard, giving the entire country the shape of a soup-plate and making it almost impossible for the few rivers to wend their way towards the sea without developing such a large number of curves as to be practically unnavigable.

The climate? No, for it is not very different from that of England, only perhaps a trifle more moist and a little more foggy.

The geographic situation? Again the answer is no, for after the discovery of America Ireland was the nearest and the most conveniently located of all European countries to engage in commerce with the New World.

Then what? Once more I am afraid it was the incalculable human element which upset all prophecies, turned every natural advantage into a physical disability, victories into defeat and courage into a sullen acceptance of a dreary and not very cheerful fate.

Has the atmosphere anything to do with it? We have all of

If the British Channel should run dry

us heard how dearly the Irish people love their fairy stories. Every Irish play and every Irish peasant tale mentions elves and werewolves and goblins and leprechauns and, truth to tell, in these prosaic days we sometimes get a little tired of their kobolds and pixies and all their whimsical relatives.

Ireland

Wandering again, you will say. What, if you please, has all this got to do with geography? Nothing with the geography that consists of the enumeration of mountains and rivers and cities and vital statistics upon the export of coal and the import of woollens. But man is not merely a tummy in search of food. He has also got a mind and the gift of imagination. And there is something unnatural about this country called Ireland. When you see other countries from a distance, you say to yourself, "There is a piece of land. It seems to be high or flat, brown or black or green. There are people there and they probably eat and drink, are all handsome or ugly, happy or miserable, and they live and die and are buried with or without the benefit of clergy."

But with Ireland it is different. Ireland has an air of other-worldliness or rather un-worldliness. An air of solitude pervades the sky. The loneliness of the atmosphere becomes almost tangible. Whatever was true yesterday is now surrounded by doubt. What seemed so simple only a few hours before has suddenly become complicated. Just towards the west lies the deep abyss of the silent ocean. It is less mysterious than the land at your feet.

The Irish, conscious of their unhappy past, have blamed everybody and everything for that terrible fate which made them a subject race for a longer period than any other nation. But there must have been a quality in their own mental make-up, a subtle defect of perception, which allowed the uninterrupted continuation of conditions that were wellnigh unique in the annals of history. And this weakness, for all I know, may have grown out of that very soil for which they were ever ready to die but rarely prepared to live.

As soon as the Norman conquerors of England had put their recently acquired house more or less in order they cast covetous glances across the Irish Sea which, like the North Sea, is really a submerged valley rather than a bona fide part of the ocean. Circumstances favored their ambitious designs upon this rich island. The native chiefs were forever quarrelling among each other. All efforts to turn the entire island into a single monarchy had failed. To the contemporaries of William the Conqueror, Ireland was "the trembling sod". The country was full of wide-eyed priests eager to bring the blessings of Christianity unto the heathen of all the world, but there were no roads, there were no bridges, there were no means of communication of any sort. All those little elements that are of such tremendous importance in making ordinary daily life more agreeable and more harmonious had been conveniently overlooked. The center of the island, being so much lower than the border regions, was a bog and

stayed a bog. For marshes have an unfortunate habit of refus-
ing to drain themselves and when the human soul is filled with
poetry, the human hand is apt to neglect washing the dishes.

The rulers of England and France, being mighty sovereigns,
were on excellent terms with the powers that ruled the world
at that time. Had not Pope Innocent III rushed to the aid of
his beloved son John, declaring Magna Charta "null and void"
and damning the nobles to perdition who had dared to force
their King to sign so outrageous a document? When one of the
warring Irish chieftains appealed to Henry II for aid against
his more successful rivals (I have forgotten exactly how many
there were of them at that moment) certain invisible wires were
pulled in Rome and Pope Adrian IV obligingly signed a piece
of parchment which granted unto His English Majesty the
hereditary lordship over Ireland. A Norman army, composed
of 200 knights and less than a thousand other troops, thereupon
occupied Ireland and forced the feudal system upon a people
who still dwelled amidst the simple virtues and pleasures of a
tribal system long since obsolete in the rest of the world. That
was the beginning of a quarrel which officially at least did not
end until only a few years ago, which even today may break
into the front page news with the suddenness and the violence
of a volcanic eruption.

For the Irish landscape, like the Irish soul, lent itself ideally
to a warfare of murder and ambush, a conflict in which high
ideals and low deeds of treachery got themselves so hopelessly
intermixed that it looked as if nothing short of the complete
extermination of the original natives could settle the problem.
Alas, these are no idle words. Upon several occasions the conquerors tried the experiment of wholesale slaughter and deportation, followed by the confiscation of all the worldly goods
for the benefit of the King and his henchmen. What Cromwell,
for example, did to the Irish after suppressing the rebellion of
1650, when the Irish with their marvellous sense of the unreal
and their great intuitive gift for doing the wrong thing at the
wrong moment had taken the side of worthless King Charles,

is still in the memory of many who were born centuries after that foul crime. As a result of this attempt to settle the Irish question definitely and for all time, the population of the island was reduced to 800,000 and the rate of starvation (the rate of living had never been very high) was raised to such proportions that those who could beg, borrow or steal the money necessary for a short sea voyage moved hastily to foreign shores. The others remained behind, nursing their grievances, tending their cemeteries and living on a diet of potatoes and hope that had to support them until the exigencies of the Great War brought them final relief.

Geographically speaking, Ireland has always been part of northern Europe. Spiritually speaking, Ireland until very recently was located somewhere in the heart of the Mediterranean. And even today, when the island has attained the rank of a dominion and enjoys the same wide degree of self-government as Canada or Australia or South Africa, it continues to be a world apart. Instead of working for a united fatherland, the people have divided themselves into two separate and mutually hostile parts. The southern and Catholic half, containing about 75% of the entire population, enjoys the status of a "free state" and has retained Dublin as its capital. The northern half, usually known as Ulster, and consisting of six counties, inhabited almost exclusively by the descendants of Protestant immigrants, remains a part of England and continues to send its representatives directly to the British Parliament in London.

That is the situation at the moment of sending this volume to the binder. What it will be one year or ten years from now, no one can foretell. But for the first time in over a thousand years, the fate of Ireland is in Irish hands. They now are at liberty to develop their ocean ports and turn Cork and Limerick and Galway into real harbors. They can experiment with those cooperative systems of agriculture which have proved such a success in Denmark. Their dairy products are able to compete on an equal basis with those of the rest of the world. As free and independent citizens, they can at last play their role among the other nations of the world.

But can they forget their past sufficiently well to prepare intelligently for the future?

XXII

RUSSIA, THE COUNTRY WHICH WAS PREVENTED BY ITS
GEOGRAPHICAL LOCATION FROM EVER FINDING
OUT WHETHER IT WAS PART OF EUROPE
OR OF ASIA

As FAR as the American government is concerned, Russia does
not exist. Its rulers have been outlawed, its diplomatic representatives are stopped at the frontier, American citizens are
warned that if they go to Russia they do so at their own risk
and must not count upon Washington to come to their assistance
if they should get into difficulties. But, geographically speaking,
Russia occupies one-seventh of all the dry land of our planet,
it is twice as large as the whole of Europe and three times as
large as our own country and it has as many inhabitants as the
four biggest countries of Europe combined. Yet we have a minister in Monrovia and in Addis Ababa, but none in Moscow.

For all this there must be a reason. This reason, outwardly
seen, is a political one. In reality it is of a decidedly geographic
origin, for the Russian state, more than any other country I can
think of, is a product of its physical background. It has never
been quite able to make up its mind whether it wanted to be
a part of Europe or of Asia. These mixed emotions caused a
conflict of civilizations, and this conflict of civilizations is responsible for the present condition of affairs. All of which I
hope to make clear with the help of a very simple map.

But first of all let us try to answer the question, is Russia a European nation or an Asiatic one? For the sake of argument suppose that you belonged to the tribe of the Chukchi and were
living on the shores of the Bering Strait and that you did not

like the life you were leading (for which I would not blame you, for it is pretty poor pickings in that frozen corner of eastern Siberia) and suppose that you decided you would follow Horace Greeley's advice and go west. And suppose that you were not much of a mountaineer and decided to stick to the flat plains of your childhood days. Well, you could walk west for a couple of years without any hindrances except the nuisance of being forced to swim across a dozen very wide rivers. In the end you would of course find yourself face to face with the Ural Mountains. But these Ural Mountains, which on all maps are shown as the dividing line between Asia and Europe, are not really much of an obstacle, for the first Russian explorers who moved into Siberia (fugitives from justice but elevated to the dignity of "explorers" as soon as they had found something valuable) carried their boats across the Urals; and you try to carry a boat across the Rockies or the Alps!

After leaving the Urals, another trek of half a year or so would bring you to the Baltic. You would therefore have wandered from the Pacific to the Atlantic (for the Baltic after all is merely a branch of the Atlantic) without ever having left fairly flat country. And all that country would have been part of a plain which covers almost one-third of Asia and one-half of Europe (for it connects with the great German plain which only stops when it reaches the North Sea) and which suffers from one tremendous physical disadvantage, in that it looks out upon the Arctic Sea.

That was the curse of the old Russian Empire, which during hundreds of years spent most of its blood and treasure upon costly and useless efforts to reach "warm water"; and it is one of the greatest handicaps of the U. S. S. R., the Union of Soviet Socialist Republics (the political successors to the ancient and defunct house of Romanov) which is not unlike a structure consisting of eighty floors and eight thousand rooms, but with no other means of entrance or exit than two little windows connecting with the fire-escape of the third floor rear.

You are accustomed to think of our own Republic as one of

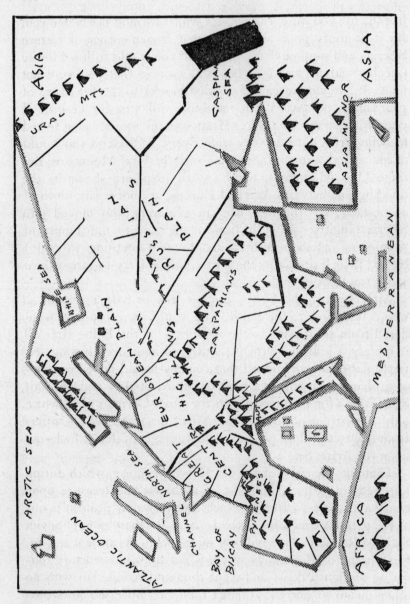

Europe

enormous proportions, compared to such funny little countries as France or England. But this plain, which flies the Russian flag from one end to the other, is forty times as large as France and one hundred and sixty times as large as England and three times as big as Europe, and it contains one-seventh of all the land of our entire planet. Its main river, the Ob, is as long as the Amazon. Its second biggest river, the Lena, is as long as the Missouri. Of its lakes and inland seas, the Caspian in the west is as large as Lakes Superior, Huron, Michigan and Erie combined. The Aral Sea in the center is four thousand square miles larger than Lake Huron while the Baikal Lake in the east is almost twice as large as Lake Ontario.

The mountain peaks in the south, which cut this plain off from the rest of Asia, rise to a height which compares well with the highest summits of our own continent, for Mt. McKinley in Alaska is 20,300 feet and Mt. Elbruz in the Caucasus is 18,200 feet. The coldest spot on the surface of the earth is found in north-eastern Siberia, and the part of the plain that lies well within the Arctic Circle is as large as France, England, Germany and Spain put together.

In every possible way this region encourages extremes. No wonder therefore that the character of the people who inhabit these steppes and tundras has been so very definitely influenced by their natural surroundings and that they think and act according to a system or pattern which would be considered grotesque in any other part of the world. No wonder that for centuries they were able to practice a most devout form of piety and then suddenly could drop all ideas of God and banish Him and His name from even the curriculum of their schools. No wonder that for hundreds of years they were willing to submit to the rule of a man whom they considered infallible and divinely inspired, to arise one day and destroy him, and thereupon accept the tyranny of an impersonal economic doctrine which may promise to bring them great blessings in the future but which for the moment is quite as cruel and relentless and autocratic as any Czar has ever dared to be.

The Russian landscape

The Romans had apparently never heard of Russia. The
Greeks who went to the Black Sea for their grain (remember the
story of the Golden Fleece?) just as we do today had there encountered certain tribes of wild men whom they called the
"mare-milkers" and who, judging by a few pictures on vases
that have come down to us, may well have been the ancestors of
the modern Cossacks. But when the Russians made their definite
appearance upon the horizon of history, they lived in the square
formed by the Carpathian Mountains and the Dniester in the
south, the Vistula in the west and the Pripet marshes and the
Dnieper in the north and east. To the north, in the Baltic plains,
lived their cousins, the Lithuanians and the Letts and the Prussians, for the latter, who have given their name to the leading
German power of modern times, were originally a Slavic tribe.
To the east of them lived the Finns who are now restricted
to the territory that lies between the Arctic, the White Sea and

the Baltic, and to the south there were Celts and Germans or a mixture of both.

A little later, when the Germanic tribes began their wanderings through central Europe, they found it convenient whenever they were in need of servants to raid the encampments of their northern neighbors. For they were a docile race and accepted whatever Fate brought them with a shrug of the shoulders and a silent, "Well, such is life!"

These northern neighbors seem to have had a name for themselves which to the Greeks sounded something like "Sclaveni". The dealers in human flesh, who raided the region of the Carpathians to stock up on their living merchandise, used to say that they had caught so many Slavs or slaves, until gradually the word "slave" became a trade-name for all those unfortunate creatures who were the legal property of another. That those same Slavs or slaves should eventually have developed into the largest and most powerful centralized state of the modern world is one of the great jokes of history, but unfortunately, the joke is on us. If our immediate ancestors had only been a little more far-sighted, we would never have found ourselves in our present predicament. As I shall try to explain to you in a very few words.

The Slavs lived peacefully in their little triangle. They bred profusely. Soon they needed more land. The road to the west was blocked by powerful German tribes. Rome and Byzantium closed the gateways that led to the fleshpots of the Mediterranean. There only remained the east and so eastward they flocked in search of further territory. They crossed the Dniester and the Dnieper and did not stop until they reached the Volga, the Big River, the mother of all rivers, as the Russian peasant calls it, because with its superabundant fish-supply it was able to feed hundreds of thousands of people.

This Volga, the biggest of all European rivers, takes its origin way up in the north among the low hills of the central Russian plateau, those same hills which offered such splendid opportunities for the building of fortresses that most of the early Rus-

The old Russian trade-route

sian cities are to be found right there. In order to reach the sea, the Volga is obliged to skirt these mountains and to make a wide circle towards the east. It follows the outline of this ridge so carefully that the right bank is high and steep while the left bank is low and flat. The detour caused by the hills is quite considerable. In a straight line, the distance from Tver, near where the Volga begins, to the Caspian Sea is only 1000 miles. But the road the river actually travels is 2300 miles long. As for the drainage or basin area of this biggest of all European rivers, it beats that of the Missouri by some 40,000 square miles (Volga 563,000 and Missouri 527,000) and it covers a territory as big as Germany, France and England put together. But like everything else in Russia, this river must do something just a little queer. The Volga is an eminently navigable river (before the war it had a fleet of its own of 40,000 little boats), but when it reaches the city of Saratov it has descended to sea-level. The last hundreds of miles are therefore run below sea-level. This however is not as impossible as it sounds. For the Caspian Sea

Europe: The Continent of coasts, islands and rivers

into which it flows, situated in the midst of its salty desert, has shrunk so considerably that it now lies 85 feet below the level of the Mediterranean. Another million years and it will be a fit rival for the Dead Sea, which holds the record with 1290 feet below sea-level.

Incidentally it is the Volga which is supposed to be the mother of all the caviar we eat. I purposely use the expression "is supposed to be" for very often the Volga is only the caviar's step-mother and the tunny-fish rather than the sturgeon has been responsible for that far-famed Russian delicacy.

Until the general introduction of the railroads, rivers and oceans were the natural routes which people followed in search of trade or plunder. Cut off from the open sea by their Teutonic enemies of the west and their Byzantine competitors from the south, the Russians were forced to depend upon their rivers as soon as they were obliged to look for more free land. And the history of Russia from the year 600 until the present day is forever connected with the two big rivers, one the Volga, which I have just mentioned, and the other the Dnieper. But of the two, the Dnieper was by far the more important, for it was part of the main road that led from the Baltic to the Black Sea, and that was undoubtedly as old as the caravan route that led through the great German plain. Please look at the map and try to follow me there.

Starting in the north we find that the Gulf of Finland is connected with Lake Ladoga (about the size of our Lake Ontario) by means of the Neva, the river on which Leningrad is situated. Then there is a small stream running due south from Lake Ladoga and which is known as the Volkhov, the connect-ing link between Lake Ladoga and Lake Ilmen. On the south side of Lake Ilmen we find the Lovat River. The distance between the Lovat River and the Duna River is not very great and the country is flat enough to allow people to use it as a portage. Once he had overcome this difficulty, the traveller from the north could then float leisurely down the Dnieper until he finally reached the Black Sea, a few miles west of the Crimean Peninsula.

Trade is no respecter of boundaries and commerce is not very much interested in race. There were profits to be made by those who carried merchandise from the land of the Norsemen to that of the Byzantines and that is why they came to establish themselves definitely in these parts of the world. All during the first five or six hundred years of our era this was a trade-route, pure and simple, and it followed the geological depression between the hills of Galicia and Podolia (the outskirts of the Carpathians) on the one side and the central Russian plateau on the other.

But when this region got gradually filled up with Slavic immigrants, conditions changed. For then the trader became the political overlord and he ceased his endless wanderings and settled down to become the founder of a dynasty. The Russians, with all their brilliant qualities of mind, have never been very good administrators. They lack the more rigid mental precision of their Teutonic neighbors. Their soul is too full of doubt. Their mind is too often upon other things. And they are too fond of talk and speculation to be very good at a game that demands concentration and quick decisions. Hence the comparative ease with which a number of men were able to set themselves up as local potentates. Of course, at first their ambitions did not reach very far. But they needed a place to live. And when they had built themselves a semi-royal residence, they needed homes for their retainers. That is the way most of the old Russian cities came into being.

Cities, however, especially when they are young and vigorous, are apt to attract the attention of the outside world. Missionaries in Constantinople heard of this wonderful new opportunity to save souls. They paddled northward along the river Dnieper as the Norsemen had paddled southward several centuries before. They combined forces with the local rulers. The monastery became the annex of the palace. The stage was set for the Russia of the Romanovs. Kiev in the south and the rich commercial city of Novgorod the Great (no relation to Nizhni-

Novgorod, which is situated on the Volga where the Oka joins it) became so opulent and famous that even western Europe heard of their existence.

Meanwhile the patient peasants continued to increase their numbers as they had done during the last ten thousand years

The Old Russia

and, once more finding themselves in need of more farms, they burst the bonds of their homeland, that fertile valley of the Ukraine, the richest granary of all Europe, and they began to move into the central Russian plateau. As soon as they had reached the highest point, they followed the river that ran eastward. Very slowly (what is "time" to a Russian peasant?) they crept down the valley of the Oka until at last they reached the Volga and founded another New-Town or Novgorod, which was to command the plains that were to be theirs for all eternity.

But "all eternity", in history at least, never seems to last so very long. For early in the thirteenth century the Great Disaster put a temporary check upon all their ambitions. Through the wide gap that lay between the Ural Mountains and the Caspian Sea, the salt-infested wilderness of the Ural River, thousands of little yellow men came trotting westward until at last it seemed as if Asia was to pour its entire population into the heart of Europe. The little Norse-Slavic principalities of the west were caught completely by surprise. In less than three years the whole of the Russian plain, rivers, seas, hills, were all of them in the hands of the Tartars, and it was only a matter of great good luck (an epidemic among the Tartar ponies) which saved Germany and France and the rest of western Europe from a similar fate.

As soon as they had raised a new crop of horses, the Tartars once more tried their luck. But the bulwark of Germany and Bohemia held fast and the invaders, describing a wide circle, hacked and plundered and burned and murdered their way through Hungary and then settled down in eastern and southern Russia to enjoy the spoils of victory. During the next two centuries Christian men and women and children were forced to kneel in the dust whenever they met a descendant of the terrible Genghis Khan and kiss the stirrup of his horse or suffer the penalty of instant death.

Europe heard of this, but Europe did not care. For the Slavs worshipped God according to the Greek rites and western Europe worshipped God according to the rites of the Romans. Therefore, let the heathen rage and let the Russian people become the most abjectly miserable slaves that ever trembled at the crack of a foreign whip, for they were heretics and deserved no better fate. In the end, this indifference was to cost Europe very heavily, for those patient Russian shoulders, which accept whatever burden is put upon them by "those in power", acquired that disastrous habit of unreasoning submission during the two and a half centuries of Tartar domination.

Left to themselves, they would never have been able to throw off that terrible yoke. The rulers of the little principality of Moscow, an old frontier post of the Slavs in the east, were responsible for setting their country free. In the year 1480, John III (the Ivan the Great of Russian history) refused to pay the annual tribute to the master of the Golden Horde. That was the beginning of open resistance. Half a century later, the foreign visitation came to an end. But although the Tartars disappeared, their system survived.

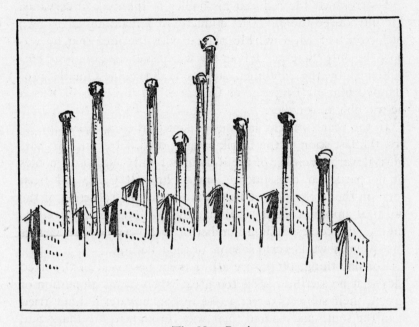

The New Russia

The new rulers had a fine natural feeling for the "realities" of life. Some thirty years before, Constantinople had been captured by the Turks, and the last of the Eastern Roman Emperors had been killed on the steps of the church of the Holy Sofia. But he left a distant relative behind, a woman by the name of Zoe Palaeologa. She happened to be a Catholic. The Pope, seeing a chance of bringing the straying sheep of the Greek church back into his own fold, suggested a marriage between Ivan and Zoe. The wedding took place and Zoe changed her name to

Sophia. But nothing came of the deeply laid plans of the Pope. Instead, Ivan grew more independent than ever. He realized that this was his opportunity to assume the role formerly played by the rulers of Byzantium. He adopted the coat-of-arms of Constantinople, the famous double-headed eagle, representing both the eastern and western Roman Empires. He made himself sacrosanct. He reduced his nobles to the rank of servants. He introduced the old strict etiquette of Byzantium at his own little court of Moscow. He played with the idea that he was now the only "Caesar" left in the world and his grandson, emboldened by the continued success of his house, finally proclaimed himself Emperor or Caesar of all the parts of Russia he was able to conquer.

In the year 1598 the last descendant of the old Norse invaders, the last scion of the Rurik family, died. After fifteen years of civil war, a member of the Romanov family—Moscow nobles of no particular consequence—made himself Czar, and from then on the geography of Russia is merely the reflection of the political ambitions of these Romanovs, who had many positive faults but a corresponding number of such very positive virtues that we may well overlook some of their failings.

For one thing, they were all of them possessed of the fixed idea that no sacrifices were too great when it was a question of giving their subjects direct access to "open water". They tried it in the south and hacked their way through to the Black Sea, to Azov and Sebastopol, only to find that the Turks cut them off from the Mediterranean. But these campaigns assured them the royal allegiance of the ten Cossack tribes, the descendants of the old Kazaki or free-booters, adventurers or runaway serfs who during the previous five centuries had fled into the wilderness to escape from their Polish or Tartar masters. They engaged in a war with the Swedes who had held practically all the territory around the Baltic since their successful participation in the Thirty Years War, and finally, after half a century of fighting, Czar Peter could order hundreds of thousands of his subjects into the marshes of the Neva to build him his new capital of St.

Petersburg. But the Finnish Gulf was frozen over for four months of every year, and "open water" was as far off as ever. They followed the Onega River and the Dwina River right through the heart of the Tundra region—the mossy plains of the Arctic—and they built themselves a new city on the White Sea which they called after the Archangel Michael; but the inhospitable Kanin peninsula was as far removed from Europe as the frozen shores of the Hudson Bay, and the Murman coast was carefully avoided by all Dutch and English skippers. The task seemed hopeless. There remained no other way out than to try the eastern route.

In the year 1581 a band of runaway slaves and adventurers and prisoners of war from half a dozen European nations, all in all some sixteen hundred men, had crossed the Ural Mountains and, driven by necessity, had attacked the first Tartar Khan whom they met on their way east, the ruler of a region called Sibir or Siberia. They had defeated him and had divided his possessions among themselves. But knowing that the arm of Moscow reached far, they had offered this territory to the Czar rather than await the day the troops of the Little Father should follow them to hang them as deserters and rebels, instead of rewarding them as true patriots who had contributed to the glory of their beloved sovereign.

This strange method of colonization was kept up for almost a century and a half. The vast plain that lay stretched out before these "bad men" was sparsely populated. It was fertile. The northern half was prairie but the southern half was covered with woods. Soon they had left the river Ob behind them. Then the Yenisei was reached. As early as 1628 the advance-guard of this unsavory army of invasion reached the Lena and in 1639 they stood on the shores of the Sea of Okhotsk. Further towards the south they built their earliest fortress on Lake Baikal, shortly after the year 1640. They explored the Amur River in 1648. In the same year a Cossack by the name of Dejnev had sailed down the Kolyma River in northern Siberia, had followed the shores of the Arctic Ocean until he reached the strait that sepa-

rates Asia from America and had returned to tell the tale, which
however attracted so little attention that when Vitus Bering, a
Danish navigator in Russian employ, rediscovered these straits
eighty years later he was permitted to give them his own name.

From 1581 till 1648 is a period of 67 years. When you consider that it took our own ancestors about two centuries to cover
the distance between the Alleghenies and the Pacific coast, it
becomes evident that the Russians are not always as slow as we
are sometimes led to believe. But not content with having added
the whole of Siberia to their original holdings, the Russians
finally crossed from Asia into America, and long before George
Washington was carried to his grave, there was quite a thriving
Russian colony around a fort called after the Archangel Gabriel,
now known as Sitka, the town in which the formal transfer of
Alaska from Russia to America took place in the year 1867.

As far as energy and personal courage and reckless bravery

Eastern Siberia

were concerned, these earliest Russian pioneers compared more than favorably with our own. But the Asiatic conception of Empire that still dominated the minds of those in power in Moscow and Petersburg prevented the normal development of a region where riches of every sort awaited the men who would know how to exploit them. Instead of developing the pastures and the forests and the mines, Russia turned Siberia into a gigantic jail.

The first prisoners arrived during the middle of the seventeenth century, fifty years after Yermak had crossed the Urals, and they consisted of priests who refused to say mass according to the orthodox formula and who were therefore sent to the banks of the Amur to starve and freeze to death. Since then there has never been any interruption of that endless procession of men and women (and ofttimes children) who were being driven into the wilderness because their European sense of individualism had come into conflict with the Asiatic notion of conformity that was the basic law of the old Russian form of government. The peak of these deportations was reached in the year 1863, shortly after the last great Polish revolution when more than 50,000 Polish patriots were moved from the Vistula River to the neighborhood of Tomsk and Irkutsk. No precise statistics have ever been kept of the total number of these involuntary emigrants, but from 1800 to 1900, when the system was slightly modified under heavy pressure from abroad, the mean annual average of exiles was about 20,000. That, however, did not take into account the ordinary criminals, the murderers and petty thieves and pickpockets, who as often as not were shackled to men and women of great spiritual refinement whose only error consisted in loving their fellow-men more than they deserved.

When their actual time of punishment had come to an end, the survivors were given little pieces of land near one of the exile villages and were allowed to become independent farmers. On paper this was a marvellous scheme to get the country inhabited by white men, and it allowed the imperial government to show its European stock-holders that it was really not as bad as it was sometimes painted—that there was some system in all this Siberian madness—the "criminal" was being educated to become a useful and productive member of society. In practice, however, it worked so well that the greater part of these so-called "free settlers" disappeared from the face of the earth without leaving trace of their whereabouts. Perhaps they went to live with one of the native tribes, became Mohammedans or heathen, and bade farewell to Christian civilization. Perhaps they tried to escape and were eaten by the wolves. We don't know. Russian police statistics show that there were always between thirty and fifty thousand ex-convicts on the loose, hiding in the forest or the mountains, preferring any sort of hardship to the prison-yards of the Little White Father. But the imperial flag no longer flies over the Siberian bull-pen. It is now the flag of the Soviets. There has been a new deal. But the cards are the same, and they are of Tartar origin.

What happened to Russia when the old agricultural system of barter and serfdom came to an end and was replaced by capitalism and industrialism is a matter of general knowledge. A few years before Lincoln signed the act of emancipation, the Russian serfs had been set free. In order to keep them alive, they were given a little bit of land, but never quite enough, and the land that was given unto the slave was taken away from the master. As a result, neither the master nor his former servant got enough to be able to pay his way. And all the time, foreign capital was reaching out after the hidden mineral treasures of the vast Russian plain. Railroads were built—steamship lines were organized—and European engineers waded through the mud of semi-Asiatic villages built around a replica of the Paris grand opera and asked themselves whether such things could be.

That primitive barbaric strength that had given the founders of the Russian dynasty the courage to attempt the impossible had spent itself. A weak man, surrounded by priests and women, now sat on the throne of the great Peter. And when he pawned that throne to the money-lenders of London and Paris and accepted their terms which forced him to take part in a war that was abhorrent in the eyes of most of his subjects, he signed his own death-warrant.

A little, bald-headed man, a graduate of the great Siberian school of exile, took hold of the ruin and began the work of reconstruction. He discarded the old European model and he discarded the old Asiatic model. He discarded everything old. He built ever with an eye for the future, but it was still the eye of the Tartar.

What that future will be, we shall know a hundred years hence. Here it is sufficient if we give you a vague outline of the modern Soviet state, but only a very vague one, for the system is in a constant state of flux. The Bolshevists are engaged in an experiment, and they are as ruthless in discarding what proves impracticable as a chemist who suddenly realizes that he has been working according to the wrong formula. Furthermore, the system is so absolutely different from anything to which we ourselves have been accustomed these last five hundred years that it is difficult to reduce it to the usual European or American terminology of statecraft with its continual references to "representative government" and "democracy" and "the sacred rights of the minority". These terms mean nothing to a youngster brought up in a Bolshevist school. He has never even heard of them, except as an example of the folly of his ancestors.

In the first place, the Bolshevist conception of government is not based upon that rule of government of all the people, by all the people, for the benefit of all the people, which we teach our children as the most desirable ideal of statesmanship, whether we quite believe in it or not. Bolshevism recognizes only one class of society, that of the proletarians, the wage-earners, the workers, preferably those who work with their hands. And in order that this class may attain some of the good things of this world from which it has so far been deprived, it has declared a ruthless war upon all those who in any way could remind the

The Great Russian Plain.

people of the year 1932 of the old "bourgeois" or middle-class form of government which was based upon private profit and private gain.

So far so good. Violent upheavals are nothing new in this world. Charles of England and Louis of France lost their heads a long time before Lenin was born. But when they died, a man, rather than a system, came to an end. When Nicholas II was murdered, it was not only a man but also the entire system this man had embodied and represented which was scrapped and which was forcibly removed from the Russian consciousness. The old account was closed and two little red lines were drawn at the bottom of the page. Then a fresh, new page was started and at the top of it appeared the name, "The Communist Party of Russia, Inc."

Now Communism as an economic system is nothing new. The old monastic orders were really communistic institutions and they in turn were based upon the communism of the early Christian Church, which recognized neither rich nor poor and did not believe in private property. The Pilgrims, when they came to America, intended to form a communistic community. But all these efforts to bring about a more equitable division of this world's goods had been conducted on a relatively small basis. They had never touched the lives of the people at large. And there is where the Bolshevist experiment differs from all others. It has turned the whole of the Russian plain from the Baltic to the Pacific into one vast political and economic laboratory where everybody is supposed to work for just one purpose— the well-being and happiness of the mass, regardless of the present happiness and well-being of the individuals. But just as in the older days it was never quite possible for a Russian to rid himself of that duality of character which had been caused by the dual nature of his country, half-Asiatic and half-European, so the new Russian too is suffering from a conflict of enthusiasms which very frequently defeat their own ends.

The basic structure of the new Soviet Society is undoubtedly of European origin. The methods employed to put it into action are entirely Asiatic. Karl Marx and Genghis Khan have joined forces to bring about the Millennium and what will come of this extraordinary experiment I do not know. One prophecy is as good as the next.

But already Bolshevism has accomplished certain results with which the rest of humanity will have to deal very seriously at the risk of seeing its own civilizations go to pieces.

In the older days, Russia was ruled for the sole benefit of a small group of land-owners and supporters of the Czar, just as it had been in the days of the Tartars. It is still being ruled by a small group of people. But now they belong to the inner circle of the Communist party. They are fewer in number than the old-style nobility but even more devoted in their loyalty to the principle of autocracy.

There is however a great difference between the dictatorship of the Czars and that of the Bolshevists. The small group of people who are now governing Russia are not working for their own benefit. They receive such wages as any American plumber or stevedore would sniff at, provided he happened to have work and was receiving any wages at all. And the truly gigantic energy developed by these new tyrants (who are infinitely more ruthless than the Czar's ministers ever dared to be) is directed towards one single object—to make everybody in the world work and to see to it that the workers, in exchange for their labors, are guaranteed enough food, enough living space and every possible opportunity for leisure of the more intelligent sort.

To our western way of thinking, all this is about as topsy-turvy as Einstein's conception of a four or five dimensional universe. But one-seventh of all the land of this planet, a country three times as large as our United States, is now living under this system and it is making itself felt all over the world. It is not being preached by some poor little country like Norway or Switzerland, but by one of the richest nations on earth, possessed of every form of wealth. Pious prayers and angry editorials will hardly upset it because the Russian people are completely cut off from the rest of the world, read very few foreign books, never see any but strictly censored foreign newspapers, and might as well be living on the planet Mars for all they really know about their neighbors. The leaders, of course, are aware of the criticism that is levelled against them, but they don't care. They are too busy doing other things, organizing their White Russian Republics and their Ukrainian Soviet Republic and their Trans-Caucasian Federation of Soviet Republics and their Kirghiz Soviet Republic and their Bashkir Republic and their Tartar Soviet Republics, to spend much time worrying about the approval and disapproval of that western world which they profess to regard as a pathetic historical revival, a nice exhibition for the museum of anti-religion, opened a year ago in the Czar's former palace.

Time will show us what is to become of this strange experiment, this Asiatic mysticism combined with the European sense of actuality. But the Great Russian Plain has come to life and the rest of the world would do well to take notice, for Bolshevism may be only a dream, but Russia is a fact.

XXIII

POLAND, THE COUNTRY THAT HAD ALWAYS SUFFERED FROM BEING A CORRIDOR AND THEREFORE NOW HAS A CORRIDOR OF ITS OWN

POLAND suffers from two great natural disadvantages. Its geographic position is most unfortunate, and its nearest neighbors are its fellow-Slavs of Russia. A real feeling of brotherhood is said to be a wonderful thing, but rarely as practiced between nations of a similar race.

We do not know where the Poles originally came from. Like the Irish, whom they resemble in so many ways, the Poles are intensely patriotic, ever ready to die for their country, but rarely willing to live and work for it. The record of the valorous deeds of their ancestors, as compiled by their own leading historians, makes the earliest Polish heroes stow-aways on Noah's Ark. But when the Poles are first mentioned in any reliable historical document, Charlemagne and his braves had been in their graves for almost two entire centuries. Some fifty years after the battle of Hastings, however, the word Poland began to mean something more than the name of a vague territory that was supposed to lie somewhere in the wilderness of the Far East.

To the best of our present knowledge, the Poles lived originally near the mouth of the Danube, were set upon by invaders from the east, were forced to pull up stakes, and moved westward until they reached the Carpathian Mountains. They thereupon passed through the regions just evacuated by the other great branch of the Slavic race, the Russians, and finally found a safe place of refuge among the primeval forests and the marshes of that part of the great European plain which is situated between the Oder and the Vistula.

They could not possibly have chosen a worse location. A man

The North Pole

sitting on a chair in the middle of the main entrance to the Grand
Central Station enjoys about as much quiet and privacy as a
farmer in this territory, which is in reality the front door of
Europe and the only passageway at the disposal of those who
wanted to go west to conquer the European lands bordering on
the North Sea, or those who wanted to go east to plunder Russia.
The constant necessity of being prepared to fight on two fronts
at the same time, gradually turned every Polish land-owner
into a professional soldier and made every castle into a fortress.
As a result, the military side of life was stressed at the expense
of everything else. And commerce never took hold in a country
where a state of war was the normal condition of life.

There were a few towns but all of them were situated in the
center of the country and along the banks of the Vistula. Krakow,
in the south, has been built where the Carpathian Mountains dissolved themselves into the plains of Galicia. Warsaw, in the
middle of the Polish plain, and Danzig, near the mouth of the
river, depended for their business life on foreign merchants.
Further inland, however, the country was almost empty, for
there were no other rivers until one reached the Dnieper, which
was in Russian territory, and Vilna, the old capital of Lithuania,
never grew beyond the status of a small princely residence.

Such buying and selling as were absolutely necessary were
in the hands of the Jews, who had fled to the outskirts of Europe when the Crusaders in their holy zeal had slaughtered the
inmates of several of the better known ghettos of the Rhine
region. A few hardy Norsemen, such as had founded the Russian
state, might have done the country no end of good. But they
never came to this part of the world. Why should they? There
was no convenient trade-route running north and south or east
and west and there was no city of Constantinople at the other
end of the long trail to reward them for the fatigue and the hardships of their trip.

And so the Polish people were caught between the Germans,
who hated them because, although they were fellow-Roman-
Catholics, they also were Slavs, and the Russians, who despised

them because, although they were fellow-Slavs, they were not Greek Catholics, and the Turks who loathed them because they were both Christians and Slavs.

If the energetic Lithuanian dynasty, which did so much for the country during the days of the Middle Ages, had survived, things might have gone a great deal better, but in the year 1572 the Jagiellans died out and upon the death of the last king the nobles, grown rich during the many years of frontier fighting and enjoying almost despotic rights on their vast but isolated estates, succeeded in turning the country into an elective monarchy. That elective monarchy lasted from 1572 until 1791 and when it was destroyed, it had long since degenerated into a very painful joke.

For the throne of Poland was simply sold to the highest bidder and no questions asked. Frenchmen and Hungarians and Swedes in turn were rulers of a kingdom which meant nothing to them except as a possible source of graft and revenue. When these monarchs omitted to surrender part of their spoils to their henchmen, the Polish nobles did what their Irish friends had done a thousand years before. They called in their neighbors to come and help them "get their rights". Those neighbors, Prussia and Russia and Austria, were only too happy to oblige, and Poland ceased to exist as an independent nation.

In 1795, during the last of the three great divisions, Russia got 180,000 square miles with 6,000,000 people. Austria got 45,000 square miles with 3,700,000 people, and Prussia got 57,000 square miles with 2,500,000 people. This hideous wrong was not undone until one hundred and twenty-five years later. And then the Allies, in their fear of Russia, went to another extreme. They not only made the new Polish Republic much larger than it had any right to be, but furthermore, in order to give Poland a direct outlet to the sea, they established the so-called "Polish Corridor", a strip of land which runs from the old province of Posen to the Baltic Sea and which cuts Prussia into two parts which now have no longer any direct connection with each other.

It takes no profound knowledge of either geography or history to predict what will happen in connection with this unfortunate corridor. It will remain an object of hatred and distrust between Germany and Poland until either country shall have grown strong enough to destroy the other and then poor Poland will become once more what it has always been, a buffer-state between Russia and Europe.

In the first flush of victory it seemed a glorious achievement. But building spite-fences across each other's territory is not going to bring the economic and social problems of our time any nearer to their final solution.

XXIV

CZECHOSLOVAKIA, THE ONLY CHILD OF THE VERSAILLES TREATY THAT HAS MADE GOOD

FIVE years ago I began to write this book. Since then I have had little reason to change my opinion about most of the countries that came up for discussion. If I were rather harsh on them then, what could I say now, when almost all of them are rushing from one mistake and blunder to the next, when revolution and counter-revolution are following each other with increasing rapidity, when dictatorships are destroying the last vestiges of that Democratic Ideal of live and let live that was to be the reward for those four dreadful years of wholesale murder and destruction?

The one country that stands forth as an exception is Czechoslovakia. If ever it was clearly demonstrated that men are infinitely more important than measures, it is in the case of the old land of Bohemia. For the new republic of Czechoslovakia too was an artificial state, a commonwealth created by a stroke of the pen of the Old Men of Versailles. It is true, it was founded upon the ruins of what had once been an independent kingdom. But for so many centuries Bohemia had ceased to function as an independent unit, that most people had forgotten its ancient glory. When several other parts of the former Austro-Hungarian monarchy were added to the Czech nucleus, it seemed that the world was once more to witness the sad spectacle of a man-made community which like all the others would soon become a menace to the peace of Europe.

Today, after it has been thoroughly tried out in the cauldron which the late Georges Clemenceau left us as his sole legacy, it has a much better chance of survival than any of the other nations which made their appearance upon our map when the Congress of Versailles finally rested from its futile labors.

The country started out with one very definite disadvantage. It was entirely landlocked and found itself caught between two powerful rivals, Germany and Poland. And the second menace to its safety was the amalgamation of several Slavonic tribes which had been living separated from each other for almost four centuries and which had gone through entirely different processes of training. For whereas the Austrian monarchy had been either too wise or too happy-go-lucky to destroy all spirit of independence in Bohemia, the Hungarians and the Russians, with their aggressive and narrow minded nationalism, had done everything within their power to retard the cultural progress of those parts of modern Czechoslovakia which had fallen into their hands as the result of the wars of conquest of the previous four centuries.

Hence the highly educated Czechs might very easily have used or rather abused their own superior abilities to turn the Slovaks and the Moravians and the Salicians and the inhabitants of the Carpathian Mountains into a subject race. And, for a while it looked as if Czechoslovakia would also find itself with a "minority problem" upon its hands. But within a short space of time, these difficulties were most successfully overcome. The Slovaks, who were essentially peasant people without ever having enjoyed any of the educational advantages which the Habsburgs had established within the frontiers of old Bohemia, were encouraged to make up for lost time. They were given all the schools they needed. They were also taught the new trade of administration, without which no modern state can possibly hope to survive, and they were readily admitted to the government at Prague, as soon as they had qualified themselves for their new duties. Until today the country offers almost the only example (together with Switzerland) of a European nation in which people with different national backgrounds live in peace and amity with each other, and are also eager to coöperate for a common national ideal. Once their President Thomas Masaryk (himself born in Moravia of a father who was a native of Slovakia) and his able Minister of Foreign Affairs, Edward Beneš, had accomplished this; they had to face a most difficult economic problem.

The old Bohemia had been not only one of the richest agricultural possessions of the ancient Habsburg monarchy but it also had been developed into a highly industrial province with a great deal of iron and coal and a world-famous ability in the difficult art of glass making. Furthermore the industrious Czech peasants had always been exceedingly clever at different forms of home industries (after twelve hours in the fields they must have something to do in their spare hours) and Bohemian rugs and shoes were famous all the world over.

But the old territory into which these products could be imported free of duty—one of the few but very concrete advantages of the ancient Habsburg monarchy—had now been divided into a dozen small and mutually jealous little nations and principalities, each one of which had surrounded itself with heavily spiked tariff walls, not merely in order to protect itself but also in the faint hope of thereby killing as many of its neighbors as possible. And whereas formerly a wagon load of beer from Pilsen (Plzen, if you want to find it on the map) could have been sent to Fiume without being once stopped on the way by customs officers, it must now change cars at three different frontiers (most of these pleasant new nations did not even trust each other with their railroad cars) and it is obliged to pay duty at almost every little frontier station, and when it finally gets to its destination after some four or five weeks (the trip could easily be done in four or five days) the beer has most likely turned sour and is fit to be thrown away.

It is to the everlasting credit of the ruler of Czechoslovakia and of his main advisor that they alone among the statesmen of the new Europe have recognized that such a policy must inevitably lead to suicide, for all the nations concerned, and that they have tried to take the steps necessary to bring about a definite eastern European customs union, which as much as possible shall follow the lines of the old Habsburg monarchy.

Writing this as an American who still believes that a reasonable democracy is the best because also the most human form of government, I sincerely wish that the whole central European muddle could be left to Masaryk and Beneš. A pious hope but a futile one. The only consolation I can possibly find in the present sad state of affairs is the fact that under these two practical leaders Czechoslovakia has now become so well prepared for all eventualities that in case of a conflict it is the only country that is bound to survive. Then, when the final debris is being cleared away, Masaryk and Beneš may be the engineers who can reconstruct that new central European community of interest that is as necessary to our peace and well-being as Austria was to the peace and well-being of the Europe of four centuries ago.

If Masaryk had been born fifty years later, we might even have a chance at a United States of Europe. But in that case there would not now be an independent state called Czechoslovakia. And as it is the only country of eastern Europe that seems to speak the same language as we do on our side of the Ocean, that would deprive us of the one dependable friend in that distant and little known part of the world. Wherefore we had better not indulge in any further useless ifs and should gratefully accept the fact that there is at least one country in central Europe that has come safely through the ordeals and trials of the post-war period and that has not let its national aspirations blind it to the demands of international common sense and decency.

XXV

YUGOSLAVIA, ANOTHER PRODUCT OF THE TREATY OF VERSAILLES

The official name of this country is the Kingdom of the Serbs, Croats and the Slovenes. Of these three ethnical groups (tribes sounds too much like African natives and might offend them) the Serbs, who are the most important, live in the east along the banks of the Save which joins the Danube at a point where the capital Belgrade has been built. The Croats live in the center between the Drave, also a tributary of the Danube, and the Adriatic, while the Slovenes occupy the little triangle between the Drave, the Istrian peninsula and Croatia. Modern Serbia however is composed of several other racial groups. It has absorbed Montenegro, the picturesque mountain state, famous for its four hundred years of war against the Turks, and affectionately remembered ever since the days we danced to the tune of "The Merry Widow" waltz. And it also has annexed a well-known remnant of the old Austrian Empire, the provinces of Bosnia and Herzegovina, old Serbian territory, but taken away from Turkey by the Austrians, and the source of that ill-feeling between the Serbians and the Austrians which finally ended in the murder of Serajevo in 1914, the immediate (although by no means the real) cause of the Great War.

Serbia (the old habit is too strong—hereafter when I write Serbia I really mean the Kingdom of the Serbs, Croats and Slovenes) is essentially a Balkan state and its history is essentially that of a country subjected to five hundred years of Moslem slavery. Since the war it has a sea-front on the Adriatic, but it remains cut off from its own sea-front by the Dinaric Alps. Even if it could build railroads across the Dinaric Alps (and railroads cost a lot of money) there would be no convenient harbors ex-

Cold

cept perhaps Ragusa (or Dubrovnik, as it is now called), one of the great medieval distributing centers for colonial merchandise. It was the only Mediterranean city which refused to accept defeat after the discovery of the direct ocean routes to America and India and it continued to send its far-famed Argosies (ships from Aragusia) to Calicut and Cuba until a foolish participation in the ill-fated expedition of the Armada deprived it of its last remaining squadrons.

Unfortunately Dubrovnik offers no facilities to modern steamers. As for Fiume and Trieste, the natural outlets for Serbia, the Old Men of Versailles gave one of these cities to Italy and the other one she took for herself, although she really had no need for them as they would only compete with Venice, which aspired to regain its ancient and honorable position as mistress of the Adriatic. As a result, the grass now grows in the dockyards of Trieste and Fiume while Serbia, as of old, must send its agricultural products by one of three routes. It may send them down the Danube to the Black Sea, which is about as practical as if New York should export its merchandise to London by way of Lake Erie and the St. Lawrence River. It may send them up the Danube to Vienna and from there through one of the mountain passes to Bremen, Hamburg or Rotterdam, which is also an exceedingly expensive procedure. Or it may send them by rail to Fiume, where the Italians of course do their best to ruin their Slavic competitors.

In this respect, therefore, nothing has been changed since the days before the war when Serbia was kept a land-locked state at the instigation of the Austrian Empire. It is a bit sad to reflect that pigs were primarily responsible for the outbreak of that terrible disaster. For Serbia had only one great article of export —pigs—and by putting impossible duties on pigs, the Austrians and the Hungarians were able to ruin the only trade from which Serbia derived any profit at all. The dead Austrian Grand Duke was the pretext for the mobilization of all the armed forces of Europe. But the underlying cause of all the ill-feeling in the north-eastern corner of the Balkans was the duty on pigs.

And speaking of pigs, pigs prosper on acorns. That is why they were so plentiful in the triangle between the Adriatic and the Danube and the mountains of Macedonia, for it is densely covered with oak forests. There would be more forests today if the Romans and the Venetians had not denuded these hills in a most irresponsible fashion to get wood for their vessels.

What other resources does the country have to feed and clothe its 12,000,000 inhabitants, outside of pigs? There is some coal and iron but there seems to be already by far too much coal and iron in this world, and it would be very costly to carry it all the way by rail to one of the German ports, and as I have said before, Serbia has no decent harbor of its own.

After the war Serbia got part of the great Hungarian plain, the so-called Voyvodika, which is good agricultural land. The valleys of the Drave and Save will provide it with enough grain and corn for its own people. The Morava valley connecting with that of the Vardar River is a good enough trade-route which connects northern Europe with Saloniki on the Aegean Sea. It is really a branch of the great trunk lines connecting Nish (the birthplace of Constantine the Great and the spot where Frederick Barbarossa, on his ill-fated expedition to the Holy Land, was entertained for a while by the famous Serbian Prince Stephen) with Constantinople and Asia Minor.

But, generally speaking, Serbia cannot look forward to a great future as an industrial state. Like Bulgaria it will have to remain a nation of fairly prosperous Slavic farmers. Who has ever been able to compare a six-foot peasant from Skoplje (or Uskub) or Mitrovitsa to a cockney workman from Manchester or Sheffield will have some doubts whether such a fate is entirely without its compensations. Belgrade may forever remain an amiable little country town like Oslo or Bern, but does it really want to compete in size with Birmingham or Chicago? Perhaps it does. The modern soul is a strange thing and the Serbian peasant would not be the first to have his sound ancestral standard of values upset by the counterfeit cultural ideals of our Hollywood prophets.

XXVI

BULGARIA, THE SOUNDEST OF ALL BALKAN COUNTRIES, WHOSE BUTTERFLY-COLLECTING KING BET ON THE WRONG HORSE DURING THE GREAT WAR AND SUFFERED THE CONSEQUENCES

THIS is the last of the little principalities that grew out of the great Slavic invasion of some twenty centuries ago. It would be more important in size and number of inhabitants if during the World War it had not taken what ultimately proved to be the wrong side. But such things will happen even in the best regulated nations. Better luck next time. On the Balkan peninsula, the "next time", when speaking of war, means a dozen or half a dozen years hence. We are apt to speak in a slightly contemptuous manner of these half-civilized Balkan people who are forever fighting among each other. But do we ever realize with what sort of an inheritance of strife and cruelty and bloodshed and slavery and plunder and rape and arson the average Serbian or Bulgarian boy starts out upon his career through life?

Of the earliest inhabitants of Bulgaria we know nothing. We have found their skeletons, but skulls do not talk. Were they perhaps related to those mysterious Albanians, the Illyrians of Greek history, compatriots of the long-suffering Odysseus, that mysterious race which speaks a tongue unlike that of any other people on earth, who ever since the beginning of history have maintained themselves among the Dinaric Alps along the coast of the Adriatic and who today form an independent state, ruled over by a native tribal leader who made himself their legitimate sovereign as soon as a Vienna tailor had provided him with a nice, new uniform in which to hold court at Tirano, the new capital of a nation of 98% analphabets? Or is this the home country of the Romani, who were also known as the Wlachs and who must have spread all over Europe as they also bestowed their name upon Wales and the Welsh and the Walloons of Belgium? We had better leave the solution of that puzzle to the philologists and confess that we do not know.

But when we reach the era of the written chronicles, what endless invasions, wars and calamities! There were, as I have already told you, two main routes leading from the gap between the Urals and the Caspian Sea to the west. One went northward of the Carpathians and led to the impenetrable forests of the northern European plain. The other followed the Danube and by means of the Brenner Pass carried the hungry savages to the heart of Italy. The Romans knew this and they therefore used the Balkans as their first line of defence against that "foreign scum", as they were pleased to call those despised barbarians who eventually were to destroy them. Lack of soldiers gradually forced them to retreat to their own peninsula and leave the Balkan peoples to their fate. When the great migrations had come to an end, not a trace remained of the original Bulgarians. The Slavs had assimilated them so completely that not a single word of the ancient Bulgarian tongue survives in the Slavic dialect spoken by the so-called Bulgarians of today.

The position however of the new conquerors was exceedingly precarious. In the south they had to deal with Byzantium, that eastern remnant of the Roman Empire which was Roman in name only but Greek in purpose and structure. From the north and the west they were forever threatened by raids on the part of the Hungarians and the Albanians. Next the Crusaders passed through their territory, an unholy army of holy men, the disinherited from all nations, ready to plunder Turk or Slav with equal ferocity. Finally the threat of an all-overpowering Turkish invasion and those last desperate appeals to Europe to come and protect the common soil of Christendom against the degrading touch of the infidel. And the sudden hush that spread through the land when fugitives from the Bosporus told how the Moslem Sultan had ridden his horse up the steps of Saint Sofia to desecrate the most holy of all the holy shrines of the Greek church. Followed by the panic when the reddening sky of burning villages told of the steady advance of Turkish troops, marching westward through the blood-soaked valley of the Maritza. And thereafter four entire centuries of Turkish mis-rule. And then, at last, during the beginning of the last century, a first faint stirring of hope. A swineherd in Serbia started a rebellion that was to make him a king. Next that terrible war of extermination between Greek and Ottoman, turned into a major European issue by an English poet who hobbled to his welcome death in the pestiferous village of Missolonghi. And then the beginning of that great struggle for liberty which was to last for another hundred years. Let us be lenient in judging our Balkan friends. They have been the leading actors in the tragedy of man's martyrdom.

Among the modern Balkan states, Bulgaria is one of the most important. It is composed of two very fertile regions, both of them excellently suited to all sorts of agriculture: the plain in the north between the high ridge of the Balkan Mountains and the Danube, and the plain of Philippopolis in the south between the Balkans and the Rhodope Mountains. This valley, protected on both sides, enjoys a mild Mediterranean climate. It exports its products through the harbor of Burgas, just as the sterner products of the northern plain, grain and corn, are sent abroad by way of Varna.

Otherwise there are very few towns, for the Bulgarians are essentially a peasant people. Sofia, the present capital, lies on the old trade-routes from north to south and east to west. For almost four hundred years it was the residence of the Turkish governors who, from their fortified palace on the Struma River, ruled the whole of the Balkan peninsula, with the exception of Bosnia and Greece.

When Europe finally became conscious of the plight of its fellow-Christians, delivered to the mercies of the Moslem invaders, Mr. Gladstone's constituents did a great deal of talking

about the Bulgarian atrocities; but the Russians were the first
to take action. Twice their armies crossed the Balkan Mountains. The fighting to force the Shipka Pass and to subdue the
fortress of Plevna will be remembered as long as people realize
that there have been a few wars which were absolutely unavoidable, if the world was ever to progress from slavery to comparative freedom.

As a result of the last of these Slavic relief-expeditions, the
great Russo-Turkish conflict of 1877–1878, Bulgaria was made
an independent principality under a ruler of German origin.
This meant that the patient and intelligent Bulgarian peasants
got trained by people with a Teutonic sense of order. That may
be responsible for the fact that today Bulgaria has the best schools
of all the different Balkan states. The large land-owners have
completely disappeared. The peasant owns his own land as he
does in Denmark and in France. The illiteracy percentage has
been sharply reduced and everybody works. It is a simple country of farmers and lumbermen. It is a veritable reservoir of
physical endurance and energy. Like Serbia, it may never be
able to compete with the industrialized states of western Europe.
But it may still be there when the others are gone.

XXVII

ROUMANIA, A COUNTRY WHICH HAS OIL AND A ROYAL FAMILY

THE list of the Slavic nations of the Balkans has come to an end. But there exists one other Balkan state which none of us, however, is likely to forget, as it has a habit of crashing into the front pages of our newspapers with a frequency that is at times a bit painful. That is not the fault of the Roumanian peasants. They are born and till their fields and die very much as peasants are in the habit of doing all the world over. It is due to the incurable vulgarity and the unspeakable bad taste of that Anglo-German dynasty which thirty years ago succeeded the highly respectable Prince Charles of Hohenzollern on the throne of a kingdom founded by the grace of God, Prince Bismarck and a certain Benjamin Disraeli.

It was in the year 1878 that these two gentlemen came together in Berlin and after paying their duties to the Deity decided to elevate Walachia (the land of the Wlachs) to the rank of an independent principality. If the present reigning family can ever be persuaded to remove itself to Paris, where people do not care how much dirty laundry is washed, as long as it is done with French soap, Roumania may go far, for Nature has been extraordinarily kind to this great plain between the Carpathians, the Transylvanian Alps and the Black Sea. Not only could it be turned into a granary as rich as that of the Russian Ukraine, of which it is the natural continuation, but the richest oil deposits of Europe are to be found near the city of Ploesci, where the Transylvanian Mountains join the plains of Walachia.

Unfortunately, the farms both of Walachia and Bessarabia between the Danube and the Prut are in the hands of large landowners, most of them absentee landlords who spend their revenues in Bucharest, the capital, or in Paris, but never among the people whose labor makes them rich.

As for the petroleum, the capital invested is usually owned abroad; and the same is true of the iron deposits of Siebenbergen or Transylvania, the enormous complex of mountains taken away from Hungary and given to Roumania in exchange for the more than highly doubtful services which the latter country had rendered the Allies during the Great War. But as Transylvania had originally been part of the old Roman province of Dacia, and had been made part of Hungary as late as the twelfth century, and as the Hungarians had treated the Roumanians of Transylvania very much as the Roumanians of old Roumania treat the Hungarian minority of Transylvania today, we might just as well forget about it. These hopeless and intricate national puzzles can never be solved until every idea of nationalism shall have disappeared from the face of the earth. At the moment of going to press there seems to be little chance that such a miracle will happen.

According to the latest available statistics, the former Kingdom of Roumania counted 5,500,000 Roumanians and 500,000 Gypsies, Jews, Bulgarians, Hungarians, Armenians and Greeks. The new Roumania, the so-called Greater Roumania, has 17,-000,000 inhabitants, of which 73% are Roumanians, 11% Hungarians, 4.8% Ukrainians, 4.3% Germans and 3.3% Russians in Bessarabia and the Dubrudja, the land south of the delta of the Danube. As all these races dislike each other most cordially, do not in any way belong to the same ethnographical stock, but happen to have been thrown together by the artificial decisions of a peace conference, the material is there for a first-rate civil war, unless the foreign creditors intervene to save their investments.

Bismarck once said that the whole of the Balkans was not worth the bones of a single Pomeranian grenadier. One feels that in this, as in so many other things, the grouchy old founder of the last German Empire may have been right.

XXVIII

HUNGARY, OR WHAT REMAINS OF IT

THE Hungarians, or Magyars, as they prefer to call themselves, are very proud of the fact that they are the only people of Mongolian origin who were able to maintain themselves on European soil and to found a kingdom of their own, for their distant cousins, the Finns, were until very recently always a part of somebody else's empire or kingdom. Perhaps the Hungarians in their present misery have stressed their great warlike qualities a little more than was strictly necessary. But no one can deny that as a bulwark against the Turks they have rendered a tremendously important service to the rest of Europe. The Pope recognized the value of this buffer state when he raised the Magyar chieftain, Stephen, to the rank of Apostolic King of Hungary.

For when the Turks overran eastern Europe, it was Hungary which kept them within bounds. They were the first barrier, as Poland was to prove the second when Hungary at last was overrun. Under the leadership of one John Hunyadi, a humble nobleman of Vladic origin, Hungary became in truth one of the few defenders of the faith who was entitled to that name. But those same wide plains on both sides of the Tisia and Danube, which had so greatly attracted the Tartar horsemen that they had decided to settle down for good, were to prove the source of many internal evils.

Wide open spaces make it comparatively easy for a few strong men to dominate their neighbors. For where can the poor peasants go when there is neither sea nor mountains? Hungary therefore became a country of large land-owners. Far removed from the center of government, the land-owners maltreated their peasants so outrageously that soon the latter cared very little whether they were Magyar or Turk.

When Sultan Suleiman the Great marched against the West in the year 1526, the last of the Hungarian kings could not collect more than 25,000 men when he tried to stop the Mohammedans. On the plain of Mohács this Hungarian army was completely annihilated. Twenty-four thousand out of a total of 25,000 perished. The King himself was killed, together with all his advisers, and more than 100,000 Hungarians were dragged back to Constantinople to be sold to the slave-dealers of Asia Minor. The greater part of Hungary was annexed to Turkey. The rest was occupied by the Austrian Habsburgs who then began a tug of war with the Mohammedans for the unhappy land until the beginning of the eighteenth century when all of Hungary became part of the Habsburg domains.

Then, however, a new struggle for independence was started, the war against the German masters, and it continued for two entire centuries. The Hungarians fought with reckless bravery, and at last they were able to achieve a semblance of independence by recognizing the Emperor of Austria as Apostolic King of Hungary, and acquiring the status of a dominion.

But no sooner had they obtained what they considered merely to be their own good right than they must start upon a policy of persecution against all those who were not of Magyar blood. This policy was so short-sighted and deprived of common sense that soon they were without a friend in the whole wide world. They noticed this during the Congress of Versailles, when the number of inhabitants of the ancient Apostolic kingdom was reduced from 21,000,000 to 8,000,000 and three-fourths of all its former territory bestowed upon deserving neighbors.

This left Hungary a mere shadow of its old glorious self, a state not unlike Austria, one big city without any hinterland. Hungary was never very much of an industrial country. The large land-owners had had a prejudice against those ungainly chimneys that are an indispensable part of all well-regulated factories and they had not cared for the smell of smoke. As a result the Hungarian plain remained available for the purposes of agriculture, and Hungary today has the highest percentage of agricultural land of any country. Since most of this has always been under cultivation, the people should have been comparatively well off; yet the prevailing poverty has been so great that between 1896 and 1910 the country lost almost a million inhabitants through emigration.

As for the subject races of the old kingdom, the Magyar minority knew so well how to make its subjects uncomfortable that they too moved away by the boatload and the trainful, to help in the development of our own nation. We may as well give you a few figures, for what happened in Hungary happened to a lesser extent in practically all those countries where a small class of hereditary landlords had succeeded in making themselves supreme.

Just before the beginning of the Turkish wars of the sixteenth century, the Hungarian plain was densely populated and had more than 5,000,000 inhabitants. The Turkish domination reduced that number to 3,000,000 in a little less than two centuries. When finally the Austrians had driven the Turks away from the Puszta (the Magyar name for the plains), Hungary was so sparsely populated that immigrants from all over central Europe hastened to occupy the deserted farms. But the Magyar nobles, considering themselves the dominant race, the fighting race *par excellence*, would grant unto those newcomers none of the rights which they themselves enjoyed. The subject races, therefore, who accounted for almost one-half of the total population never were able to feel any real affection towards their adopted country.

Was it any wonder that during the Great War they felt a lack of inner loyalty which in the end caused the dual monarchy to crumble to dust, like an old building shaken by an earthquake?

XXIX

FINLAND, ANOTHER EXAMPLE OF WHAT HARD WORK AND INTELLIGENCE CAN ACHIEVE AMID HOSTILE NATURAL SURROUNDINGS

THERE only remains one more country before we leave Europe. Turkey today retains little of her former European possessions except Constantinople and a small slice of the Thracian plain and we had therefore better save our Turkey for tomorrow. But the Finns are part of Europe, and very much so.

They used to live all over Russia, but the more numerous Slavs pushed them northward until they reached that strip of dry land which connects Russia with Scandinavia. There they settled down, and there they have been ever since. The few Lapps who were living in the forests offered no difficulties, for they moved to Lapland in the Scandinavian peninsula, and were contented to give European civilization a wide berth.

As for Finland, it is unlike any other country in Europe. For tens of thousands of years it had been covered by glaciers. These have scraped the original soil so completely away that today only ten percent of the land is fit for cultivation. The moraines of the glaciers, the stones and the dirt carried down by these slow-running rivers of ice had filled up the ends of a great many valleys. When the great thaw set in, these valleys were filled with water, and that was the origin of those endless mountain lakes with which Finland is dotted. The word "mountain lake", however, should not call forth the image of another Switzerland, for Finland is a low country and rarely rises above a height of 500 feet. The number of these lakes is around 40,000. Together with the marshland that stretches between them, they occupy 30% of the total area of the state. They are entirely surrounded by those valuable forests which cover 62% or two-thirds of the total area and which provide the greater part of the world with the woodpulp necessary for the manufacture of books and magazines. Part of this wood is manufactured into paper on the spot. But Finland has no coal. It has enough fast-running rivers to be able to develop some water-power. But the climate, which is not unlike that of Sweden, turns these rivers into ice for five months of every year, and then the power stations are, of course, unable to function. The wood therefore has to be carried away by ships. Helsinki (Helsingfors until the late war) is not only the political capital but also the chief export-harbor for Finnish lumber.

But ere I finish this chapter, let me draw your attention to an interesting object lesson of what education may do for a people. The granite bridge connecting Scandinavia with Russia was entirely inhabited by people of Mongolian origin. But the western half, the so-called Finnish half, was conquered by the Swedes while the eastern half, inhabited by the Karelians, became Russian territory. After five centuries of Swedish influence and domination, the Finns of the east had become a civilized European nation, superior in many ways to several countries which enjoyed a much better geographical situation. But the Karelians, after an equally long period under the rule of the Russians, who some day hoped to exploit the riches of the Kola peninsula and the Murmansk coast, were exactly where they had been when the Muscovite Czars first insisted upon their submission. Whereas in Finland proper, which did not get in touch with Slavic culture until the year 1809 when Sweden lost this province to Russia, the number of analphabets is one percent, it is 97% in Karelia, which has always been under Muscovite influence. Yet the two people are the same and probably have the same natural ability for spelling c-a-t cat and t-a-i-l tail.

XXX

THE DISCOVERY OF ASIA

Two thousand years ago the Greek geographers were fighting among themselves about the original meaning of the word Asia. So there is no use in trying to solve the problem today. The theory that the word *Ereb* or "darkness" was the name which the sailors from Asia Minor had bestowed upon the land in the west where the sun went down and *Açu* or "glorious" upon the land in the east where the sun arose seems to be as good or as bad as any other.

Then we come to the next point, which is of greater importance. How and when did the people of Europe begin to suspect that they were not the center of the world? That their own home was but the small peninsula of an infinitely larger piece of land inhabited by ever so many more people, many of whom enjoyed a much higher degree of civilization, so that the Trojan heroes were fighting each other with weapons of such prehistoric shape that the intelligent Chinese had long since placed them in their museums of obsolete historical curiosities?

Usually Marco Polo is mentioned as the first European to visit Asia, but there had been others before him, although we know very little definite about them. As has happened so often in the realm of geography, it was war rather than peace which widened our knowledge of the Asiatic map. The chance to do business with the people over seas made the Greeks familiar with Asia Minor. The Trojan war was not without its educational side. The three great Persian expeditions against the west helped matters along very nicely. I doubt whether the Persians knew where they were going. Did the Greeks mean much more to them than the Indians of the west meant to General Braddock when

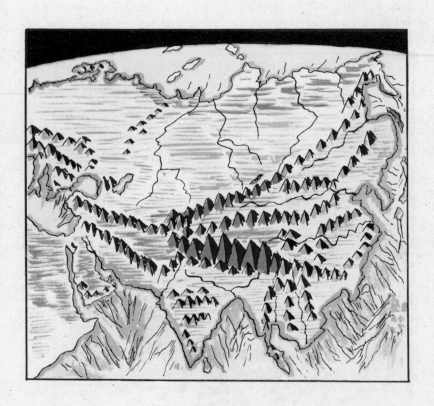

The Great Asiatic-European Plain

he moved into the wilderness to attack Fort Duquesne? I doubt it. The return visit of Alexander the Great, a couple of centuries later, was already something more than a mere military campaign, and Europe got its first scientific ideas about the territory lying between the Mediterranean and the Indian Ocean.

The Romans were by far too much pleased with themselves to take a really serious interest in "foreign" lands. As a source of revenue, to allow them to live a more luxurious existence at

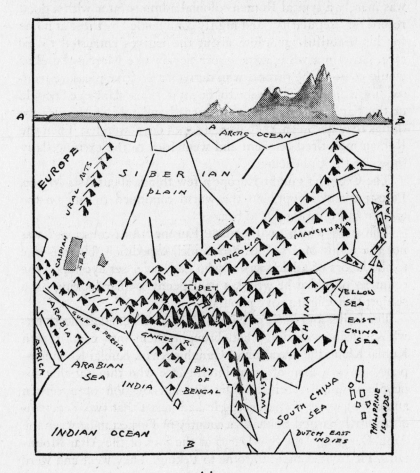

Asia

home, all foreign countries were grist to their mill. But the people whom they administered meant nothing to them whatsoever. Provided they paid their taxes and worked on the roads, they could live and die and quarrel among themselves as they pleased. They never even tried to understand what happened around them. In a crisis they called for the guards, did enough shooting to reestablish order, and washed their hands of the whole affair.

Pontius Pilate was neither a weakling nor a scoundrel. He was merely a typical Roman colonial administrator with a good record for "regularity" and highly commended by those at home for his beautiful ignorance about the natives entrusted to his care. Once in a while some queer person like Marcus Aurelius would come to the throne, who derived a positive pleasure from sending a diplomatic mission to the mysterious, slant-eyed people of the Far East. When they returned and told of the strange things they had seen, they were a seven days' wonder. Then the Roman mob tired of them and went back to the exciting daily shows of the Colosseum.

The Crusades taught Europe a few things about Asia Minor, Palestine and Egypt, but the world continued to end on the eastern shores of the Dead Sea.

The story which finally made Europe "Asia-conscious" was not the result of a serious "scientific" expedition, but was due to the labors of a hack-writer who had never set eyes upon the countries of which he wrote, a poor penny-a-liner looking for a subject that might prove popular.

The father and uncle of Marco Polo were Venetian merchants whose business dealings had brought them into contact with Kublai Khan, the grandson of Genghis Khan. Kublai Khan happened to be a man of great intelligence who thought that his people would be benefited by the introduction of a certain amount of western efficiency. He had heard that two Venetians occasionally visited Bokhara, a country in Turkestan between the Amu-Darya and the Syr-Darya at the foot of the Altai Mountains. He invited them to come to Peking. They went and were received with great honors. After several years they decided that their families needed them. The Khan bade them go home for a while and return and bring their bright young son and nephew Marco, about whom they had been talking so much.

In the year 1275, after a trip of three and a half years, the Polo family returned to Peking. Young Marco was all he had been said to be. He became a favorite at the court of Peking, was made governor of a province, received titles and honors, but after two dozen years he got homesick and so returned to Venice by way of India (he did that part of the voyage on ship-board) and Persia and Syria.

His neighbors, not in the least interested in tall stories, nick-named him Marco Millions, for he was forever telling them how rich the Khan was and how many golden statues there were in this temple or that, and how many silken gowns the concubines of such and such a prime-minister owned. Why should they believe such yarns, when it was well-known that even the wife of the Emperor of Constantinople had only a single pair of silk stockings?

And Marco Millions might have died and his story might have died with him if Venice and Genoa had not engaged in one of their little quarrels just then, and if Marco, as commander of a Venetian galley, had not been taken prisoner by the victorious Genoese. He remained in prison for a year, sharing his cell with a citizen from Pisa by the name of Rusticiano. This Rusticiano had had some experience as a writer. He had popularized a number of Arthurian tales and cheap French novels, the Nick Carter stuff of the Middle Ages. He quickly recognized the publicity value of the great Polo story, and during their time in jail he pumped Marco dry for information. Taking down everything Marco told him, he gave the world a book which is read quite as much today as when it was first published in the fourteenth century.

What probably gave the book its success was its constant references to gold and to riches of all sorts. The Romans and the Greeks had vaguely spoken of the opulence of eastern potentates but Polo had been on the spot, had seen all these things with his own eyes. The efforts to find a short-cut to the Indies really date from that time. But the task was difficult.

Finally in 1498 the Portuguese got as far as the Cape of Good Hope. Ten years later they were in India. Forty years later they were in Japan. Meanwhile Magellan, coming from the east, had reached the Philippine Islands, and by that time the exploitation of southern Asia was in full swing.

So much for the general outline. How Siberia was discovered, I have already told. The first visitors to the other countries will be given honorable mention when we get to them.

XXXI

WHAT ASIA HAS MEANT TO THE REST OF THE WORLD

EUROPE gave us our civilization but Asia gave us our religion. What is even more interesting, Asia gave the world the three great monotheistic religions which now dominate mankind. Judaism, Christianity and Mohammedanism are all of Asiatic origin. It is curious to reflect that when the Inquisitioners were burning their Jews, both the executioners and their victims were appealing to deities of Asiatic origin; that when the Crusaders were killing the Mohammedans and vice versa, it was a conflict of two Asiatic creeds which bade them do murder upon each other; and that whenever a Christian missionary gets into a dispute with a follower of Confucius, the two are merely engaged in a purely Asiatic exchange of opinions.

But Asia did not only give us our religious beliefs. It also gave us the fundamentals upon which we have constructed the entire fabric of civilization. In the pride of our recent technical inventions, we may loudly boast of "our great western progress" (we occasionally do), but that much vaunted progress of the west is merely a continuation of the progress that was begun in the east. It is highly doubtful whether the west would have been able to do anything at all if it had not learned the rudiments of everything it knows in the schools of the east.

The knowledge of the Greeks was not the result of cerebral spontaneous combustion. Mathematics and astronomy and architecture and medicine did not, like Pallas Athene, jump forth from the head of Zeus, armed from head to foot, ready for the glorious battle upon human stupidity. They were the result of slow and painful and deliberate growth, and the real pioneering work was done along the banks of the Euphrates and the Tigris.

289

From Babylon the arts and sciences then travelled to Africa. Here the dark-skinned Egyptians took them in hand until the Greeks had at last reached a sufficiently high degree of civilization to appreciate the beauty of a geometrical problem and the loveliness of a perfectly balanced equation. From that moment on, we can speak of a truly "European" science. But that truly "European" science had had an Asiatic ancestor who had lived and prospered more than 2000 years before.

And Asia bestowed further blessings upon us. The domestic animals, the dog and the cat and the useful quadrupeds, the docile cow and the faithful horse, together with the sheep and the hog, were all of them of Asiatic origin. When we think of the role played by these useful creatures during the era before the invention of the steam-engine, we begin to realize the debt we owe to Asia. To which we must add the greater part of our bill-of-fare, for practically all of our fruits and vegetables, most of our flowers and practically all of our poultry is of Asiatic origin and was brought to Europe by the Greeks, the Romans or the Crusaders.

Asia, however, was not always a Lady Bountiful from the east, carrying rich blessings from the banks of the Ganges and the Yellow River to the poor barbarians of the west. Asia could also be a terrible taskmaster. The Huns, who during the fifth century ravaged central Europe, were of Asiatic origin. The Tartars, who followed them seven centuries later and turned Russia into an Asiatic dependency to the everlasting detriment of all the other European nations, hailed from the desert regions of central Asia. The Turks, who during five long centuries caused so much bloodshed and misery and made eastern Europe into what it is today, were an Asiatic tribe. And another hundred years may see a united Asia once more upon the warpath and eager to repay us for some of the things we have done to her children since Berthold Schwartz invented his gunpowder.

XXXII

THE CENTRAL ASIATIC HIGHLANDS

THE 17,000,000 square miles of Asia are divided into five unequal parts.

First of all, and nearest to the Arctic, lies the great plain which I have already mentioned when I spoke of Russia. Next come the central highlands. Then the high plateaus of the south-west. Next the peninsulas of the south; and finally the peninsulas of the east. As I have already described the great Arctic plain, I can continue at once with the second part of the program.

The central Asiatic highlands begin rather mildly with a series of low mountain chains which form more or less parallel lines running invariably from east to west or from south-east to north-west, but never from north to south. In many places, however, the crust of the earth has been badly broken and twisted and folded and tortured by great volcanic upheavals. Thus we get the irregular contours of the Yablonoi Mountains east of Lake Baikal, the Khangai and Altai Mountains west of Baikal, and the Tien-shan Mountains just east of the Balkash Lake. To the west of these mountains are the plains. To the east lies the high plateau of Mongolia where the Gobi desert is situated, the home of the ancestors of Genghis Khan.

West of the Gobi desert lies the slightly lower plateau of east Turkestan. It is the valley of the Pamir River, which aimlessly loses itself in the nearby lake of Lob-nor, famous through the discoveries of the Swedish traveller, Sven Hedin. On the map the Pamir looks like a small desert brook. Yet it is one and a half times as long as the Rhine. For remember, Asia is the country of the gigantic proportions.

Just north of Turkestan there is a gap between the Altai and

Tien-shan Mountains. It is the land mentioned on our atlases as Jungaria, and it leads up to the Khirgiz steppes. It consists of an enormous valley which was the gateway through which all the desert tribes, the Huns, the Tartars and the Turks, started upon their marauding expeditions against Europe.

South of the Tarim basin, due south-west to be more accurate, the landscape becomes exceedingly complicated. The Tarim basin is cut off from the valley of the Oxus or the Amu-Darya (which loses itself in the Aral Sea) by a high plateau, the Plateau of Pamir, also called the Roof of the World. The Pamir Mountains, already known to the Greeks, were on the direct route from Asia Minor and Mesopotamia to China. They were a good deal of a barrier but could be crossed by a number of mountain passes. These passes average between 15,000 and 16,000 feet in height. Remember that Mount Ranier is only a little over 14,000 feet high, Mont Blanc a little over 15,000 feet. Then you get some idea of a mountainous territory where the passes lie at a higher altitude than the highest mountain tops of America and Europe, where the mountains themselves therefore dwarf anything we ourselves have to offer in the shape of crinkled globe-crust.

But the Pamir plateau is merely a beginning. It is a sort of terminal from which the big mountain-ranges radiate in all directions. There is the Tien-shan range, which I have already mentioned, running northward. There is the Kuen-lun range, which cuts Tibet off from the Tarim basin. There is the Karakoram, which is short but very, very steep; and finally we have the Himalaya range, which in the south cuts Tibet off from India and which breaks all records for "highest above sea-level", with altitudes of more than 29,000 feet or over five and one half miles, reached by both Everest and Kanchanjanga.

As for the plateau of Tibet, with an average height of 15,000 feet, it is indeed the most elevated country in the whole world. The Bolivian plateau in South America is between 11,000 and 13,000 feet high but it is practically uninhabited, whereas Tibet, which covers an area equal to two-fifths of that of Russia, has a population of almost two million people.

This shows to what extremes of air-pressure the human body can accustom itself. Those Americans who have crossed the Rio Grande know the discomforts they experience when they are allowed to spend a few days in the delightful Mexican capital which is only 7400 feet high. They are warned beforehand not to hustle as they do at home, and to take it easy until their heart

The High Plateau of Tibet

ceases to pump like a sledgehammer whenever they walk half a block. The Tibetans not only walk a hundred blocks in a day but they carry everything the country needs on their backs across mountain passes which are quite frequently too steep for mules and horses but which are the only connection they have with the outside world.

Although Tibet is about sixty miles further south than the semi-tropical island of Sicily, the snow remains on the ground for at least six months of every year and the thermometer not infrequently goes down to—30°. Nevertheless, this high plateau with its terrible wind storms, raging across the bleak salt-bogs of the south, its dust and snow and general discomforts of living, has become the home of an exceedingly curious religious experiment.

During the seventh century, Tibet was merely a principality like so many other Asiatic states, ruled over by a king who lived in Lhasa, the City of God. One of these kings was converted to Buddhism by his Chinese wife. Since that day, Buddhism has flourished in Tibet as nowhere else in Asia. Lhasa is to the Buddhists what Rome is to the Catholics, or Mecca to the Mohammedans—the holy of holies.

The Buddhism of Tibet is not the pure original doctrine of the gentle Indian prince who lived and died six centuries before the birth of Christ. It is the usual degenerate form, full of devils and spooks, and it has forgotten a great many of the noble teachings of the founder of that great Asiatic faith. But Tibet has been a bulwark of Buddhism which has been of great help in preserving that religion against the attacks of the Mohammedans from the west and the pagan creeds of southern India. Its uninterrupted success may in part have been the result of a very extraordinary arrangement which that church provides for an almost automatic continuation of the institution of the Buddhistic papacy.

The Buddhists have always believed in the reincarnation of the soul. It follows that the soul of Gotama himself must continue somewhere on this earth. All that was necessary was to find him and make him head of all the faithful. Now it is well to remember that Christianity, which is so much younger than Buddhism, has a great many ideas and institutions in common with its old neighbor and rival. Pious Buddhists were in the habit of eschewing the Devil and the flesh long before John the Baptist retired into the wilderness. Their monks practiced celibacy, poverty and chastity ages before Saint Simeon climbed to the top of his pillar in the valley of the Nile. They also exercised high political functions. During the reign of Kublai Khan, the grandson of Genghis Khan and an ardent convert to Buddhism, the abbots of an important Tibetan monastery were recognized as the political rulers of all Tibet. In return for this favor, the new Dalai Lama, in his quality of spiritual over-lord of the whole Buddhist world, officially crowned the Tartar Khan Emperor of Mongolia, just as Pope Leo III had crowned Charlemagne. In order to keep the dignity of Lama (or superior spiritual ruler) in the same family, the first Lamas broke the rules of celibacy and remained married until they had begotten a son to succeed them. But during the fourteenth century a great reformer arose among the Tibetan monks, a sort of Martin Luther of Buddhism. When he died, the old monastic orders had been reestablished in all their former rigor and their head, the Dalai Lama, "the Lama as big as the ocean", was once more recognized as their spiritual shepherd by one-quarter of all the people on earth. He was to be assisted in his task by the Pantshen Lama or Glorious Teacher, who was to be a sort of vice-pope. The method of succession, which was then introduced, has never been changed.

When either the Dalai Lama or the Pantshen Lama dies, the survivor sends for a list of all the male children born in Tibet immediately after the demise of his colleague, for the spirit of the dead man must now live in one of those babies. After prolonged prayers, three names are chosen, and these names are written on slips of paper. These are then thrown in a golden casket, provided several centuries ago for the occasion by one of the Chinese emperors. Then the abbots of all the great monasteries of Tibet gather together in the immense palace of the Dalai Lama. There are 3000 such monasteries in the country, but only a few are big enough to send delegates to this Buddhistic college of cardinals. After a week of fasting and praying, they draw one name out of the golden casket. The child who bears that name is held to be the reincarnation of the Buddha and is surrendered to the monks to be prepared for his task.

His fate is not a very happy one. It is to the advantage of the powerful abbots to keep him in the background and to make him a weakling, so that he may do their bidding and let them live comfortably at the expense of the other five-sixths of the populace, who are not monks but who are engaged in some productive labor and must therefore support their spiritual mentors. Should the poor youngster prove "difficult", then there are several subtle ways and means to allow him to "return to Paradise". Does he come up to the just expectations of his tutors, then he leads a terribly dull and monotonous existence and dies young anyway from sheer lack of exercise and boredom.

Nevertheless and notwithstanding, the system continues. Systems of that sort always do, whether 12,000 feet up in the air

The Mountain Gap

or at sea-level. As for the mountain-ranges which protect Tibet against the neighbors from the south and which protect it so well that until only a few years ago no foreigner had set foot upon this holy land of the living Buddha for more than seven hundred years, these mountain-ranges are so much in the public prints that they are better known and to a larger number of people than the mountains of Vermont. For our time, which loves records, has cast an envious eye upon the last remaining mountain top of any importance that remains unscaled. Mount Everest was called after the colonel of engineers who brought this part of the Himalayas into maps for the English geodetic survey, some time during the middle of the last century. It is 29,000 feet high, which makes it just twice as high as Mount Ranier. It has defied all attempts of man to reach the summit. The last of the great Everest expeditions in 1924 got to within a few hundred yards of the top. Two men volunteered to make the final climb. Armed with oxygen apparatus, they bade farewell to the rest of the party. They were last observed when they were within 600 feet of the final pinnacle. After that, they were never seen again. Mount Everest remains unconquered.

But for ambitious mountaineers this is an ideal region. Being situated in the heart of Asia, the country of the Gigantic Dimensions, the mountains must of course assume proportions compared to which the Swiss Alps become little sand piles made by boys and girls playing along the sea-shore. In the first place, these mountains of eternal snow, as the Hindus call them, are almost twice as wide as the Alps and cover thirteen times more territory. Some of their glaciers are four times as long as the most important glacier of Switzerland. There are forty individual mountain tops of more than 22,000 feet height and several of the mountain passes are more than twice as high as those of the Alps.

Like all other parts of the Great Fold which runs all the way from Spain to New Zealand, the Himalayas are of comparatively recent date (even younger than the Alps) and count their age in millions of years and not in hundreds of millions. It will take a great deal of sunshine and rain to destroy them and reduce them to flat country, but the forces of Nature, hostile to rock formations, are busily engaged. Already the Himalayas are cut into irregular pieces by the deep ravines of half a hundred brooks and rivers. The Indus, the Ganges and the Brahmaputra, the three most important rivers of India, help this labor of disintegration along at a merry clip.

Politically speaking, too, the Himalayas, with their tremendous length of 1500 miles, offer a more diversified spectacle than any other mountain-range. For they are not merely the natural frontier between two adjoining countries, as are the Alps and the Pyrenees. They happen to be so wide that quite a number of independent states are tucked away in them. Some of these, like Nepal, the home of the famous Gurkhas, who have retained a certain degree of independence, are four times as large as the republic of Switzerland and have almost 6,000,000 inhabitants. Others, like Kashmir (where our grandmothers got their shawls and where the English recruit their famous Sikh regiments), which is now part of the British domains, have an area of some 85,000 square miles with a population of over 3,000,000.

Finally, if you will look once more at the map, you will see a curious thing in regard to two of the big rivers, the Indus and the Brahmaputra. They do not run down from the Himalayas the way the Rhine runs down from the Alps, or the Missouri runs down from the Rockies. Instead they take their rise behind the main chain of the Himalayas. The Indus originates between the Himalayas and the Karakoram ridge. The Brahmaputra flows first from west to east through the plateau of Tibet. Then it makes a sharp turn and starts upon that short voyage from east to west to join the Ganges which runs through the heart of the broad valley between the Himalayas and the plateau of Deccan, in the central part of the Indian peninsula.

Running water, of course, has a terrific erosive power, but it does not seem likely that these two rivers could have dug their way through the Himalayas if they had begun to flow after the mountains had been made. And we are therefore obliged to draw the conclusion that these rivers must be older than the mountains. The Indus and the Brahmaputra were there before the crust of the earth began to heave and groan and very slowly produced those gigantic folds which were to become the highest mountain ranges of the modern world. But their growth was so slow (time is after all only an invention of man, eternity is timeless) that the rivers, by dint of their erosive energies, managed to remain on the ground floor, so to speak.

There are geologists who claim that even now the Himalayas are still gaining. Since the thin concrete shell on which we live contracts and expands like the skin of our body, these geologists may be right. The Swiss Alps, as we know for a fact, are travelling slowly from east to west. The Himalayas, like the Andes of South America, may be moving upward. There is only one law in the laboratory of Nature which holds good for all creation—there must be constant change and the punishment for those who fail to obey is death.

XXXIII

THE GREAT WESTERN PLATEAU OF ASIA

FROM Pamir in the center a wide mountain-range, which is really nothing but a series of high plateaus, runs due west until at last it is stopped by the waters of the Black Sea and the Aegean.

All of these plateaus have familiar names, for they have played a most important role in the history of human progress. I might go a little further and say *the* most important role. For unless all our present ethnological speculations are wrong, these highlands and valleys between the Indus river and the shores of the eastern Mediterranean were not only the nursery which hatched that branch of the human race to which we ourselves happen to belong, but they also acted as a sort of grammar school in which we learned the rudiments of those sciences and the first principles of those moral tenets which eventually were to set Man apart from the rest of the animal world.

In order of their succession, the first of these highlands is the plateau of Iran. It is a vast salty desert about 3000 feet high, entirely surrounded by high mountain-ranges. Even in the north where it borders upon the Caspian Sea and the Turanian desert and in the south where it borders upon the Persian Gulf and the Arabian Sea, there is not a sufficient amount of rainfall to let this region have a single river worth the name. Baluchistan, separated from India proper by the high Kirthar range, and since 1887 part of the British domains, has a few indifferent streams which lose themselves into the Indus river, but its deserts have been feared ever since a greater part of Alexander's armies perished there from thirst on the way back from India.

Afghanistan, which was so much in the limelight a few years ago when it fell into the hands of a ruler who tried to publicize himself and his country by a very spectacular trip through Europe, has a river, the Helmund. This begins in the Hindu Kush, one of the high mountain-ranges that radiate southward from Pamir and which loses itself in the salty Lake of Seistan on the border between Persia and Afghanistan. Afghanistan, however, enjoys a much better climate than Baluchistan and in many other ways this country is of much greater importance. The original trade-route between India and northern Asia and Europe ran through the heart of this country. It went from Peshawar, the capital of the north-west frontier province, to Kabul, the capital of Afghanistan, by way of the famous Khyber Pass, and then crossed the high Afghan plateau until it reached Herat in the west.

About fifty years ago Russia and England began their fight for the ultimate control of this buffer state. As the Afghans happened to be excellent fighting men, those peaceful penetrations from south and north had to be accomplished with more than the usual care and circumspection. The disaster of the first Afghan war of 1838–1842, when a mere handful of English returned to tell how all the others had been massacred during the attempt to force an unpopular ruler upon the unwilling Afghan people, was never quite forgotten; and thereafter England proceeded across the Khyber Pass with careful tread. But when the Russians in 1873 occupied Khiva and were known to be heading for Tashkend and Samarkand, the English from their side were forced to make some move lest they wake up one morning to hear the armies of the Czar doing a little practice shooting on the other side of the Suliman Mountains. And so, while His Imperial Majesty's representatives in London and Her Royal Majesty's representatives in St. Petersburg were assuring the respective imperial and royal governments that their intentions towards Afghanistan were wholly unselfish and of a most respectable and laudatory nature, the engineers of both governments were working on elaborate plans to bless poor Afghanistan, "cut off by cruel Nature from direct access to the sea", with a railroad system that should henceforth allow the benighted Afghans to partake at first hand of the blessings of western civilization.

The World War unfortunately interfered with these projects. The Russians got as far as Herat, from where today you may travel by rail via Merv in the Turkoman Socialist Soviet Republic to the harbor of Krasnovodsk on the Caspian Sea and thence by boat to Baku and western Europe. Another line runs from Merv by way of Bokhara to Kokand in the Uzbeg Republic and is to continue from there to Balkh. Balkh is at present a third-rate village, situated among the vast ruins of that ancient Bactria which 3000 years ago was as important as Paris is today. It was the original center of that highly ethical religious movement started by Zoroaster (or Zarathustra) which not only conquered Persia and penetrated as far as the Mediterranean, but which in a modified form was so popular among the Romans that for a long time it was one of the most serious rivals of Christianity.

England meanwhile has been pushing her railroad from Hyderabad to Quetta in Baluchistan, and from there to Kandahar, where in the year 1880 the British had avenged themselves for their defeat of the first Afghan war.

But there is still another part of the Iranian plateau which deserves some attention. Today it is merely the shadow of its former greatness but it must have been an extraordinarily interesting land when the name of Persia stood for all that was most excellent in painting and literature and above all things in the difficult art of living. The first period of glory came six centuries before Christ, when Persia was the center of an empire which reached all the way from Macedonia to India. This was destroyed by Alexander, but five hundred years later, under the dynasty of the Sassanids, the Persians restored the ancient realm of Xerxes and Cambyses. They restored the Zoroastrian faith in all its former purity, collected the sacred writings into one volume, the famous Zend-Avesta, and made the desert flower with the roses of Ispahan.

Early during the seventh century the Arabs conquered Persia and Mohammed defeated Zoroaster. But if it is true that one

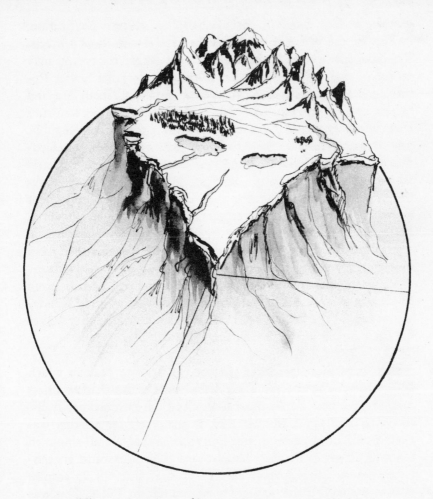

The total amount of land and water on our planet

The Land Bridge from Asia to Europe

shall know a country by its literature, then the works of Omar, the tent-maker's son from Nishapur, bear witness to the exquisite taste that flourished once upon a time in these desert lands between Kurdistan and Khorasan. A professor of mathematics, dividing his time between algebra and quatrains upon the delights of love and the beauties of old red wine, is a phenomenon of such rare occurrence that only a civilization both wise and mellow would have tolerated his presence in the hallowed halls of pedagogy.

Today's interest however in Persia is of a more prosaic nature. The country has oil, and that is about the worst thing that could possibly happen to a nation too weak to defend its own interests. Theoretically speaking, the natives of any given place are supposed to be the chief beneficiaries of the treasures that lie hidden beneath their ancestral grave-yards. In practice it works out differently. A few of the Sultan's intimate friends in far away Teheran grow rich from granting concessions, and several thousand men and women living near the wells may find occasional employment at pretty meagre wages. But the rest goes to the foreign investor who thinks that Persia is the name of a rug.

Unfortunately, Persia seems to be one of those countries which will always be poor and badly administered. Its geographical location is very little of a blessing and very much of a curse. It is a desert, but when a desert is situated on the main road, which in turn is part of a land bridge connecting two of the most important parts of the world, then that desert will forever be a battle-field and a bone of contention between opposing interests. And what I have just said of Persia holds true of this entire western part of Asia.

The final highlands in the chain of plateaus that run all the way from Pamir to the Mediterranean are Armenia and Asia Minor. Armenia, the westward continuation of the great platform of Iran, is a very old land, old in the formation of its volcanic soil and old in the suffering of its people. It is another bridge country. Whosoever wanted to wander from Europe to India had to pass through the valleys of the high Kurdistan Mountains, and among those travellers have been some of the most notorious cut-throats of all time. Its history goes back to the days of the deluge. It was on the top of Mount Ararat, the highest mountain of this entire region, which rises 17,000 feet above sea-level and almost 10,000 feet above the plain of Erivan, that Noah's ark landed when the waters of the earth had begun to recede. This we know for certain because when Sir John de Mandeville, the Belgian physician, visited these regions in the beginning of the fourteenth century, he still found parts of the old craft lying around near the top. But when the Armenians themselves, who belong to the racial group of the Mediterranean and who therefore are our very near cousins, moved into these hills is still quite uncertain. At the recent rate of extinction, however, there soon won't be any more of them left. In one single year, 1895–1896, the Turks, who were then the masters of the Armenian plateau, murdered several hundred thousand of them; and the Turks are by no means their worst enemies and not half as savage with them as the Kurds.

The Armenians have always been very pious Christians. But although they had adopted Christianity long before Rome, their church had retained several institutions, such as an hereditary priesthood, which made it a most obnoxious organization in the eyes of all good Catholics of the west. Europe therefore sat quietly by while the Mohammedan Kurds slaughtered Armenians and stole their territory.

Then came the Great War, and the Allies, trying to get into Turkey by the back door in order to relieve the English in Mesopotamia, stamped across all this territory. Such names as Lake Van and Lake Urmia, of which the world had never heard before, although they are among the biggest of all mountain lakes, suddenly appeared in the news of the day; and Erzerum, an Asiatic frontier town of the old Byzantine Empire, attracted more attention than it had done since the days of the Crusades.

When the fighting came to an end, it is small cause for surprise that the surviving Armenians wished a plague upon all of their tormentors and joined the Soviet Union. They were allowed to form the republics of Azerbaijan and Armenia, between the Caspian and the Black Sea at the foot of the Caucasian Mountains, which Russia had added to its territory during the first half of the nineteenth century.

Then, turning from the traditional victims of Turkish wrath to the Turks themselves, we wander a little further westward and enter the plateau of Asia Minor.

Asia Minor, once merely a province of the empire of the old Sultan, is today all that remains of that Turkish dream of world dominion. On the north it is bounded by the Black Sea, on the west by the Sea of Marmora, the Bosporus and the Dardanelles, which cut it off from Europe, and in the south by the Mediterranean, from which the interior is separated by the Taurus Mountains. Across this territory, which is considerably lower than Iran, Persia or Armenia, runs a famous railroad, the so-called Bagdad railroad which has played such an important part in the history of the last thirty years. For both England and Germany wanted to have the concessions for the railroad that was to connect Constantinople with Bagdad on the Tigris and Smyrna, the great harbor of the Asiatic west coast, with Damascus in Syria and with Medina, the holy city of the Arabs.

No sooner had these two nations reached a compromise than French capital insisted upon a share in the future revenue. The French were thereupon given the northern part of Asia Minor where Trebizond, the export harbor for Armenia and Persia, was still waiting for suitable communications with the west. Foreign engineers then began to survey their roads through these ancient lands where the Greek philosophers of the Athenian colonies had first speculated upon the true nature of man and the universe, where solemn church councils had given the world the iron-bound faith by which the people of Europe had lived for over a thousand years, where Paul of Tarsus was born and where he had preached, where Turk and Christian had fought for the supremacy of the Mediterranean world, and where in some forsaken desert hamlet an Arab camel-driver had dreamed his first dreams of being Allah's one and only prophet.

This railroad as planned was to keep well away from the coast-line, skirting those almost mythical seaports of ancient and medieval history—Adana and Alexandretta and Antioch and Tripoli and Beirut and Tyre and Sidon and Jaffa, the only harbor of the rocky land of Palestine—and devoting itself chiefly to the mountains.

When the war broke out, the railroad played exactly that role which the Germans had expected. The railroad, with its excellent German equipment, together with the presence of two big German battle-ships in Constantinople, were the two highly practical "considerations" which made the Turks join the Central Powers rather than the Allies. And how well that road had been planned from a strategical point of view was shown during the next four years. For the war was finally decided on the ocean and in the west. The eastern front never collapsed until long after the western front had begun to melt away. And the world learned to its surprise that the Turk made as good a soldier in the year 1918 as he had done in 1288 when the Seljuk Turks conquered the whole of Asia and cast their first longing glances across the Bosporus at the impregnable walls of imperial Constantinople.

Up to then that mountainous plateau had been quite well-to-do. For Asia Minor, although part of the land bridge between Asia and Europe, had never quite suffered the fate of Armenia and the Persian plateau of Iran. This had been due to the fact that Asia Minor was not only part of a commercial highroad but also the terminal station for all the routes leading from India and China to Greece and Rome. For when the world was still young, the most active intellectual and commercial life of the Mediterranean was not to be found in Hellas itself. It flourished among the cities of western Asia which the Greek cities of the mainland had converted into Greek colonies. Where the ancient blood of Asia had mingled with the new race until it produced a mixture that for sheer intelligence and sharpness of wit has rarely found its equal. Even in the modern Levantines, of highly unsavory reputation in regard to business integrity and general honesty, we can detect traits of the old stock which for half a thousand years had been able to hold its own against its many enemies.

The final disintegration under the rule of the Seljuks was inevitable. As a degenerative force, the Turks have always been

Jerusalem

without a single rival. But today this small peninsula is practically all that remains of the ancient glories of the Ottoman Empire. The Sultans themselves are gone. Their ancestors, after residing for almost a century in Adrianople, the only other Turkish city left in Europe outside of Constantinople, had moved to the latter city in the year 1453, and from there had ruled a territory which included the whole of the Balkans, all of Hungary and the greater part of southern Russia.

Four centuries of inexpressible mismanagement sufficed to

ruin this empire and make it what it is today. Constantinople, the oldest and most important example of a commercial monopoly which for thousands of years held the key to the grain trade of southern Russia, that same Constantinople, so favored by Nature that its harbor came to be known as the Golden Horn, the Horn of Plenty, so filled with fish that no one ever need go hungry, was reduced to the rank of a third-rate provincial city. For the masters of the New Turkey, who had salvaged what was left when peace was declared, wisely concluded that the degenerate background of Constantinople, a hodge-podge of Greeks and Armenians and Levantines and Slavs and the accumulated riff-raff of all the Crusades, was not the place from which to try the well nigh impossible task of rejuvenating the Turkish people and turning them into a modern nation. They therefore chose themselves a new capital, the city of Angora in the heart of the Anatolian Mountains, more than 200 miles east of Constantinople.

Angora was old, very old. Four hundred years before our era, a tribe of Gauls had lived here, the same sort of Gauls who afterwards took possession of the plains of France. It had passed through all the vicissitudes of all the cities situated on this main road of trade. The Crusaders had captured the city. The Tartars had done likewise. Even as late as 1832 an Egyptian army had destroyed that whole neighborhood. But it was there that Kemal Pasha founded the capital city of his new fatherland. He purged it of all the elements that could not be assimilated. He swapped his Greeks and Armenians for Turks who lived in these other countries. He built up his army and his credit with equal brilliancy. And he made the New Turkey a going concern, though Heaven knows, the mountains of Anatolia, after fifteen centuries of warfare and neglect, yield little enough that is considered of any value to a Wall Street banker who is looking around for possible prospects in the loan market.

All the same, Asia Minor is generally recognized as being of the utmost importance for the future trade between Asia and Europe. Smyrna is regaining the position it already held when the Amazons, the female warriors of the ancient world, ruled this part of Asia and founded their curious state in which all male children were put to death and in which no man was allowed to set foot except once a year and then exclusively for the purpose of continuing the race.

Ephesus, where Paul still found the natives worshipping the image of the Chaste Diana, the ideal goddess, by the way, for a race of Amazons, has disappeared from the face of the earth, but the region nearby may become one of the most lucrative fig gardens of the world.

Further towards the north, past the ruins of Pergamum (the great literary center of the ancient world which gave us our word parchment), the railroad skirts the plain of Troy to connect with Panderma on the Sea of Marmora. Panderma is only a day's trip by boat removed from Scutari where the famous Orient Express (London–Calais–Paris–Vienna–Belgrade–Sofia–Constantinople) has connections with the trains that run to Angora and Medina and those which via Aleppo–Damascus–Nazareth–Ludd (change cars for Jerusalem and Jaffa)—Gaza–Ismailia–Kantara connect with Suez and from there up the Nile as far as the Sudan.

If it had not been for the Great War, that road could have been made profitable by transporting goods and passengers for India and China and Japan from western Europe by rail as far as Suez and then sending them the rest of the way by ship. But by the time the damage of four years' fighting shall have been repaired, the aeroplane will probably be in general use for the passenger traffic.

The eastern part of Asia Minor is inhabited by the Kurds, the ancient enemies of the Armenians. The Kurds, like the Scotch and most mountain peoples, are divided into clans and have too much individual pride to take kindly to a commercial or an industrial civilization. They are a terribly old race, already mentioned in the cuneiform inscriptions of the Babylonians and by Xenephon in his "Retreat of the Ten Thousand" (what a dull book!) They belong to the same original stock as we do but they have been converted to Mohammedanism. As such they have never trusted their Christian neighbors, but this holds good of all the other Moslem states that were founded in consequence of the Great War, and not without cause as all of us who lived during those days, when "official misstatements" were part of the national strategy, have every reason to remember.

When peace was finally declared, nobody was satisfied and many new feuds and quarrels were added to the old ones, all the more as several European powers now installed themselves as "mandatory rulers" over parts of the old Turkish Empire and proved to be but little less cruel in their dealings with native races than the Turks had been.

The French, who had invested a great deal of money in Syria, took hold of Syria, and a French High Commission, amply supplied with money and troops, undertook to rule the three million odd Syrians who most certainly had not asked to be turned into a European "mandate", which meant a colony but with a slightly less offensive name. Soon different elements that had been part of the old Syria were beginning to forget their dislike for each other in one common hatred for the French. The Kurds made peace with their hereditary enemies, the Roman Catholic Maronites of Lebanon (the old home of the Phoenicians), and the Christians ceased to maltreat the Jews, and the Jews ceased to despise both Christians and Mohammedans, and the French were obliged to erect a great many gallows in order to maintain themselves. But order apparently has been reestablished and Syria is rapidly becoming another Algeria. That does not mean that the people like their mandatory rulers any better than before but merely that the leaders have been hanged and the others lack the courage to go on fighting.

As for the valley of the Tigris and the Euphrates, it was elevated to the rank of a monarchy and the ruins of Babylon and Nineveh are now part of the Kingdom of Irak. But the new potentates hardly enjoy the freedom of action of Hammurabi or Assur-Bani-Pal, for they have been forced to recognize England's suzerainty. King Feisal has to await word from London whenever he wants to decide upon something more important than the re-digging of a few ancient Babylonian drainage canals.

As for Palestine (the land of the Philistines), which is also part of this region, it is so strange a country that I shall have to be very short about it for fear of filling the rest of this book with a description of a little state, no larger than some ninth-rate European principality like Schleswig-Holstein, but which somehow or other has played a greater role in human history than many a first-class empire.

The original ancestors of the Jews, after leaving their miserable villages in eastern Mesopotamia, and after wandering through the northern part of the Arabian desert, and crossing the plains between Mount Sinai and the Mediterranean, and spending a few centuries in Egypt, finally retraced their steps. They stopped when they had reached the narrow strip of fertile land between the mountain-ridge of Judea and the Mediterranean and engaged in bitter warfare with the original natives, whom they finally deprived of a sufficient number of villages and cities to found an independent Jewish state of their own.

Their lives cannot have been very comfortable. In the west, the Philistines, non-Semitic settlers from the island of Crete, were in full possession of the coastal region, cutting the Jews completely off from the open sea. In the east, one of the strangest natural phenomena of which we have any record, an enormous rift in the rocks, running a straight course from north to south and going as deep as 1300 feet below sea-level, separated their country from the rest of Asia. This sink, which is very much to-day as it was when John the Baptist chose it as his place of residence, begins in the north between the Lebanon and the Anti-Lebanon and follows the valley of the Jordan, the Lake of Tiberias or Sea of Galilee, which is 526 feet below sea-level, the Dead Sea, which is 1292 feet below sea-level (the Death Valley in California is only 276 feet, and the deepest spot on the American continent) and from there (for the River Jordan stops dead in the Dead Sea, which contains 25% salt on account of the constant evaporation) through the ancient land of Edom (where

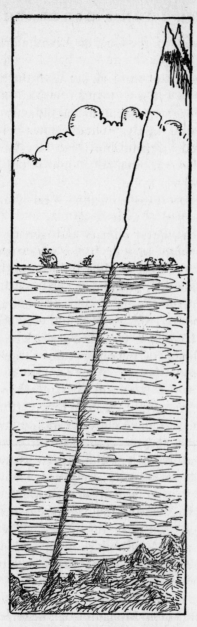

The distance between the highest mountain top and
the lowest ocean depth is 11½ miles or
1/700 of the earth's diameter

the Moabites lived) to the Gulf of Akaba, a branch of the Red Sea.

The southern part of this sink is one of the hottest and most desolate regions of the world, full of asphalt and sulphur and phosphates and other diabolical ingredients which modern chemistry has made highly profitable (just before the war the Germans founded a formidable Dead Sea Asphalt Company) but which must have inspired the people of long ago with horror and fear, and which made them attribute the destruction of Sodom and Gomorrah by an ordinary earthquake to an act of vengeance on the part of their Gods.

The sudden change of climate and scenery when they had crossed the mountain ridge of Judea, which runs parallel with this great rift, must have made a tremendous impression upon the earliest invaders from the east and probably inspired that jubilant cry of a land "overflowing with milk and honey". For the modern visitor to Palestine will find very little milk and the bees apparently have long since died for lack of a sufficient number of flowers. That, however, is not due to a change in the climate, as one hears so often said, for the climate today seems little different from the climate in the days when the disciples of Jesus wandered from Dan to Beersheba without bothering much about the problem of their daily bread and butter, since there were enough dates and there was enough native wine for the simple needs of all travellers. But the Turks and the Crusaders between them played the role of climate. The Crusaders began by destroying whatever remained of the old irrigation works which had been built during the days of independence and during the centuries of Roman domination. The Turks had, as usual, done the rest. A soil which only needed water to bring forth rich harvests was systematically neglected until nine-tenths of the farmer populace had either died or moved away. Jerusalem became a sort of Bedouin village where a dozen Christian sects and their Mohammedan neighbors were forever engaged in far from edifying quarrels. For to the Moham-medans, Jerusalem is also a very Holy City. The Arabs consider themselves the direct descendants of that unfortunate Ishmael who together with his mother Hagar was driven into the wilderness by Abraham at the request of the latter's wedded wife, the redoubtable Sarah.

But Ishmael and Hagar had not perished of thirst, as seems to have been Sarah's little plan, but Ishmael had married an Egyptian girl and had become the founder of the whole of the Arabian nation. Today therefore he and his mother lie buried just outside the Kaaba, the center of the most holy of all places of worship in Mecca which all Mohammedans must visit at least once during their lifetime, no matter how difficult the voyage or how far the distance that separates them from that hallowed spot.

As soon as the Arabs had conquered Jerusalem, they erected a mosque over the rock upon which, according to tradition, their distant cousin Solomon, another direct descendant of Abraham, had built his famous temple. That happened Heaven only knows how many centuries ago. But the fight for the ownership of that rock and the walls around it, part of which is the traditional "wailing wall" of the orthodox Jews, is responsible for the continual quarrels between the two races that now make up the population of the Palestinian mandate.

And what can one hope for the future? When the English captured Jerusalem, they found the people to consist of 80% Moslems (Syrians and Arabs) and 20% Jews and Gentile Christians. The English, as the rulers of the largest Mohammedan empire of the modern world, could not afford to hurt the feelings of so many of their loyal subjects and dared not surrender half a million Palestine Moslems to the mercies of less than a hundred thousand Jews, who had many entirely justifiable axes to grind.

The result was the usual post-Versailles compromise which satisfied nobody. Palestine today is a British mandate and British troops maintain order between the different nationalities. The governors are selected from among the best-known English Jews but the country is nevertheless a colony and does not enjoy that complete political independence of which Mr. Balfour had spoken so eloquently but also so vaguely when at the beginning of the Palestine campaign he referred to those regions as the future home of the Jewish race.

Matters would become a great deal simpler if the Jews themselves knew what they wanted to do with the old mother-country. The orthodox Jews of eastern Europe and especially those of Russia want to keep it as it is now, a vast theological seminary with a little museum of Hebrew antiquities. The younger generation, remembering the wise words of the Prophet that "the dead should bury the dead", and feeling that too much weeping about the past joys and glories of bygone days is apt to interfere quite seriously with the glories and the joys of tomorrow, hope to make Palestine into a normal, modern state, something like Switzerland or Denmark, a going concern of men and women who have rid themselves of the memories of the Ghetto and who are more interested in good roads and good irrigation canals than in squabbling with their Arab neighbors about a few old stones which may or may not have been the well from which Rebecca drew the water but which are now merely a hindrance to progress.

Since most of Palestine consists of rolling territory with a decided slope from east to west, it is indeed possible to reclaim the neglected and exhausted soil for purposes of agriculture. The sea winds which blow the greater part of each day spread their heavy dew across the entire landscape and make it ideally fit for the cultivation of olives, and Jericho, the only city of any importance ever built in the terrible Dead Sea region, may once more become a center for the trade in dates.

And as the soil of Palestine contains neither coal nor oil, it will escape the attentions of the foreign promoter and will be allowed to work out its own problems as Yahweh and the Mohammedan majority will permit.

XXXIV

ARABIA—OR WHEN IS A PART OF ASIA NOT A PART OF ASIA?

ACCORDING to the maps in our ordinary atlases and according to the handbooks on geography, Arabia is a part of Asia. But the proverbial visitor from Mars, ignorant of the history of our planet, would probably come to a different conclusion and would decide that Nejd, the famous Arabian desert, is really nothing but a continuation of the Sahara from which it is separated by an inconsequential and rather shallow bay of the Indian Ocean known as the Red Sea.

This Red Sea is almost six times as long as it is wide and full of reefs. Its mean depth is about 300 fathoms, but where it connects with the Gulf of Aden, which is really part of the Indian Ocean, the depth varies between only two and sixteen fathoms. It is possible that the Red Sea, which is full of little volcanic islands, was originally an inland lake which did not get elevated to the rank of a sea until the Straits of Persia were formed, just as the North Sea did not really become a sea until after the formation of the British Channel.

As for the Arabs themselves, they seem to have no desire to be either African or Asiatic, for they call their country "the island of the Arabians", which is rather a large order for a piece of territory six times as large as the whole of Germany. The number of inhabitants is not at all in proportion to the size of their country. It does not exceed that of greater London. But the original ancestors of these 7,000,000 modern Arabs must have been possessed of extraordinary physical and mental qualities for they have been able to impress themselves upon the world at large in quite an extraordinary fashion, and that without the slightest assistance from the side of Mother Nature.

In the first place, they lived in a country with a climate that is not fit for human beings. Not only is this continuation of the Sahara Desert completely deprived of rivers, but it is also one of the hottest places on earth, except in the extreme south and east where the coast is so damp and moist as to be practically uninhabitable for Europeans. But in the center of the peninsula and in the south-west where the mountain-ranges reach a height of almost 6000 feet, the life of both Man and beast is made intolerable by those sudden changes in temperature which take place immediately after dark and which cause the thermometer to fall from 80° to 20° in less than half an hour's time.

If it were not for the underground water the interior would be entirely uninhabitable. As for the coastal regions they are not much better off except the territory immediately north of the British settlement of Aden.

From a commercial point of view, however, the whole blessed peninsula is not worth as much as the lower part of the island of Manhattan. But the island of Manhattan will have to do a great deal better than it has done so far if it ever wants to equal Arabia in its general influence upon the cultural development of the world.

Curiously enough the Arab peninsula has never been a country as France or Sweden are countries. As a result of the irresponsible promises made to everybody and everything during the Great War when the Allies were badly in need of a few extra men, a baker's dozen of so-called independent states now stretches all the way from the Persian Gulf to the Gulf of Akaba and even further northward where Transjordania, ruled by an Emir who takes his orders from Jerusalem, separates Palestine from the Syrian desert. But most of them are mere names like El Hasa and Oman, along the Persian Gulf, Hadramut in the south and Yemen and Asir along the Red Sea, just south of El Hejaz which is perhaps the only one of any importance. For the Hejaz not only has a railroad of its own (the final part of the Bagdad road which now runs as far as Medina and which eventually will be continued to Mecca) but it also is in control of the two holy cities of the Moslem world, Mecca, the place where Mohammed was born, the Bethlehem of the Moslems, and Medina where he lies buried.

Neither of these two oasis cities amounted to much early during the seventh century when they became the center of such stirring events. Mohammed, who was responsible for their fame, was born in 567 or 569, several months after the death of his father. Soon afterwards his mother died too and he was thereupon entrusted to the care of an impecunious grandfather. At an early age he became a camel-driver and travelled all over Arabia with the caravans who hired his services. He may even have crossed the Red Sea, and there is a possibility that he visited Abyssinia which was then trying to turn Arabia into an African colony (and having an easy time of it as the different desert tribes hated each other too cordially to be able to put up a concerted fight).

At an uncertain age he married a widow. Her property allowed him to give up his wandering life and open a little store of nis own, dealing in grain and camel-feed. Like many other people suffering from epileptic fits, he had strange hallucinations when in a state of semi-consciousness, and, like many other people affected by that unpleasant ailment, he tried to console himself for his unfortunate affliction by telling his neighbors that he had gone into a trance in order to receive a revelation from God. Not being a man of great originality of thought, he did not find it easy to develop some definite and new system of religion of his own. He vaguely talked about restoring the ancient faith of Abraham and Ishmael. For a time he even seems to have played with the idea of adapting the Christian faith to the needs of his wild neighbors who would never have listened to any one talking to them of meekness and asking them to turn the other cheek to their enemies. In the end, and under the pressure of his Meccan neighbors, who laughed rather heartily at the vegetable-vender turned prophet and who threatened his life when he began to take himself a bit too seriously, he fled to Medina and there he started upon his career as a preacher in all seriousness.

I cannot go into details about his doctrines. If you are interested, buy a Koran and try to read it, though you will find it hard sledding. Suffice it here to state that as a result of Mohammed's labors, the different Semite tribes of the great Arabian desert suddenly became conscious of having to fulfil a mission. In less than a century they had conquered all of Asia Minor and Syria and Palestine, together with the whole of the northern coast of Africa and Spain. Until the end of the eighteenth century they were a constant menace to the safety of Europe.

Well, a people who could do all that and in only a few years must have been possessed of extraordinary mental and physical abilities. According to all those who have ever had anything to do with them (including Napoleon, who was a bad judge of women but who knew a good soldier when he saw one) the Arabs are terrific fighters, and their medieval universities were concrete proof of their intellectual gifts and their interest in science. Why in the end they should have lost so much of their former prestige, I could not say. It would be very easy here to indulge in a few high sounding theories about the influence of the geographical background upon the character of men and then prove that desert tribes have always been great world conquerors, but there are just as many desert people who have never amounted to anything. Also there are just as many mountaineers who have done all sorts of wonderful things. And then again there are other mountaineers who have never risen far above the ranks of drunken and careless and lazy loafers. No, I am sorry, but I have never been able to draw a single general moral lesson from success or the lack thereof on the part of any nation.

But what has happened once may happen again. The great reform movement of the middle of the eighteenth century which purged Mohammedanism of all forms of idolatry and which gave rise to the puritannical sect of the Wahhabites with their insistence upon frugal and simple living, may cause the Arabs to go on the warpath once more; and if Europe continues to waste its strength on civil warfare they may become as dangerous to us as they were twelve centuries ago. Their terrible peninsula is a vast reservoir of "hard" people, of people who rarely smile, who rarely play, who take themselves with dignified seriousness and who cannot be corrupted by the pleasant prospects of material wealth because their needs are so simple that they have never felt the lack of anything better.

Such nations are ever a potential source of danger. Especially when they have a just reason to feel themselves aggrieved. And in the case of Arabia, as in that of all Asia, Africa, America and Australia, the White Man's conscience is not quite as clear as we might wish.

XXXV

INDIA, WHERE NATURE AND MAN ARE ENGAGED IN
MASS-PRODUCTION

ALEXANDER THE GREAT discovered India. That happened three hundred years before the birth of Christ. But Alexander did not get very far beyond the Indus River, and although he crossed the Punjab, the home of the Sikhs, he never penetrated the heart of the country of the true Hindus who lived then as they do now in the wide valley of the Ganges, situated between the Himalayas in the north and the plateau of Deccan in the south. Eighteen centuries had to go by before the people of Europe got their first reliable information about this wonder-land of Marco Polo. That happened when the Portuguese Vasco da Gama reached Goa on the coast of Malabar.

Once the sea route from Europe to the land of the spices and the elephants and the golden temples had been established, information poured in upon the geographers at such a vast rate that the map-makers of Amsterdam were kept working over-time. Since then every nook and corner of the teeming peninsula has been thoroughly explored. This is the lay of the land in as few words as possible.

In the north-west India is cut off from the rest of the world by the Khirdar Mountains and the Suliman range which run from the Arabian Sea as far as the Hindu Kush. In the north the barrier consists of the Himalayas which run in a semi-circle all the way from Hindu Kush to the Gulf of Bengal.

Please remember that everything connected with India is on a scale which dwarfs the geographical proportions of Europe and makes them look almost ridiculous. In the first place, India itself is as large as all of Europe outside of Russia. The Hima-

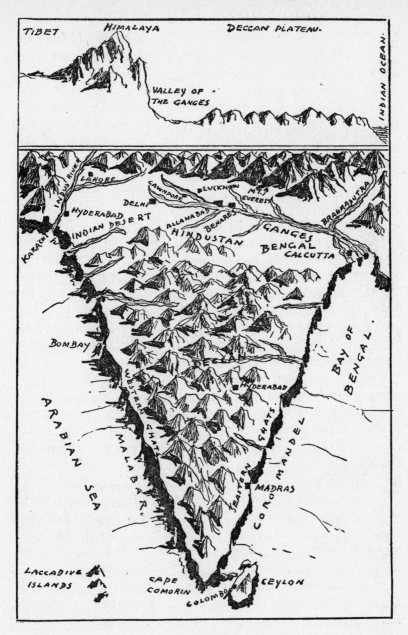

India

layas, if they were a European mountain-range, would run from Calais to the Black Sea. The Himalayas have forty peaks which are higher than the highest mountain of Europe. Their glaciers are on the average four times as long as the glaciers of the Alps.

India is one of the hottest countries on earth and at the same time in several parts it has the records for the world's annual rainfall (1270 cm. per annum). It has a population of over 350,000,000 people who speak 150 different languages and dialects. Nine-tenths of them still depend for their livelihood upon their own crops and when the annual rainfall is insufficient, they die of starvation at a rate of 2,000,000 per year. (I am giving you the figures for the decade between 1890 and 1900.) But now that the English have stamped out the plague, have made an end to inter-racial warfare, have built vast irrigation works and have introduced the first rudiments of hygiene (paid for of course by the Indians themselves) they are increasing at such a rate that soon they will be just as badly off as they were in the days when pestilence and hunger and the death-rate of their babies kept the ghats of Benares working twenty-four hours each day.

The big rivers of India run parallel with the mountain-ranges. In the west it is the Indus which runs first of all through the Punjab and then breaks through the mountains of the north, where it provided the prospective conquerors from northern Asia with a convenient passage-way to the heart of Hindustan. As for the Ganges, the holy river of the Hindus, it follows a course which runs almost due east. Before it reaches the Gulf of Bengal, the Ganges is joined by the Brahmaputra which also takes its origin among the peaks of the Himalayas and which runs due east until it is forced to make a detour by the Khasi Hills, changes its course from east to west and shortly afterwards joins the Ganges.

The valleys of the Ganges and the Brahmaputra are the most densely populated part of all India. Only in China are there a few spots where quite so many millions of people must fight each other for the barest necessities of life. On the western banks of the moist and marshy delta of these two enormous rivers lies the city of Calcutta, the chief manufacturing center of India.

As for the products of the Ganges valley, more commonly known as Hindustan, or the land of the true Hindus, they are numerous and would probably be profitable if that whole part of the world did not suffer so hopelessly from chronic overpopulation. In the first place, there is rice. The people of India and Japan and Java do not eat rice because they happen to be so fond of it, but they eat rice because rice yields more food per square mile (and per square foot and per square inch) than any other plant that has thus far been domesticated.

The cultivation of rice is both difficult and messy. That is not a pleasant word, but it happens to be the only word that will adequately describe a procedure which forces hundreds of millions of men and women to spend the greater part of their time wading through mud and liquid manure. For the rice is originally sown in mud. When the little plants are about nine inches high they are dug out by hand and transplanted into flooded fields which must remain under water until it is time for the harvest, when the disgusting pap is allowed to run away by means of a highly complicated system of drainage ditches until it finally reaches the Ganges. At this point the Ganges provides both bathing and drinking water for the pious who have gathered together in Benares, the Rome of the Hindus and probably the oldest city in the world. By this time that putrid liquid has acquired such a degree of holiness that it can whiten sins which no other form of ablution could possibly hope to cleanse.

Another product of the Ganges valley is jute, a vegetable fibre which was first sent to Europe a century and a half ago to be used as a substitute for cotton and flax. Jute is the inner bark of a plant which needs almost as much moisture as rice. The bark itself has to be soaked in water for weeks before the fibre can be extracted and sent to the Calcutta factories to be changed into ropes and jute bags and a coarse sort of clothing which the natives wear.

Then there is the indigo plant from which we used to get our

blue color until the recent discovery that it could be extracted
much more economically from coal-tar.

Finally there is opium, which was originally grown to deaden
the pain of that rheumatism which was inevitable in a country
where the greater part of the population spent so much of its time
slushing knee-deep through mud, cultivating its meagre daily
portion of rice.

Outside of the valley on the slopes of the hills, tea plantations

Rice

have taken the place of the old forests. For the shrub which produces these tiny but valuable leaves needs a great deal of hot
moisture and therefore grows best on mountain slopes where the
water does not hurt the tender roots.

Southward of the Ganges valley lies the triangular plateau of
Deccan which has three different types of vegetation. The northern mountains and those of the west are the center for the trade
in teakwood, a very durable sort of timber which does not warp
or shrink and which does not corrode iron. It used to be in great
demand for ship-building purposes until the introduction of the

iron steamer, but is still used for a number of purposes. The interior of Deccan, which has very little rain and is another dreaded hunger spot, raises cotton and a very little wheat.

As for the coastal regions, Malabar on the west and Coromandel on the east, they enjoy enough rain to support a large population providing them amply with rice and millet, a sort of grain which we import for chicken feed but which the natives of India eat instead of bread.

The Deccan is the only part of India where coal and iron and gold are found, but these deposits have never yet been seriously exploited, for the rivers of Deccan have too many rapids to be of any use, and the construction of railroads would hardly pay in a part of the world where the natives, being totally without worldly goods, never stir beyond their own villages.

The island of Ceylon, east of Cape Comorin, is really a part of the Indian peninsula. The Palk Strait which separates it from Deccan is so filled with reefs that it must be dredged continually in order to be kept navigable. The reefs and sandbanks which form a sort of natural bridge between Ceylon and the mainland are called Adam's Bridge, because Adam and Eve escaped that way from Paradise after they had incurred the wrath of God by their disobedience. For according to the people of this part of the world, Ceylon was the original Paradise. It still is a Paradise compared to the rest of India. Not only on account of the climate and its fertility and the abundance (but not superabundance) of rain and its moderate temperature, but because it has escaped one of the worst evils of India. By remaining faithful to Buddhism, which the Indians rejected as being of such sublime spiritual value as to be entirely beyond the grasp of the average man, it has escaped the rigors of the caste system which until very recently was an inseparable part of the Hindu religion.

Geography and religion are much more closely connected than we usually suppose. In India, where everything is done on a superlative scale, religion has since thousand of years dominated Man's mind so completely and absolutely that it has become an integral part of everything the Hindu says and thinks and does and eats and drinks or carefully avoids to say or do or eat or drink.

In other countries, too, religion has often interfered with the normal development of life. The Chinese, with their veneration for the departed ancestors, bury grandpa and grandma on the southern slopes of their mountains. That leaves them only the cold and wind-swept northern slopes open for the cultivation of their daily bread. As a result of this otherwise highly laudable affection for the departed relatives, their own children starve to death or are sold into slavery. Indeed almost every race (we ourselves included) is handicapped by strange taboos or mysterious ancient laws of divine origin which quite frequently interfere with the progress of the whole nation.

In order to understand how religion has affected the Hindu country, we must go back to almost prehistoric times, to at least thirty centuries before the first of the Greeks had reached the shores of the Aegean Sea.

At that time the Indian peninsula was inhabited by a race of dark-skinned people, the Dravidians, who were probably the original inhabitants of the Deccan. The Aryan stock (the same stock from which we ourselves have sprung) divided itself into two groups and left its ancient home in central Asia in search of more agreeable climes. One part moved westward and settled down in Europe, afterwards crossing the ocean and taking possession of northern America. The other trekked southwards through the mountain passes between the Hindu Kush and the Himalayas and took possession of the valleys of the Indus and the Ganges and the Brahmaputra and from there penetrated into the plateau of Deccan. By following the coastal region between the western Ghats and the Arabian Sea they finally reached southern India and Ceylon.

The newcomers, being infinitely better armed than the natives, treated the latter as the stronger races have always treated the weaker ones. They spoke derisively of them as the Black Men, took their rice fields away from them, stole their women whenever their own supply ran out (the trip across the Khyber

Pass was too difficult to let them bring many women all the way from central Asia), killed them whenever they showed the least signs of rebellion, and forced the survivors to retire to the most undesirable parts of the peninsula where they could live or

India is full of Indians

starve as they wanted. But there were by far more Dravidians than Aryans and as a result there was a constant menace that the lower form of civilization would influence the higher one. The only way by which this could be prevented was by keeping the Black Man strictly in his place.

Now the Aryans, like all the people of our race, have always had a tendency towards dividing society into a number of sharply differentiated social layers or castes. The idea of "caste" is known all over the world and it exists in America even in this year of enlightenment. It runs all the way from our discrimination against the Jews, based upon our unwritten code of social prejudice, to the formal laws of certain southern states which force Negroes to ride in Jim Crow cars. New York is a proverbially broad-minded city but I would not for the life of me know where to take a dark-skinned friend (Negro or Hindu or even Javanese) for dinner, and our trains pay homage to our feeling of caste by providing us with Pullman cars and day-coaches. I don't know much about the caste system of the Negroes in Harlem, but I have seen enough of the mortification of German-Jewish families when their daughters married men of Polish-Jewish descent to realize how wide-spread this feeling of "being something different from the common run of humanity" is in all of us.

But with us the caste system has never developed into a hard and fast rule of social and economic behavior. The doors leading from one class to another are supposed to be kept carefully closed but we all know that those who can push hard enough or who have a little golden key or who are merely able to make enough noise banging the windows outside will sooner or later be admitted. The conquering Aryans of the Indies, on the other hand, had the doors leading from one class to another filled up with masonry; and from that moment on each group of society was locked up in its own little compartment and it has been forced to stay there ever since.

Now a system like that is never an accident. People don't just suddenly invent it to please themselves or to be nasty to their neighbors. In India it was the result of fear. The priests and the warriors and the farmers and the day-laborers, the original classes of the Aryan conquerors, were of course hopelessly outnumbered by the Dravidians whose country they had just taken away. They were bound to take some desperate measure by which to keep the black man in "his proper place". But when they had done this, they went one step further, a step which no other race has ever quite dared to take. They gave their artificial "caste" system a religious twist and decreed that Brahmanism was to be the exclusive possession of the three upper classes, leaving their humbler brethren to shift for themselves outside the true spiritual pale. And thereupon, in order to keep themselves free from the defiling touch of all people of humbler birth, each individual caste surrounded itself by such a complicated barrier of ritual ceremonies and sacred usages that finally no one but a native was able to find his way in that maze of meaningless "verbotens".

If you want to know how such a system would work out in practical every-day life, try to imagine what would have happened to our own civilization if nobody during the last three thousand years had been allowed to proceed beyond the status of his father, grandfather or great-grandfather. What would have become of the personal initiative of the individual?

There are signs all around that India is on the eve of a great social and spiritual awakening, but until very recently such a change was deliberately held back by those who dominated all classes of Indian society, by the Brahmans, the hereditary members of the highest of all castes, that of the priests. The faith of which they were the undisputed leaders was known by the rather vague name of Brahmanism. Brahma, around whose personality this religion was built up, might be called the Zeus or Jupiter of the Hindu Olympus, the divine essence enhancing all creation, the beginning and end of all things. But Brahma, as a mere all-embodying idea, was much too vague, too unsubstantial for the average person, and therefore, while he continued to be worshipped in a general way as a venerable old gentleman who had done his duty when he created this world, the actual management of our planet was thought to have been surrendered to certain of Brahma's deputies, a number of Gods and Devils of not quite such excellent social standing as Brahma himself, but relatives of the All-Highest nevertheless, and as such to be treated with the utmost consideration.

That opened the door wide for the introduction of all sorts of strange, supernatural creatures, like Siva and Vishnu and a whole army of spirits and spooks and ghouls. They introduced the fear element into Brahmanism. People no longer tried to be good because being good was in itself something after which Man should strive but because it was the only way in which he could hope to escape the wrath of all the evil ogres.

Buddha, the great reformer who was born six centuries before Christ and who knew what a noble thing Brahmanism in its purer form could be, tried to make the prevailing creed of his day the spiritual power it had been once upon a time. But although at first he was victorious, his ideas proved too unpractical, too noble, too elevated for the vast majority of his fellow-countrymen. As soon as the first enthusiasm had died down, the old Brahmans returned in full force. It is only during the last fifty years that the leaders of India have come to realize that a religion based (as far as the man in the street is concerned) almost completely upon ritual and empty ceremonial acts of devotion must eventually perish as a hollow tree must perish when it no longer is able to extract its nourishment from the living earth. And Hinduism is no longer that dead and hideous spiritual affliction which it may have been a few generations ago. The doors and windows of the old temples are being opened up wide. The younger men and women of India are conscious of the disaster that might have destroyed them if, divided against themselves, they had been unable to offer a united front against the foreign master. Strange things are happening along the banks of the Ganges. When strange things happen among 350,000,000 people, they are apt to form a new chapter in the history of the world.

India, although it has several large towns, is still essentially a country of villages, for 71% of the people continue to live in the country. The rest are spread among the cities of which you should at least know the names. There is Calcutta, at the mouth of the Ganges and Brahmaputra. It began as an insignificant fishing village, but during the eighteenth century it became the

center for Clive's operations against the French and developed
into the leading harbor of all India. It lost a great deal of its
former importance when the Suez Canal was opened, because
steamers found it more convenient to go directly to Bombay or
to Karachi than to Calcutta when they happened to have a cargo
for the Indus region or the Punjab. Bombay on its little island
is also a creation of the East India Company, which intended to
use it as a naval base and a harbor of export for the Deccan cotton trade. It was so eminently suited for this purpose that it attracted settlers from all over Asia and became the home of the
last remaining group of followers of the Persian prophet,
Zoroaster. These Parsees belong to the richest and most intelligent group of natives. Their worship of fire as something holy
which must not be defiled, makes it impossible for them to burn
their dead. Hence Bombay has attracted a sort of lugubrious attention as the city where the Parsee corpses are thrown to the
vultures, a form of extinction which is so swift that it seems almost preferable to the slower method of being eaten by ordinary worms.

On the eastern shores of the Deccan peninsula lies Madras,
the main port of the coast of Coromandel. The French city of
Pondicherry, a little towards the south, is a reminder of the
days when the French were the most serious rivals of the English and when Dupleix and Clive fought for the possession of
the whole of India, in that war that led up to the ghastly incident
of the Black Hole of Calcutta.

But most of the important cities are naturally situated in the
valley of the Ganges. In the west there is first of all Delhi, the
old residence of the Mogul emperors who had chosen this city
because it commanded the entrance gate from central Asia into
the valley of the Ganges so thoroughly that he who was master
of Delhi was also master of all India. Further down the river
lies Agra, the residence of four members of the Mogul dynasty,
one of whom erected the Taj-Mahal in memory of a woman
whom he had greatly loved. Still further towards the south

is Allahabad, a holy city of the Mohammedans, as the name implies. In this same neighborhood lie Lucknow and Cawnpore, well known for their connection with the great mutiny of 1857.

Then further down the river we reach Benares, the Rome and Mecca of all good Hindus who not only come here to bathe in the holy waters of the river but also to die that they may be burned in one of the ghats on its shores and their ashes strewn upon the river of their desire.

But I had better stop right here. Whenever you touch upon a subject of India, whether you approach it as an historian, a chemist, a geographer, an engineer or a mere traveller, you find yourself right in the heart of profound moral and spiritual problems. And we people of the west should proceed carefully when we enter into this labyrinth in which we are both strangers and newcomers.

Two thousand years before the learned councils of holy men in Nicea and Constantinople tried to formulate the creed which afterwards was to conquer the western world, the ancestors of these people about whom I am writing in so familiar a fashion had already settled obscure points of doctrine and faith which to this very day disturb the minds of my own neighbors and will probably continue to disturb them for another dozen centuries or so. It is easy, far too easy, to condemn things that are strange to us. Most of what I know about India is strange to me and gives me a feeling of discomfort, a bewildered sense of uneasy irritation.

But then I remember that I used to feel the same way towards my grandfather and grandmother.

And now at last I am beginning to realize that they were right. Or at least, that, if they were not always entirely right, neither were they always as absolutely wrong as I used to think them to be. It was a hard lesson. But it tended to teach me a little humility. And Heaven knows, I needed it!

XXXVI

BURMA, SIAM, ANAM AND MALACCA, WHICH OCCUPY THE OTHER GREAT SOUTHERN PENINSULA OF ASIA

THE peninsula which contains these four ancient kingdoms, independent, semi-independent and subject, is four times as large as the Balkan peninsula. The first of the four when we start from the west, Burma, enjoyed complete independence until the year 1885 when the English, to the general approval of the natives and the world at large, sent the last of the local rulers into exile and annexed the country and made it part of their empire. Nobody objected much except the king himself but he was a true representative of a type that has no longer any reason to exist, except in the movies, the proverbial "Oriental potentate" who as a rule was nothing but an undetected lunatic. Needless to say that he was not even a local product but an import from the north. The peninsula as a whole has suffered a good deal from that kind of gentry. The situation of the local mountain-ranges was chiefly responsible. Whereas India was cut off from the north by high mountains which ran from east to west and therefore enjoyed a certain natural protection, the whole of this unfortunate peninsula is taken up by five independent mountain ridges which run from south to north and thereby offer almost ideal means of access to any one wishing to move from the harsh grass-land of central Asia to the rich coast-land of the Bay of Bengal and the Gulf of Siam and the South China Sea. And the sort of men bred by central Asia we have already met wherever our maps were dotted by an abundance of ruined cities and pillaged farms.

Lest you should shed unnecessary tears over the fate of the last of the independent Burmese potentates, know ye that in order to celebrate his accession to the throne he had revived the good old Asiatic custom of killing all his relatives. The Turkish sultans had always done that as a mere matter of precaution, like taking out accident insurance when you are elected president of a South American republic. But in the eighties of the last century the story of these hundred odd brothers and cousins and nephews, slaughtered in cold blood, did not read quite so well, and an English governor took the place of the former monarch. Since then the country, whose population consists of only three percent Hindus but ninety percent Buddhists, has greatly prospered and the Irrawaddy River, which is navigable all the way from Rangoon to Mandalay, has become an artery of trade such as it had never been before. It has seen more rice boats and oil tankers and ships of all sorts than ever before during its long history.

As for Siam, the country just east of Burma and separated from it by the Dawna Range and the Tanen-Tanng-gyi Mountains, it owes its continued independence to a combination of circumstances of which the mutual jealousy between England in the west and France in the east is most certainly not one of the least important. And furthermore, Siam has been singularly fortunate in its rulers. Old King Chulalongkorn, who held the throne for over forty years, was a descendant of a Chinaman who during the latter half of the eighteenth century had delivered Siam from the Burmese. By cleverly playing his western neighbors against those from the east, and by a few trivial concessions and above all things by not surrounding himself with English and French advisers but by choosing his experts from among the much less dangerous smaller nations, this enlightened Siamese reduced the number of analphabets in his domains from 90% to 20%, founded a university, developed railroads, made the Menam River navigable for over 400 miles, installed an excellent postal and telegraphic system and trained his army sufficiently well to make himself not only a desirable ally but also a potentially dangerous enemy.

Bangkok on the Menam delta grew until it finally had almost a million inhabitants, a great many of whom still live on rafts

anchored in the river, which gives Bangkok the aspect of a sort
of eastern Venice. Instead of closing the country to foreign immigration, the industrious Chinese were liberally encouraged to
settle down in the capital and they now form one-ninth of the
total population and have greatly contributed towards making
Siam one of the most important rice exporting nations. The interior is still densely covered with very valuable forests and
teakwood is an important article of export. And good luck or
good sense made the Siamese rulers retain at least a part of the
Malacca peninsula which contains the richest tin deposits of the
world.

On the whole, however, the government of Siam has been
opposed to the industrialization of the country. The inhabitants
of all tropical lands will have to remain primarily interested in
agriculture and other simple pursuits if they wish to survive.
Siam seems to be one of the few Asiatic countries where the desirability of such a policy has been understood. Let Europe have
its factories and slums, as long as Asia can keep its villages and
fields. They may not be the sort of villages the westerling likes,
but they suit the eastern temperament, and the factory does not.

By the way, the agricultural riches of Siam are somewhat different from those of most other countries. Outside of a million
hogs, raised by the Chinese, the country can boast of no less than
6,000,000 tame buffaloes and 6822 elephants, which are in
domestic service and hire out as derricks and trucks.

French Indo-China, the name usually given to all the French
possessions in the peninsula, consists of five parts. The first one
of these, going from south to north, is Cambodia, which occupies
the valley of the big Mekong River as far as the delta. It raises
cotton and grows pepper. Nominally it is still a kingdom, but
under French supervision. In the interior, in the midst of the
dense forests just north of the great lake called Tonlé-Sap, lie
some of the most interesting ruins that have ever been uncov-
ered. They were built by a mysterious race, the Khmers, of
whom we know remarkably little. During the ninth century of
our era, these Khmers built themselves a capital in northern

Cambodia called Angkor. It was no small affair, for the walls formed a square each side of which was not less than two miles long and thirty feet high. At first, under the influence of Hindu missionaries, the Khmers were Brahmans, but in the tenth century Buddhism was accepted as the official religion of the state. The spiritual explosion caused by this change from Brahmanism to Buddhism found an expression in the construction of a vast number of temples and palaces, all of which were built between the twelfth and fifteenth centuries when Angkor, the capital, was destroyed, leaving behind those most stupendous architectural ruins, compared to which the far famed efforts of our own Mayans were the work of simple-minded beginners.

There is a theory that Angkor was originally built on the sea and long before the delta of the Mekong had been formed. But in that case, the sea would have retreated more than 300 miles. That would be a record. For in historical times the sea has never retreated much more than five miles in the case of Ravenna and seven miles in the case of Pisa. The why and how and wherefore of Angkor will probably always remain a secret. But here stood a city that was as important in its time as New York is today. And it is gone. It has become a subject for picture postal cards, sold at a penny a piece to the visitors of the Paris colonial exhibition. And yet, once upon a time, it was a center of civilization while Paris was still a collection of evil-smelling mud hovels. It is all very strange!

As for the delta of the Mekong, today it is part of the French colony of Cochin-China which the French occupied in 1867 when their imperial prestige needed a little boosting after the disastrous failure of the great Mexican expedition. It has one excellent harbor, Saigon, where a few thousand French officials eagerly await the day when they can return to the home country to rest in peace and honor from their difficult labors in administering the four million Cochin-China entrusted to their care.

To the east of Cochin-China lies Anam, which also continues to be a kingdom although since 1886 it has enjoyed the "protection" of the French. The interior produces timber but the coun-

The mountain passes of Asia

try is mountainous and has no roads and has therefore remained almost completely undeveloped.

Tongking in the north is much more important because it not only has an excellent river, the Song-Koi, but also on account of the presence of coal and cement. It really is a part of China and as such raises and exports cotton, silk and sugar. Its capital is Hanoi which since 1902 is the chief seat of government for all the French possessions in Indo-China. These include, beside the four countries just mentioned, a narrow strip of land in the interior, called Laos, annexed in 1893, and which I set down here merely for the sake of vital statistics. The southernmost part of this big peninsula is divided into two parts. The so-called "Federated Malay States" consist of four small semi-independent principalities under British protection, and the rest is a crown colony known administratively as the Straits Settlements. It was exceedingly important for England to get hold of the Malay peninsula, for the mountains, which sometimes rise to a height of 8000 feet, contain some very rich tin deposits and the climate allows a vast variety of tropical products to be grown here at practically no cost. Rubber, coffee, pepper, tapioca and gambier (necessary in the dyers' trade) are exported in large quantities from Penang, on the straits of Malacca, and from Singapore, a city of over half a million inhabitants, situated on a small island which controls all the great sea routes between north and south and east and west.

Singapore, the Lion City, is almost as old as Chicago, having been built by that famous Sir Stamford Raffles who foresaw the strategic importance of this point while administering the Dutch colonial possessions during the time Holland was part of the Napoleonic empire. In 1819 Singapore was a jungle. Today it has more than 500,000 inhabitants, the strangest variety and hodge-podge of races and languages to be found almost anywhere in the Orient. It is as strongly fortified as Gibraltar and is the terminal station of a railroad line which connects it with Bangkok in Siam, but not as yet with Rangoon in Burma. It will play a great role when the inevitable clash between the east and the west finally takes place. In anticipation of that event, it maintains a set of bar-rooms, the splendor of which is famous all over the Orient, and loses almost as much money on the annual races as the city of Dublin.

XXXVII

THE REPUBLIC OF CHINA, THE GREAT PENINSULA OF
EASTERN ASIA

CHINA is a very large country. It has a circumference of 8000 miles, a distance about equal to the diameter of the globe, and it is larger than the whole European continent.

The Chinese people form fully one-fifth of the total population of our planet and they knew how to use gunpowder and how to write letters at a time when our ancestors still painted their faces a pale blue and hunted the wild boar with a stone axe. To give an adequate description of such a country in a few pages is out of the question. All I can give you is a sketch, an outline. The details (if you are interested) you can afterwards fill in by yourself, for there is enough literature on China to upholster two or three libraries.

China, like India, is a peninsula, but a semi-circular peninsula, not a triangular one. In another very important way it is different from India. No obliging mountain-range cuts it off from the rest of the world. On the contrary, the mountains of China resemble the fingers of a hand stretching out westward. In consequence thereof, the rich Chinese plains bordering upon the Yellow Sea have at all times been wide open to the hardy pioneers of central Asia.

In order to overcome this handicap, the Chinese emperors of the third century before our era (the period during which Rome and Carthage fought for the mastery of the Mediterranean) constructed a gigantic wall, 1500 miles long and 20 feet wide and more than 30 feet high, which ran all the way from the Gulf of Liao-tung to Kiayu-Kwan, just west of Su-chow on the borders of the Gobi Desert.

341

This granite barrier has done its duty well and honorably. In the seventeenth century it fell before the onslaughts of the Manchus. All the same, a fortification which has held its own for almost twenty centuries is no mere trifle. Those we build nowadays are useless after ten years and have then got to be renewed at enormous cost.

As for China proper, not counting in Mongolia and Manchuria (which at the time of writing this chapter seems to be rapidly falling into the hands of the Japanese) and Tibet and Turkestan, it is a vast circle neatly divided into three almost equal parts by the Yangtsze-Kiang in the south and the Hwang-Ho in the north. The northern part, in which Peking is situated, has very cold winters and moderately hot summers, as a result of which the people eat millet and no rice. The central part, protected against the winds from the north by the Tsing-ling-shan range, has a much warmer climate and a much denser population which eats rice and does not know the sight or taste of grain. The third part, south China, has warm winters and very hot and moist summers and raises everything that will grow in the tropics.

Northern China is again divided into two parts, the mountain regions of the west and the plains of the east. These mountain regions of the west are the famous loess country. Loess is a very fine sort of loam, looking a yellowish gray, and it is very porous, as a result of which the rain of Heaven disappears as fast as it touches the earth, while rivers and brooks cut themselves deep ravines which makes travel from one part of the country to the other as difficult as it is in Spain.

The plain of the east is situated on the Gulf of Chih-li which is so rapidly being filled up with the deposits carried down by the Hwang-Ho that it is almost unnavigable and has no good harbor. A little further towards the north there is another river, much smaller than the Hwang-Ho but quite as useless from the point of view of navigation. That is the Pei-Ho, which has the distinction of being the Chicago River of Peking, the great drainage canal which looks after the sewage disposal of the Chinese capital. As conditions in China change from hour to

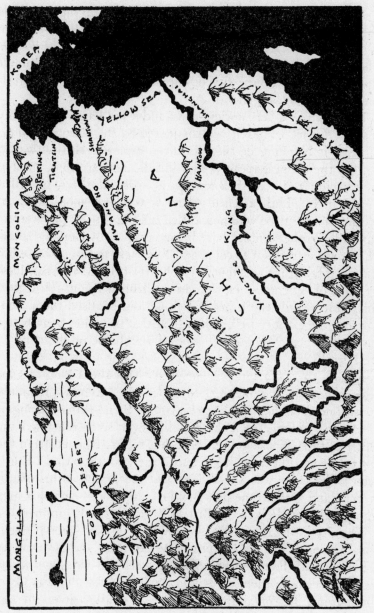

The Big Chinese Rivers

hoŭr I will merely say that Peking has been the capital of the Celestial Empire for nine centuries, or ever since the days when William the Bastard conquered England, but that I have no idea whether at the time this book goes to press it will be the Chinese capital, a mere Chinese city or the temporary or definite residence of a Japanese general.

It is however a very ancient town and it has seen a great many ups and downs. In 986 it was conquered by the Tartars who rebaptised it Nanking or the "southern capital". In the twelfth century the Chinese recaptured it but did not care to retain it as their capital and made it a second-rate provincial center, called Yen-shan Fu. Half a century later it was once more taken by another Tartar tribe who now called it Chung-tu or the "central capital". Another century later it was occupied by Genghis Khan, who however refused to come and live there in fatuous ease but remained faithful to his tent in the heart of the Mongolian Desert. One of his successors, the famous Kublai Khan, felt differently. He rebuilt the ruins of Peking and baptised them Yenking or "the great court", although at that time they were better known by their Mongolian name of Cambaluc or the "city of the Khan".

Finally these Tartars were expelled too, and a king of Chinese origin, the first one of the famous Ming dynasty, mounted the throne. Yenking or the "great court" then became Peking or the "north court". As Peking it has ever since remained the center of the Chinese government, but so far removed from the rest of the world that it was not until the year 1860 that a European ambassador was allowed to visit the capital in his official capacity and with all the pomp and circumstance befitting a man whose father had given the British Museum the Elgin marbles.

The city in the hey-day of its power must have been tremendously strong. The walls were sixty feet thick and almost fifty feet high and defended by square towers and gateways which were fortresses in themselves. On the inside, the city was like a Chinese puzzle, containing a number of smaller cities, the one inside of the other, an imperial city, and a Manchu city and a

Chinese city and, after the middle of the nineteenth century, a
foreign city.

Until the Boxer outbreak of 1900 the foreign diplomatic representatives lived in a small square of their own just between the

The Chinese wall is the only structure made by
human hands that would be visible by the
astronomers of the moon

Manchu city and the Chinese city. After the siege, this diplomatic ghetto was strongly fortified and heavily garrisoned with
troops of the different countries to prevent a recurrence of this
most unfortunate incident. Peking, of course, contains a number
of palaces and temples. But here I would like to draw attention
to a very interesting difference between the temperaments of
the people of China and those of India which explains to a certain degree why these two countries have practically nothing in

common except that they are both of them hopelessly overpopu-
lated.

The Hindus have always taken their Gods very seriously and
when they built them a temple it must be the biggest, the most
expensive and the showiest temple the money of the poor sweating peasants could buy. "Not a cent for public improvements,
but millions for the Gods!" was the slogan of the Brahmans. The
Chinese are nominally Buddhists but every Chinaman from the
humblest laundry-man in Mott Street to the most powerful of
the old Mandarins had fallen under the influence of that shrewd
old sage, Kung-fu-tsze or Confucius, who during the second half
of the sixth century had preached his gospel of common, every-
day horse-sense without wasting much time upon vague discus-
sions about the Life Hereafter. And it was completely in keeping with the Confucian notions about the "sensible thing to do"
that the Chinese rulers spent the greater part of their revenue
upon public improvements, upon canals and irrigation dams and
Chinese walls and river improvements, but just enough upon
their temples and shrines not to make the Gods feel that they
were in any way being slighted.

As the ancient Chinese were a people of tremendous artistic
ability, they could achieve much more satisfactory results and
at a much smaller cost than the natives of the Ganges valley. It
is true that nowhere in China does the traveller find anything
at all comparable to the vast structures of India. A few gigantic
statues of animals guarding the gardens of the Ming rulers,
some sixty miles north of Peking, and here and there a large
Buddha. That is all. The rest is of modest dimensions, albeit of
excellent proportions. But curiously enough, the art of China
appeals to the people of the west much more than does the art
of India. Chinese paintings and sculptures and pottery and
lacquer-work fit into a European or American home, whereas
their Indian counterparts disturb the harmony and are slightly
upsetting, even when seen in a museum.

To the modern business world China is important because it
has very large coal deposits and the second largest iron deposits

in the world. When the English and German and American mines get exhausted, we can still go to the province of Shan-si to keep warm.

To the south-east of the province of Chih-li lies the province of Shan-tung with the peninsula of that name which separates the Gulf of Chih-li from the Yellow Sea. This part of China is very mountainous, except for the valley of the Hwang-Ho, which formerly ran due south into the Yellow Sea. But it changed its course suddenly in 1852, and that little affair showed us that a flood in China really meant a flood. In order to find a parallel for the Hwang-Ho's behavior we would have to imagine the Rhine suddenly making up its mind to flow into the Baltic or the Seine deciding to run into the North Sea instead of the Gulf of Biscay. As the Hwang-Ho has changed its mouth ten times since the end of the seventeenth century we are by no means certain that the present channel will be definite. Dikes and dams which in other parts of the world are apt to keep a river within bounds are of no avail against such rivers as the Hwang-Ho and the Yang-tsze, for the dikes through which the river broke in the year 1852 were fifty feet high and they tore apart like tissue paper.

And then there is something else that makes these rivers such a nuisance. You must have heard the Chinese referred to as the yellow race and you must have seen articles in the newspapers about the Yellow Peril, etc., etc. As a rule we associate the idea of yellow and Chinese with the color of a Chinaman's face. But when the emperors of China called themselves Hwang-ti, which meant Lord of the Yellow Earth, they were not thinking of their subjects but of the land inhabited by these subjects. The yellow loess mud carried down by the Hwang-Ho turns everything in northern China yellow—the water of the river, the water of the sea, the roads, the houses, the fields, the clothes of the men and women. And it is that yellow dust which has given its name to a race which for the rest is really not much more yellow than the average city dweller of the west.

In order to permit his subjects to proceed from northern

China to central and southern China without running the risk of a long sea voyage, one of the Chinese emperors who lived during the thirteenth century ordered a canal to be built that should connect the Hwang-Ho with the Yangtsze-Kiang. It was more than a thousand miles long and fulfilled its purpose faithfully until the year 1852 when the Hwang-Ho moved from the Yellow Sea to the Gulf of Chih-li and the canal was destroyed together with the old river bed. But this Grand Canal, the longest in the world, shows that the ancient rulers of the land were men of enlightened views.

But to return to the peninsula of Shan-tung. Its hard granite coast has been responsible for the formation of several very important harbors. One of those, Wei-hai-wei, just east of Chi-fu, was until recently in English hands. The British had "rented" it from China when Russia occupied Port Arthur on the other side of the Gulf of Chih-li to use it as a naval base and a station of their Trans-Siberian railroad. The "renting contract" stipulated that England should withdraw as soon as the Russians had disappeared from the Liao-tung peninsula. But when Japan took Port Arthur in 1905, the English remained. The Germans, not to be outdone, must then occupy the bay of Kiao-Chow, further towards the south, and the city of Tsing-tao, both of them also parts of the Shan-tung peninsula. This meant that the Great War also had its reverberations in the Far East. Germans and Britons fought for the possession of something which belonged to neither of them and, as usually happens in such cases, a third party, the Japanese, got away with the stolen goods.

In order to regain a little of the goodwill of the Chinese, Wei-hai-wei and Kiao-Chow have since been returned to China. But if Japan succeeds in taking Manchuria, the old game will probably begin all over again. Look for the details in the next edition.

In the east central China consists of a wide and fertile plain which is really the continuation of the plain of northern China, but the interior is mountainous. Through these mountains the Yangtsze-Kiang wends its tortuous way until at last it reaches the East China Sea. It takes its origin in the province of Sze-chuen, a region almost as large as France, but supporting a much larger population as the red soil is exceedingly fertile. Several mountain-ranges running from south to north cut it almost completely off from the rest of the world. As a result it has suffered but little from the visitation of the White Man and is distinctly more Chinese than the rest of China.

Continuing its course towards the sea, the Yangtsze next traverses the province of Hu-peh where the famous city of Hankow is situated. This was the center of the revolution of 1911 which upset the last emperor of the Manchu dynasty and turned the oldest monarchy in the world into a republic. Up to Hankow the Yangtsze is navigable for sea-going vessels with a displacement of not more than 1000 tons. Below Hankow, the river is the main artery of commerce for central China until it reaches Shanghai, the center of China's foreign trade and one of the first Chinese harbors which was opened to foreign commerce at the conclusion of the so-called "opium war" between England and China in the year 1840–1842.

To the south of the Yangtsze delta lies Hang-chow, which Marco Polo knew as Kinsai, and in the east Su-chow, the name of which suggests tea. The suggestion is correct. The lower part of the Yangtsze valley is very fertile and it was for this reason that Nanking, which is situated where the Yangtsze begins its delta, was for a long time not only the most important city of central China but also the residence of its emperor.

Partly on account of its historical past and partly on account of its strategic position, half-way between Canton and Peking, and partly because it is not directly menaced by the guns of foreign warships, the city of Nanking was chosen as the center of that government which at the moment of writing (Jan. 2, 1932, seven minutes past midnight) seems to be the "official government" of China.

As for southern China, it is a mountainous country and, although it raises tea and silk and cotton, it has always been a comparatively poor region. Once upon a time it was covered with forests, but the forests were cut down and the soil was washed away by the rain, and the bare rocks remained. Hence wholesale emigration to all parts of the world which have not yet passed laws restricting the number of Chinese visitors.

The most important city in southern China is Canton, which is the main harbor of import into China just as Shanghai is the most important center for export to Europe. At the mouth of the Canton River (the city itself is a few miles inland) lie two foreign possessions. On the right bank, Macao, all that remains of the Portuguese possessions in China and now merely a sort of oriental Monte Carlo, and Hong-Kong, a city which the English took during the opium war and have kept ever since.

Of the two islands off the coast of southern China, Hai-nan is still Chinese, but Formosa, an old Dutch colony, has belonged to Japan since the Chinese-Japanese War of 1894–1895.

Ninety percent of the Chinese are, always have been and probably always will be farmers who live on their own products and starve when there is a bad season. But forty-eight harbors have been opened up for the foreign trade and their main exports are silk and tea and cotton. Curiously enough, there is no export of opium. The Chinese emperors have always tried to protect their people against this unfortunate habit-forming drug and gradually the old poppy fields have been changed into cotton fields.

As for railroads, the Chinese fought the idea longer than any other nation because, with their respect for the memory of their parents and ancestors, they feared to upset the peaceful slumbers of these departed worthies when the engines should come thundering down the roads of iron. The few miles built in 1875 between Shanghai and Wu Sung, its harbor, caused such a storm of protest that they were immediately discontinued. And even today the Chinese railroads describe wide circles around all cemeteries. Still, there are now over 10,000 miles of railroad in actual use and the bridge across the Hwang-Ho near Tsi-nan is the biggest railroad bridge in the world.

As for China's foreign trade, almost 60% is still in the hands of England and her colonies and that probably explains why England has been obliged to discontinue her old ruthless policy towards the inhabitants of the Celestial Empire. A boycott of English goods by these industrious Celestials would mean a loss

The Grand Canal in China

of millions of dollars a day. It is good policy to keep on friendly terms with a customer who happens to represent the interests of one-fifth of the entire human race.

When the earliest ancestors of the Chinese dimly emerged from the nebulous realm of the past, they were already living on the Yellow Earth along the banks of the Hwang-Ho, north-west from the heart of the present China. The fertile loess fields must have been very desirable in the eyes of an agricultural people.

Furthermore it also settled the housing problem, for it allowed a man to dig himself a comfortable little home in the side of a convenient hill and not bother about draughty walls or a roof that leaked.

According to reliable accounts of travellers who are familiar with that part of the world, there are spots which are known to be densely populated but where one fails to see a single vestige of human habitation until the first rays of light tell of the coming of another day. Then, like so many rabbits who swarm out of their holes to enjoy the sun, those men, women and children begin their endless tasks of gathering food until eventide, when they disappear once more into the bowels of the earth.

Having occupied the mountains, the Chinese then spread eastward. The turbulent Hwang-Ho carried millions of tons of mountain loess into the plains and thereby fertilized them until they were fit to support further millions of human beings. The Chinese followed in the wake of the river and twenty centuries before the beginning of our era (1500 years before the founding of Rome) the Chinese had wandered as far as the Yangtsze and the center of their empire had been moved from the Hwang-Ho region to the great plain of central China.

During the fifth and fourth centuries before the birth of Christ, three great moral teachers arose among them, Kung-fu-tsze or Confucius, Mang-tsze or Mencius, and Lao-tsze, whose name has not been latinized. What the religious conceptions of the Chinaman were at the time these three prophets made their appearance, we do not know. Nature apparently was worshipped as the forces of Nature will always be worshipped by those who depend upon them for their living, and not Confucius nor Mencius nor Lao-tsze were religious founders in the sense of the word as applied to Christ or Buddha or Mahommed.

They merely taught a moral code based upon the acceptance of man as a pretty inferior and not very brilliant product of creation but capable of great development provided he fell into good hands and was willing to listen to the precepts of his elders and betters. From our own Christian point of view, these three can of course be accused of preaching a very worldly and decidedly materialistic doctrine. None of them said much about humility and meekness or preached that we must return good for evil. They knew that the average man was not capable of such noble and elevated deeds, and furthermore they seem to have doubted whether such a rule of conduct was really for the ultimate good of the community at large. Wherefore they suggested such things as that evil should be answered with justice and that one should pay one's bills and keep contracts and honor the memory of honorable ancestors.

These three Chinese philosophers spread their morality pretty thin but every one got at least a smear of it. I don't say that this was a better system than ours or a worse one. But it was a system not devoid of certain very definite advantages. It gave a people consisting of 400,000,000 different individuals, speaking a couple of dozen different dialects (a Chinaman from the north finds it just as hard to understand a brother Chinaman from the south as a Swede trying to make conversation with an Italian) and living under entirely different circumstances, at least one thing in common—a decidedly Chinese attitude towards the ups and downs of life, a practical philosophy of existence which will pull the humblest of coolies through hardships that would either kill the average European or American or would drive him to commit suicide.

And these ideas were sufficiently simple to be understood by almost every one. As a proof whereof I refer you to the miracles of assimilation performed by the Chinese during the 4000 years of their history. They are preposterous and at the same time fabulous. During the tenth century China became part of the greatest empire that ever existed, that Mongolian commonwealth that reached from the Baltic to the Pacific. But all those Mongolian rulers were like Kublai Khan. They ended by becoming Chinamen. After the Mongolians came the Mings (1368–1644), the last purely Chinese dynasty to rule the country. They were succeeded by a Tartar prince who came from Manchuria and who was the founder of the Manchu dynasty.

But although the Chinese, as a token of submission to their Manchu masters, were forced to grow their hair long and wear a pig-tail and shave the rest of their heads, the Manchus soon became even more Chinese than the Chinamen themselves.

After the last Manchu invasion the Chinese were left completely to themselves and by merely guarding their harbors against all foreign visitors from the west, the civilization of China had a chance to settle down for a little rest. But the moment it did this, it petrified more completely than any other country of which we have ever heard. Its political system became even more rigid than that of the old Russia of pre-revolutionary days. Literature froze, even their incomparable art became as stereotyped as that of the Byzantine mosaic makers of ancient Constantinople. Science no longer made any progress. If by chance some one still happened to invent something new it was at once discarded as foolish and undesirable, just as the medical department of our own army tried to discourage the use of chloroform because it was both new and foolish. Because they were cut off so completely from the rest of the world and never had a chance of finding out what other nations were doing, it was easy for the Chinese to convince themselves that their own methods were best, that their own army was invincible, that their own art was the most sublime art ever wrought by the hands of human beings and that their own customs and habits were so superior to those of all other nations that it was ridiculous to compare the two. Many other countries have in a mild way tried such a policy of exclusion but it has always ended in disaster.

Since the early half of the sixteenth century the Chinese had allowed a few "foreign devils", hailing from Portugal and England and Holland, to settle in two or three of their Pacific ports for the sake of the profits that were to be derived from the trade with Europe. But the social status of those unfortunate foreigners had been most unsatisfactory. They were treated like a respectable colored doctor who by chance is obliged to travel on the same boat with a delegation of the descendants of Virginia's first settlers.

When England in 1816 sent Lord Amherst (nephew of Jeffrey and the man who interviewed Napoleon on St. Helena in 1817) to ask the Son of Heaven to mitigate the hardships from which the English merchants suffered in Canton, he was told that an interview with the Celestial Majesty depended upon his willingness to kow-tow before the imperial throne. The kow-tow, which literally meant "knocking the head three times upon the ground before the sacred throne" was something which a Dutch sea-captain could afford to do, for once he had kow-towed himself out of the reception room he knew that he could take home enough tea or spices to be comfortable for the rest of his life. But the representative of His British Majesty was somewhat differently placed. Lord Amherst curtly refused and as a result was not even allowed to enter the gates of Peking.

Meanwhile Europe, growing rich in consequence of the invention of James Watt and the application of steam for the purpose of exploiting our little planet, was clamoring for new worlds to conquer. China of course was No. 1 on the list. The direct excuse for the outbreak of hostilities was not exactly flattering to the pride of the white race, least of all for that part of it which ever since 1807, when Dr. Morrison had reached Canton as the first European missionary, had been telling the Chinese what a fine thing Christianity really was and why they should give it a chance. Even those pedantic and narrow-minded Mandarins (merely a Chinese title for administrator) who then ruled China were still sufficiently steeped in the teachings of Confucius to refuse to let their people be exposed to the unlimited importation of opium. But the British India Company was making millions of pounds out of the sale of poppy-seed to the people of the Yangtsze and the Hwang-Ho. The British India Company insisted upon importing opium into China and the Chinese authorities refused to let the stuff be landed. Opium and hurt feelings then led to the war of 1840 in which the Chinese, to their dumbfounded surprise, discovered that they were absolutely no match for the despised foreigners and that during the centuries of voluntary seclusion they had dropped so far behind the rest of humanity that it was doubtful whether they would ever be able to catch up.

This fear bids fair to come true. Ever since the disastrous days of the Opium War, China has been completely at the mercy of the westerner. The Chinese people, who are apt to go on plowing and harvesting, no matter who is fighting in the adjacent fields, have at times given evidence of the fact that they are beginning to realize that something is wrong with their country. The first outbreak of discontent occurred about eighty years ago. The Chinese then blamed the disasters of their hapless land upon the "foreign" Manchu dynasty and rose up in rebellion to set themselves free.

While the Manchus were engaged in a war with England and France, southern China started the so-called Tai-ping rebellion. They ceased to shave their heads and they cut off their pig-tails, but the imperial armies, led at first by an American engineer named Ward and afterwards by an Englishman, a certain Charles George Gordon, a sincere Christian and a profound mystic, were much too powerful for the poor misguided revolutionists. The "Emperor" whom they had elected to replace the Manchus burned himself alive with all his wives and concubines in his residence in the city of Nanking. Hundreds of thousands of people were executed and Gordon returned to England to devote himself to acts of charity and piety, performed in his leisure hours when he was not drilling troops, and to prepare for his tragic end of which you shall hear in the chapter on Africa.

Then in 1875 there was a slight difference of opinion between the Manchus and Germany, and Germany sent a squadron to purify the Chinese coast of pirates. During 1884 and 1885 there was a war with France which cost the Chinese Anam and Tongking, and in 1894 there was a war with Japan, now thoroughly Europeanized, which ended with the cession of the island of Formosa.

Then began the great European rush for armaments and strategic points. The Russians took Port Arthur, the English took Wei-hai-wei, the Germans took Kiao-Chow and the French took Kiang Hung on the left bank of the Mekong River. America, which has thus far always mixed sentiment (and often, alas, sentimentality) with its foreign policies, talked vaguely about "maintaining the open door" and the European nations were turning the territory they had stolen into impregnable fortresses and closed the door whenever their uncle from across the ocean was not looking.

The Chinese people, patient and plodding though they are by nature, began to grasp the fact that they were being cheated right and left. Once more holding the foreign Manchu dynasty responsible for all their humiliations and misery, they started the unfortunate Boxer rebellion of the year 1901. They began their operations by murdering the German ambassador (their plausible excuse was that he had first struck a Chinaman) and then besieged the foreign legations in Peking. As a result an army of Russians, Japanese, Englishmen, Austrians, Germans, Italians, French and Americans marched to the relief of the sorely beset foreign quarter, saved the ministers and their families from an untimely end, and then by way of retribution plundered Peking as that rich city had never been looted before. The Forbidden City, the heart of the imperial residence, was broken into. Nothing was spared, no matter how holy it might be to the Chinese, and the German commander-in-chief, who arrived with an extra 20,000 men (when the shooting was already over but the plundering still in full swing) had been instructed by his imperial master to "follow in the footsteps of the Huns"—an unfortunate expression which came home to roost a little over a dozen years later and which was one of the worst boomerangs old Wilhelm ever sent forth during the days when he indulged in that sport in preference to his present craze for chopping wood.

Condemned to pay enormous indemnities and humiliated in every possible way by their ever more aggressive European neighbors, the Chinese people once more rose in rebellion in the year 1911 and this time they were successful, for the Manchu dynasty was abolished and China was turned into a republic.

But this time, however, the Chinese had learned the lesson that the nations of the west are not primarily interested in chapters from the writings of Confucius, but care much more for coal concessions and iron concessions and oil concessions and that therefore those possessed of these valuable raw materials must either know how to defend their property or sink it to the bottom of the ocean if they want it to be absolutely safe. In short, China began to recognize the necessity of following the example of Japan by taking a short course in "westernization". Foreign teachers were engaged from all over the world, but principally from Japan, which was nearby and handy.

In the meantime, Russia had started upon its ambitious plan to convert one-sixth of the world into an industrial state, administered according to the Gospel of Saint Marx; and Russia, being a very close neighbor of China could whisper strange words into the ears of the long-suffering coolies who had been born to sweat and work, no matter who ruled them or whether they were being exploited by the English or the French or the Japanese.

The result of all these conflicting ideas, plans and emotions is the chaos which has descended upon China since the end of the Great War, during which it was forced to take the side of the Allies in a quarrel in which as usual it had nothing to gain and a great deal to lose.

I am no prophet. I don't know what will happen during the next ten or fifteen years. Conditions probably won't change very much, for poor China tried too late to catch up with the procession. But may the good Lord have mercy upon us if she ever does, for oh, what a bill we shall have to pay then! What a bill!

XXXVIII

KOREA, MONGOLIA AND MANCHURIA, IF THE LATTER STILL EXISTS WHEN THIS BOOK IS PUBLISHED

LET us begin with a short and elementary lesson in practical economics.

The Japanese, cooped up on their little island, and as prolific as Italians, need more land. All the pretty words in the world and all the treaties in the world and all the well-meant speeches of all the well-meaning old ladies and gentlemen in the world won't change this fact. For it is really a law of Nature which states that when I am strong but hungry and find myself on a raft somewhere in mid-ocean in the company of somebody else who is weak but who has a pocket full of ham sandwiches, I will in the end get my share of those ham sandwiches, or I shall have died in the attempt. Being a decent sort of a person, carefully brought up by God-fearing parents, I may resist the temptation for one day or for two days or even three days. But the hour will come when I will say, "Give me some of those sandwiches or I will throw you overboard—and be quick about it!"

My early training may assert itself sufficiently to let me treat the owner of the sandwiches more or less generously and allow him to keep part of the supplies, but I am going to still that terrible gnawing feeling in my entrails if I have to commit murder to do so. Multiply the case of the man on the raft by a million-fold or ten million-fold and you will begin to appreciate the problem that faces the Japanese people.

They live in a country that is smaller than California (155,-652 square miles for California and 148,756 square miles for Japan) and of these only 16,000,000 acres can be used for agriculture, which is less than 2% of all the arable land of America. If you want the comparison to come a little nearer home, it is a trifle less than the improved farmlands of New York State alone. Even with the help of one of the best staffs of scientific agricultural experts to be found anywhere in the world, you will see at a glance what sort of problem it is that faces these poor island folk. Living so near the sea-shore they would of course fish; but although they have now reached the point where they are raising certain sorts of fish in the muddy water of their rice fields, the difficulty remains unsolved and unsolvable in view of the fact that the population increases by more than 650,000 people a year.

It was inevitable therefore that Japan should look for more territory; and it was only natural that first of all she should think of the badly administered and sadly neglected lands that lay just across the China Sea. America would have suited her better, but it was too far away and besides is much too strong. Australia was also too far away, and nine-tenths of that continent are a desert and of no possible use to anybody. But Manchuria was within easy reach, and the road to Manchuria was indicated by the land bridge of the Korean peninsula from which the mainland of Japan was separated by the narrow Strait of Korea. This strait is only 102 miles wide and is conveniently divided into halves by the Tsushima islands, those islands near which the Japanese fleet destroyed the Russian squadron in the year 1905, and killed Russia as a possible rival in eastern Asia.

As for the Korean peninsula, which is situated in the same latitude as southern Italy and Sicily, although it has a much colder climate, it was in no position to defend itself. The Koreans who called their country Ch'ao Hsien or "the chosen land of the morning quiet", were descendants of Chinese immigrants who had occupied the country in the twelfth century before the birth of Christ. They had easily conquered the natives, a very primitive race who had lived in caves and subterranean holes in the mountains of the interior. These immigrants from the west had then established a kingdom of their own, which however was never able to gain complete independence from the mother

If the Pacific Ocean should run dry

KOREA, MONGOLIA AND MANCHURIA   361

country of China and which was forever being harassed by Japanese pirates.

In the year 1592 Japan made her first attempt to get hold of Korea. Japan never would have dared to start upon so ambitious a campaign unless she had been fully prepared. The preparations consisted of several hundred blunderbusses which Portugal had sold them. Relying upon her superior armament, Japan sent 300,000 men around the Strait of Korea, engaged in a war which lasted five years, and was then defeated only by the superior numbers of the Chinese who came to the assistance of the Koreans.

But it was this invasion, during which Seoul, the capital of Korea, was destroyed, and during which all sorts of horrible atrocities were committed, which accounts for the hereditary hatred of the Korean people for everything Japanese. But what will you? The Koreans were weak and the Japanese were strong; and when, during the last quarter of the nineteenth century, the Koreans were forced to grant all sorts of economic and political concessions to the Russians, the Japanese had an excellent excuse for a fresh campaign.

The immediate causes for a war are rarely interesting. It is the real underlying motives that count. In this case, as in the case of the expedition of 1592, they were to be found directly and absolutely in the necessity of the Japanese government to provide its rapidly increasing population with food.

As soon as Japan had defeated Russia and had driven the Muscovite troops back from the Yalu River, the river that separates Korea from Manchuria, Korea became a Japanese protectorate. In 1910 it became a part of the Japanese Empire quite as much as Formosa, which the Japanese had taken from the Chinese in 1895, or the southern half of the island of Sakhalin, which they had taken from the Russians in the year 1905 in lieu of a war indemnity. Today already half a million Japanese have moved in among the twenty million Koreans. The rest will follow in due course of time.

As for Manchuria, it had long been a bone of contention between the two nations that fought for supremacy in the northern half of the Pacific. After the Peace of Portsmouth, which made an end to the Russo-Japanese war, the fate of the country was sealed. Who was there left to protect Manchuria against Japan? Nominally the country still belonged to China, but China, after the Boxer Rebellion, was much too weak to protect anybody, even herself. Why didn't the Manchus put up a fight? A people energetic enough to conquer all of China and to establish themselves as the rulers of one-fifth of the total population of the earth must surely know how to fight. But the Manchus had long since moved southward into China. The six percent that remained of the original population were mainly little farmers without an interest in the land. The other sixteen million people, spread over a territory four times as large as England and Scotland, lived as they had always lived, which meant that they had just enough to eat not to die, but as for fighting, why should they?

And when Manchuria is gone, it will be the turn of Mongolia. For Mongolia is a very big country, almost 1,400,000 square miles, or eleven times as large as the British Isles and it has a population of less than 2,000,000 people. The southern regions are uninhabitable because they form part of the Gobi Desert but the rest consists of grass-lands, eminently suited for purposes of cattle-breeding. Otherwise the Mongolians, who depended for their success upon their cavalry, would never have been able to raise those tough ponies which carried them triumphantly from the Pacific to the Atlantic.

Many people seem to experience a profound indignation at what they are inclined to denounce as a brutal expression of "Japanese ambition". I would rather call them "Japanese necessities". In matters of international policy, a certain healthy egoism is rather a desirable quality. Japan has got to find an outlet for the extra people at home. It is finding such an outlet in northern Asia, in a part of the world that is very lightly populated, and that has been accustomed to such outrageous forms of government that the inhabitants cannot possibly be worse off now than they were ever before.

If the Atlantic Ocean should run dry

If this northern Asiatic safety-valve did not exist, the Philippines, the Dutch East Indies, Australia, New Zealand and the western coast of America would be forever exposed to a Japanese invasion and we would be obliged to station a battle-ship in front of every Polynesian island lest it be towed away over night by a Japanese cruiser.

On the whole, the present arrangement seems much more practical. Those who feel inclined to shed tears at these callous and selfish utterances, are politely requested to weep on the shoulders of our own Indians.

XXXIX

THE JAPANESE EMPIRE

JAPAN, before it started upon its career of world-conquest at the expense of its neighbors, consisted of more than 500 islands which follow a semi-circle reaching all the way from the peninsula of Kamchatka in the north to the coast of the Chinese province of Kwang-tung in the south, a distance equivalent to that between the North Cape of Europe and the center of the Sahara Desert in Africa.

Of these islands, which vary in size between the whole of England and Scotland and Manhattan, 518 are inhabited by some 60,000,000 people. The total number of Japanese, according to the latest statistics, is over 90,000,000 but that takes in 20,000,000 Koreans and several Polynesian islands which have been Japanese territory since the recent Great War.

For all practical purposes, however, it is sufficient to remember the names of Honshiu, the main island in the center, Hokka-ïdo, the next biggest island in the north, and Shikoku and Kiushiu, the two big islands immediately south of Honshiu. The capital is Tokio, with over 2,000,000 inhabitants, situated in a fertile plain in the center of Honshiu. The harbor of Tokio is Yokohama.

An even larger city is Osaka, in the southern part of the same island, the center of the important Japanese textile industry. North of Osaka lies Kioto (Tokio is merely Kioto turned around), the ancient capital of the Empire. Other cities, whose names you will occasionally encounter in our newspapers, are Kobe, the port of Osaka, and Nagasaki on the southern island of Kiushiu, the most convenient port for all vessels coming from Europe.

As for the word Yedo, which you will often find in your history books, it is merely the ancient name of the city of Tokio during the period when it was the residence of the Shoguns. When the Shoguns lost their power in the year 1866, the emperor moved from Kioto to Yedo, the city was rebaptised Tokio, and it began that extraordinary development which has made it one of the biggest cities of the modern world.

But all these towns live in constant peril of being wiped out. The Japanese islands, which are merely the outer edges of the great Asiatic mountains, (the Japanese Sea, the shallow Yellow Sea and the East China Sea are of very recent date, like the North Sea which turned England into an island), are part of the volcanic ridge that stretches from the island of Sakhalin to Java in the Dutch East Indies, and they are in almost constant motion. The seismographic observation statistics of Japan reported 27,485 earthquakes between 1885 and 1903. That gives an average of 1447 per year or four per day. Of course, most of these are of no particular importance. A slight shiver in a teacup, a rattling of a chair against the wall and that would be all. But one gets some idea of the danger to which this island region is exposed when you realize that Kioto, the ancient capital, was shaken 1318 times during the ten centuries of its existence. Of these 1318 shakings, 194 were classified as "strong" and 34 as absolutely "destructive". The earthquake of September, 1923, which destroyed the city of Tokio almost completely and which killed more than 150,000 people and lifted certain small islands a couple of feet in the air, while sinking others below sea-level, was of such recent date as still to be remembered by all of us.

People often associate earthquakes with volcanic disturbances. Some of them are undoubtedly the result of volcanic eruptions. But most earthquakes are caused by a sudden sliding among those layers of rocks which lie beneath the soil on which we live. When such layers move only two or three inches, the result is a commotion which may merely upset a few trees and shrubs but which, if it takes place in exactly the right spot (the **wrong spot would be better**) may cause a catastrophe like that of Lisbon in 1755, when 60,000 people were killed, or Canton in China in 1920 when the number may have been as high as 200,000. According to the conservative estimate of one of the greatest seismological experts, the earthquakes of the last forty centuries, the so-called "historical period" of man, have cost the lives of 13,000,000 people, which, when all is said and done, is quite a considerable number.

Earthquakes, of course, may happen almost anywhere. Only a year ago the bottom of the North Sea was severely shaken by an earthquake, and the mud flats of the islands at the mouth of the Scheldt and the Rhine trembled sufficiently to give the clam-diggers a moment of great uneasiness. Yet the North Sea region is as flat as a pancake. The Japanese islands, on the other hand, are situated on the top of a high ridge which on the eastern side descends into one of the deepest holes in the bottom of the ocean our scientists have so far been able to locate. The famous Tuscarora Deep descends to over 28,000 feet, which is only 6000 feet less than the record depth between the Philippines and the Marianas or Ladrones. It surely is no mere accident that more than half of all the disastrous earthquakes of Japan have taken place along the eastern shores where the coast makes a sheer drop of about six miles.

The Japanese, however, like most people who live in earthquake belts, lose little sleep on account of this eternal menace to their safety. They till their fields and play with their children and eat their meals and laugh at Charlie Chaplin just like the rest of us. The experience of ages has taught them to build a kind of cardboard house which is perhaps a little draughty in winter but which causes the minimum of danger when it comes tumbling down about its owner's ears. Of course, when they want to imitate the west and build sky-scrapers as they did in Tokio, then the damage runs into the hundreds of millions. But, generally speaking, Japan has adapted itself better than any other country to this inevitable geological handicap. Just as, generally speaking, they seem to have succeeded in making life a **much more harmonious and agreeable** adventure than most of

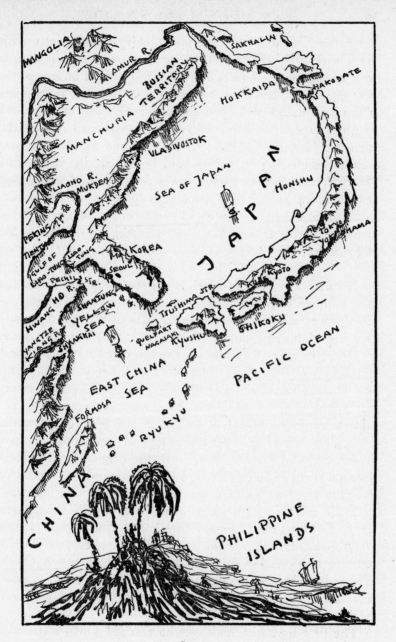

Japan

the nations of the west. I am not thinking of the pretty postal cards with little geisha girls drinking tea underneath a cherry tree, or the toy gardens of Madame Butterfly. I am merely repeating what all travellers have told us who visited Japan before it gave up its ancestral customs and habits and manners (the manners especially seem to have been exquisite) and tried to turn its islands into suburbs of Chicago and Wilkes-Barre. As that incredible change from the old Japan unto the new has had a very decided influence upon our own safety and happiness and will continue to do so in an increasing manner, we ought to know at least a few things about these people who, whether we like it or not, will be our neighbors as long as the Pacific does not run dry.

Japanese history is of much more recent date than Chinese. The Chinese calendar goes back to 2637 B. C. (about the time Cheops was building his little pyramid) but the oldest Japanese chronicle dates back only to 400 A. D. At that time the present so-called Japanese race was already in existence. Strictly speaking, however, there is no "Japanese race", for, like the English, the Japanese are a mixture. The original inhabitants were the Ainos who were gradually driven to the more remote northern islands by three successive waves of invaders from southern China and the Malayan peninsula, from central China, and from Manchuria and Korea. As a result, the original civilization of Japan was really an extension of Chinese civilization, and whatever the Japanese knew they had learned from the Chinese.

Their relations with China grew even more intimate when Japan followed the Chinese example and allowed herself to be converted to Buddhism. But when a new creed replaces an older one, the new creed cannot help being influenced to a certain extent at least by the older one. That is a lesson all missionaries have been obliged to learn, whether they preached Christianity, Mohammedanism or Buddhism.

The first Buddhist apostles who reached Japan in the sixth century of our era found that the Japanese had developed a religious system of their own which had grown out of the soil, so to speak, and which was very well suited to their needs. It was called Shinto-ism from the word Shinto which seems to be the equivalent of our expression "the divine pathway". It was a much nobler creed than the spook and devil worship so prevalent all over the rest of Asia. It accepted the world as a unit of indestructible force and taught that we are responsible for whatever use we make of that force, because, no matter how insignificant the result may be, it will be a permanent result. The present official creed of Japan is a mixture of Buddhism and Shinto-ism. It lays great stress upon one's duty towards the community at large. Like the Englishman, the Japanese, who is also essentially an island-dweller (without necessarily being an insular person), has a very sincere and deep-seated conviction that he owes his country certain very definite duties. Shinto-ism also lays stress upon the respect due the ancestors. But it does not carry this veneration to the point of absurdity which turns so much of China into a vast cemetery where the dead rule the living and where the grave-yards occupy the space that should be used to raise food for the living.

But the great cleavage between Chinese and Japanese civilization did not take place until much later, not until the latter half of the sixteenth century when, after an endless period of quarrelling and fighting between little independent potentates who paid no more attention to their emperor than a knight of the Holy Roman Empire did to his, the government fell at last into the hands of a man of power.

Eight hundred years before, in far away Europe, the Major Domos or house-stewards of the old Frankish kings had pushed their masters into a monastery and had then taken it upon themselves to rule the country. As they were much better fitted for the job than the men they replaced, nobody had objected. The Japanese people, having endured civil war for almost four centuries, did not care who ruled them as long as they got peace. And so they did not object or rush to the defence of their hereditary rulers when the highest official of the imperial court, the head of the rich and influential Tokugawa family, made himself the dictator of the country. This Japanese Major Domo promoted the Emperor to a sort of deity on earth, the spiritual father of all the Japanese, but of such remote spiritual perfection that, like the Lamas of Tibet, he must forever remain invisible to the mass of his subjects.

This arrangement lasted almost two entire centuries. The Shoguns (for that was the title by which these dictators were known and it meant as much as our "commander-in-chief") ruled in Tokio and the Emperors idled their time away behind their costly screens in the silent palace of Kioto. It was during the Shogun era that Japan adopted that strict feudal system which was to influence the character of her people in so profound a way that even today, after almost eighty years of industrialism, the Japanese are still feudalists at heart, and contemplate the problems of life from an angle that is totally different from that of their European and American competitors. It took some time to perfect the details of this new arrangement, but after the year 1600 Japanese society was divided definitely into three different groups. The highest of these castes consisted of the Daimyos, the members of the feudal nobility, the big landowners. The second one consisted of the Samurai, hereditary warriors corresponding to the knights of medieval Europe. All other people belonged to the third class, that of the Heimin or commoners.

This system was not ideal but history has quite convincingly taught us that the mass of the population is never deeply interested in any theory of government. All the average citizen asks is, "Does it work? Does it guarantee me peace and quiet and give me the assurance that whatever I have gained through my own efforts and in the sweat of my brow will actually belong to me and that no one can take it away from me without due process of law?"

And for more than two centuries the system did work. The Shogun was recognized as the political leader of the state. The Mikado was worshipped as the spiritual head of the nation. The

How Japan was made

Daimyos and the Samurai, forced to adhere to a very strict code of "noblesse oblige", either did what was expected of them or were politely requested to disembowel themselves according to the most solemn rites of hara-kiri. And the subjects labored at their different trades and professions.

Even then the country was getting to be slightly over-crowded. Often the people were obliged to subsist on very little. But they had always been very sober and frugal in their tastes and did not ask for much. And Nature appeared to be a faithful friend. The Kuro Siwo (which means the Blue Salt Current, a sort of second cousin to our own Gulf Stream) which started in the equatorial region just north of the Dutch East Indies, then flowed past the Philippines and then crossed the Pacific to bestow its blessings upon the west coast of America, provided the country with an even climate. A narrow strip of cold water just off the Japanese east coast prevented the country from enjoying quite as mild a temperature as California, but even so it was much better off than continental China.

Everything, so it seemed, was in favor of a normal and rational development of those blessed islands when a certain Mendes Pinto, a Portuguese navigator who had lost his bearings, appeared upon the scene and upset the entire future course of Japanese history. For the Portuguese not only visited distant countries to trade with them, but also to bring them the enlightened blessings of their own religious system.

At first, unless all chronicles have agreed to lie upon this one point, the Christian missionaries, whose headquarters were in Goa in India and in Macao near Canton in China, were received with great courtesy and were given every opportunity to explain the advantages of their own creed over that which for so long had ruled supreme among the Japanese. They preached their gospel and they made many converts. Then other missionaries, belonging to a different religious order, arrived from the nearby Philippine Islands which belonged to Spain. They too were welcomed, but the Shogun began to feel uneasy about their presence when he discovered (what native prince has ever failed to make that discovery sooner or later?) that these holy men were invariably accompanied by less holy men, garbed in iron armor and carrying strange iron rods that would send heavy leaden bullets through as many as three common Japanese soldiers at the same time.

It is only during the last fifty years that we have begun to

The Old Japan

understand the Japanese point of view about the very painful incidents which thereupon happened. These incidents have given the Japanese a reputation for cold-blooded cruelty which did not seem in the least in keeping with what we had learned about them from other sources. The decision of the Shogun to close Japan against all further activities on the part of the Christian missionaries was not the result of any sudden dislike on his part for the people from the west. It was caused by fear, by fear lest the whole country be rent asunder by religious strife and its riches be despoiled by the captains of those same merchantmen that carried the messengers of peace and good-will to the shores of Japan and then departed without paying for the goods that had been ordered to provide a return cargo.

The Jesuit influence had been strongest in the island of Kiushiu, nearest to the Portuguese settlements in China. At first the Fathers had humbly spoken of the Prince of Peace. As soon as they had gained the upper hand, they began to destroy Japanese temples, demolish Japanese images and force thousands of peasants and nobles to accept the cross at the point of the gun.

Toyotomi Hideyoshi, then the strong man of Japan, saw all this and realized what the inevitable end must be. "These priests," so he announced, "came here preaching virtue, but their virtue is only a means of concealing their pernicious designs against our Empire."

On July 25th of the year 1587, five years after a first Japanese embassy had paid its respects to the Pope and to the Kings of Spain and Portugal, all Christian priests were banished from Japanese territory. Merchants were given permission to visit Japan as before, but under supervision of the government. The Portuguese Jesuits left. Their place was immediately taken by Spanish Franciscans and Dominicans from the nearby Philippines. They came disguised as special ambassadors to Hideyoshi. Their trick was discovered. Nevertheless, they were treated with courtesy but were told not to preach. They disobeyed this order, built themselves a church in Yedo and began to baptise people all over the land. Next they built a church in Osaka. Next they appropriated a church in Nagasaki which had belonged to the Jesuits. Next they turned openly against their rivals, the Jesuits, and accused them of having been too conciliatory in their methods of bringing the Good Tidings to the Japanese. In short, they committed every error of judgment and taste to be found in the repertory of professional fanatics. When they were finally deported by Hideyoshi's orders, they returned as fast as they were expelled. After years of futile warnings, the Japanese, who thus far had shown the utmost patience and tolerance towards these unwelcome Spanish friars, came to the conclusion that nothing could save them but the most drastic of measures.

Rather than witness a repetition of that civil war which had been so disastrous to their country during the previous four hundred years, they voluntarily closed their country against all

The New Japan

further foreign aggression; and those Christian missionaries who disregarded that edict were put to death.

During wellnigh a century and a half Japan remained in a state of voluntary exile from the rest of the world. Almost, but not completely. One little window remained open through which a great deal of Japanese gold flowed westward and through which at least a few scraps of western science penetrated into the interior of that strange country. The Dutch East India Company had been a rival of the Portuguese for Japan's commercial favors. But the Dutch were traders, pure and simple, and had but little interest in other peoples' souls. Neither did the English. For a long time it was a toss-up which of the two nations would win out. But the English managed rather badly on this occasion, and lost.

After the execution of the last of a series of Portuguese diplomatic missions sent to Japan, an inexcusable official murder, the Dutch too were deprived of many of their former privileges. But as long as their Japanese venture paid an annual dividend of almost eighty percent, they decided to hang on. They were forced to reside on the little island of Deshima, a square rock 300 yards long and 80 yards wide, situated in the harbor of Nagasaki and hardly big enough to exercise the dogs they brought with them to keep them company. They were not allowed to bring their wives and were never permitted to set foot on the mainland.

They must for once have exercised the patience of the angels (not exactly a national characteristic) for the slightest infringement of any of the hundreds of regulations, laid down by the Japanese authorities, brought immediate reprisals. One day the East India Company decided to build a new storehouse. The date, according to the custom of the times, was painted on the façade with the usual prefix A. D. or "anno Domini". As this was a direct reference to the Dominus of those Christians whom the Japanese had come to regard as we ourselves regard Bolshevist agitators fresh from Moscow, the Shogun gave orders not only to remove the offensive letters but to tear the entire building down and raze it to the ground and to remind the Dutch of that terrible edict of expulsion of the Portuguese which had ended with the words:

"As long as the sun warms the earth, let no Christian be so bold as to come to Japan and let all people know that if King Philip himself or even the very God of the Christians break this commandment, they shall pay for it with their heads."

The officials of the Dutch East India Company seem to have taken the lesson to heart, because Deshima remained in Dutch hands for 217 years. During those 217 years there was a steady

drain of Japanese gold and silver, for the Dutch were cash traders and whatever the Japanese ordered from abroad had to be
paid for on delivery.

In this way, too, Europe got an occasional bit of news from
these hermits of the Pacific. These stories are agreed that conditions in the Empire were far from satisfactory. Japan was
rapidly becoming an object lesson of the doctrine that no nation
can ever hope to be completely sufficient unto itself. Towards
the end, too, the youth of Japan were beginning to grow increasingly restive. They had heard vague stories about the wonderful science of western Europe. They began to book-leg scientific and medical works by way of Deshima. They spelled out
queer Dutch words and learned that the world at large had been
moving at a terrific pace while Japan alone had stood still.

Then in 1847 the King of Holland sent a trunkful of scientific
books to the court of Yedo as a present, together with a map of
the world, warning the Japanese against the further folly of
isolation. All this time commercial relations between China and
Europe and America were rapidly on the increase. Vessels bound
from San Francisco for Canton sometimes suffered shipwreck
on the Japanese coast and the sailors, being without consular
or diplomatic protection, fared rather badly. In 1849 the captain of an American man-of-war threatened to bombard Nagasaki unless eighteen American seamen were returned to him at
once. Once more the King of Holland warned his Japanese colleague against the dangers of continuing a policy that could only
lead to disaster. These letters from the Hague merely expressed
what all the world had long since known. Sooner or later, Japan
would have to open her doors to western commerce, and if she
refused to do so peaceably she would be obliged to do so by
force.

Russia, which was pushing further and further down the coast
of Alaska, was slowly making plans to increase its hold upon the
western Pacific. The only country that could act without being
suspected of having territorial ambitions was America. In 1853
Commodore Perry with four warships and 560 men entered

Uraga Bay. This first visit caused such a panic as Japan had never experienced. The Emperor officially invoked the aid of Heaven and as soon as Perry was gone (he remained only ten days to deliver a letter from the President to the Emperor) the Dutch were requested to furnish a warship, forts were manned, old Portuguese guns were mounted and everything was done to prepare for a second visit of these steam-propelled monsters from the east.

All over the country the people took sides. Most of them were in favor of isolation at all costs, but others declared for the policy of the open door. The Shogun, belonging to the latter, lost much of his power and was denounced as a "friend of the foreigners". But in the end it was the Emperor who benefited most from that ever-famous visit of Admiral Perry.

The Shogunate, as the undisputed head of an absolutely feudal system of government, had long since outlived its own usefulness, as had those Daimyos and Samurai who still insisted upon carrying their swords as if they lived in 1653 instead of 1853 and were still actually engaged in the laudable task of suppressing civil war. It was time for a change all along the line.

By mere chance it so happened that the Emperor, who was then the nominal head of the nation, was also a young man of extraordinary ability and great intelligence. He prevailed upon the Shogun to resign and once more took hold of the reins of government. He let himself be persuaded that further isolation meant suicide, and now welcomed all foreigners as cordially as before that he had repelled them. And the Meiji, or era of enlightenment which he inaugurated, changed Japan from a sixteenth century feudal state into a modern, industrialized nation.

To ask whether such a complete reversion of feelings on such a tremendous scale is ever a good and desirable thing for any people is to pose a useless question. Factories and large armies and large navies and coal mines and steel foundries may make for happiness or they may not. I don't know. Some say yes and others say no. It will always depend a great deal upon the individuals in question. The Russians, ten years ago, nursed their souls and loved their saints. Today they burn their saints in the kitchen stove and their souls now dwell with perfect contentment in the exhaust pipe of an engine.

Personally I believe that such developments are absolutely inevitable. In themselves they are neither absolutely good nor absolutely bad because they are necessary and are part of that development by which we hope to set ourselves free from the worries of hunger and the fear of economic uncertainty. That the machine, who is both the father and the mother of such a change, also destroys a great deal that is desirable and beautiful, no one will dare to deny. That the Japan of Hokusai and Utamaro would have been a much more interesting country to visit than the Japan of the Japanese standard oil and the Tokio gasworks, is undoubtedly true. But Hokusai and Utamaro are dead and gone and the Tokio housewives prefer cooking on gas to cooking over a slow charcoal fire; and that is the answer.

Fujiyama, the venerable white-haired volcano which has not spoken a word since 1707, now looks down upon cigarette ads where formerly little children offered flowers to a wayside shrine. The holy deer in the temple park hurt their feet on tin cans thrown away by careless picnic parties.

But Fuji knows—some day, this too will come to an end.

XL

THE PHILIPPINES, AN OLD ADMINISTRATIVE PART OF MEXICO

THE Philippines belong to that row of islands which runs in a semi-circle from Kamchatka to Java. These bits of dry land are remnants of the outer edge of the old continent. They were high enough to remain above sea-level when the waters of the Pacific covered the bottom of those valleys since then known as the Sea of Japan, the East China Sea and the South China Sea.

There are more than 7000 islands in the Philippine group, but only 462 of these are bigger than a square mile. The others are merely large cliffs or little bits of marshland, so insignificant that only one-quarter of them have even been given a name. All of them together are about as large as England and Scotland and they have a population of 11,000,000 natives, with a very large number of Chinese and Japanese and about 100,000 whites. This whole group at one time must have been highly volcanic although today we can only locate twenty-five real volcanoes. Even those, with two or three exceptions, seem to have stopped working at their trade.

For this we ought to be duly grateful, as the Philippines are very dangerously located from a geological point of view. The deepest hole in the ocean which we have so far been able to locate lies just east of the Philippines. That is the spot of which I told you and which is so deep that if we used it as a burial ground for the Himalayas, Mount Everest, the highest mountain of our planet, would still be 5000 feet under water. If things should ever begin to slide in that little corner of the world, there would be few left to tell the tale.

The most important of the Philippine islands is Luzon. It has the shape of a pollywog and in the center rises to a height of 7000 feet. The most important city and the capital of the whole group is situated on the east coast of Luzon, and its name is Manila. The Spaniards founded it in 1571, on the ruins of an old Mohammedan settlement, and it is called after a weed, the nilad, which grew abundantly all over the place. In the year 1590 it was given those walls which were to prove more enduring than the rule of those who built them.

But even under the bad Spanish management, Manila soon developed into the most important commercial center of the whole Far East. The harbor was full of boats from China and Japan and India and even from faraway Arabia. They came to this port to exchange their merchandise for those European products which the Spaniards had brought to the Philippines by way of their Mexican possessions in Central America. For, rather than risk the voyage across the Indian Ocean and by way of the Cape, which would have exposed them to the attacks of the British and the Dutch, the Spaniards sent their vessels directly from Manila to the Gulf of Tehuantepec, then carried the goods across the American isthmus, and on the other side reloaded them into vessels that sailed for home by way of Cuba and Porto Rico.

To the south of Luzon lie a dozen fairly large islands of which Samar and Panay (with the well-known city of Iloilo, the second largest city of the Philippines) and Negros and Cebú are the best known. To the south of these lies Mindanao, only a little smaller than Luzon, and famous for the stubborn resistance with which the natives, the Mohammedan Moros, have fought both Spaniard and American to retain their independence. The biggest city of Mindanao is Zamboanga, which faces the Sulu Sea, for, generally speaking, the Philippines have always turned their back upon the Pacific. Their real interests lay in the west, they traded with the west, and it was from the west that they got their religion and their first concepts of civilization. That they were discovered by people who approached them from the east was pure accident.

Magellan, who landed here in 1521, had merely taken this unusual route to settle a point of law that was threatening difficulties between his employer, the King of Spain, and the Pope. In the year 1494 the Pope, in order to make an end to all further strife between his beloved children of the Iberian peninsula had taken a ruler and had divided the whole world into two equal parts by drawing a line from the north to the south just west of the Azores and the Cape Verde Islands (roughly corresponding to our fiftieth degree of longitude west of Greenwich). He had given the Spaniards everything to the west of that line and the Portuguese everything to the east. That was the famous treaty of Tordesillas upon which the Spaniards based their right to execute all those who dared to pass "beyond the line" and which made the first English and Dutch expeditions to the American mainland such very hazardous enterprises, for whoever was caught "beyond the line" was immediately hanged like a common pirate.

The Pope, however, who had made this venture into applied geography, the notorious Alexander VI, the father of Cesare and Lucrezia Borgia, was himself a Spaniard; and the Portuguese claimed that the treaty had not been quite fair to their interests. Hence a century of wrangling and fighting as to who owned what. In connection with this quarrel, Magellan, although a Portuguese, had been hired by the King of Spain to proceed to the Indian Ocean by way of the eastern route and to decide whether the rich spice islands of the Moluccas lay within that part of the Indies which the Pope had given to the Portuguese or to the Spaniards. The Portuguese proved to be right. They got the Moluccas, which shortly afterwards they lost to the Dutch, but the Spaniards, who had come upon the Philippines in this accidental way, kept them for their own benefit and administered them from Mexico. This meant a wholesale exodus of friars from the New Castile to a territory that promised more profitable results than would ever be obtained among the fast dwindling races of Central America.

The friars, it must be confessed, did a thorough job among

their Filipino charges. Indeed, if they had only been a little less successful, our own task in the Philippines would have been a good deal easier. For when we acquired those ancient Spanish possessions in the year 1898, we were for the first time in our political existence called upon to deal with a people who were almost 100% Catholic.

We may not be a Protestant nation in the official sense of the word, but our general philosophy of life is decidedly Protestant and very decidedly un-Catholic. We may be inspired by the best of intentions towards the Philippines, give them endless good roads, thousands of schools, three universities, hospitals, doctors, nurses, incubators, meat and fish inspection, hygiene and a thousand and one benefits of progress of which the Spaniards had never even heard. But all these generous expressions of good-will mean comparatively little to people who from their earliest childhood have been taught to regard such worldly comforts and advantages as something very nice and very pleasant but not to be compared to the chance of gaining salvation in another world, where hygiene and hospitals and good roads and schools shall no longer be of any interest to anybody.

XLI

THE DUTCH EAST INDIES, THE TAIL THAT WAGS
THE DOG

I HAVE already told you how Japan and Formosa and the Philippines are merely the outer mountainous edges of the old Asiatic continent which in the course of millions of years got separated from the mainland by the waters of the Pacific Ocean.

The Malay Islands on the other hand (Malaysia, Insulinde, Indian Archipelago, the Dutch East Indies—they are known by so many different names) are not merely part of the old outer edge of Asia. They are the remnants of an enormous peninsula as large as that of China, which reached from Burma and Siam and Cochin-China eastward to Australia. During the earliest ages of our geographical history this peninsula may have been directly connected with the Asiatic continent (then infinitely larger than today) and afterwards, during a period about which we are a little better informed, it was separated from Australia only by a narrow strip of water, not much wider than the present Torres Strait between Queensland and New Guinea.

The reason for the cataclysmic changes which have turned so vast a piece of dry land into a group of oddly shaped islands, running all the way from Borneo, which is as large as the whole of the Scandinavian peninsula, down to thousands of tiny bits of rock located wherever they happen to be most inconvenient to navigation, is not hard to discover. This part of the world was among the most volcanic regions of the earth. Even today Java retains the blue ribbon for volcanic activities. During the last three centuries, however, the hundred and twenty odd volcanoes of Java have on the whole been very well-behaved, as have those of Sumatra, a little towards the west.

When Brahmanism, the old religion of India, was prevalent among the Javanese, the priests used to placate the spirits that dwelled in the bowels of the earth by an occasional offering of human beings, who were pitched bodily into the boiling cauldron of the craters—apparently with success, for although the volcanoes continue to puff and roar and occasionally go on a rampage, there has been no major catastrophe for several centuries.

But the remnants of Krakatoa lie there as a dreadful warning of something that may happen again at any moment. On the morning of the 26th of August of the year 1883 the island of Krakatoa, situated in the Sunda Strait between Sumatra and Java, was very much as it had always been since a prehistoric eruption had blown away the top of its crater and had cut the island up into several small pieces. Two days later, the whole northern part of the island was gone. Where there had been hills 1500 feet high there now was a deep hollow, lying more than a thousand feet below the surface of the Indian Ocean. The noise of that explosion was heard 3000 miles away. Ashes were blown 17 miles up in the air. The volcanic dust spread all over Africa, Europe, Asia and America and even as far north as the North Cape. The sky for six weeks afterwards was strangely colored as if there had been a forest fire somewhere in the neighborhood.

But the disturbance caused on the ocean was much more disastrous than that caused on land, for Krakatoa was uninhabited. A tidal wave more than 50 feet high swept along the coast of Java and killed 36,000 people. It wiped out harbors and villages and destroyed large vessels as if they had been kindling wood. Ceylon and Mauritius were affected by these waves. They made themselves noticeable near Cape Horn, which is almost 8000 miles away, and they were faintly observed in the British Channel which is 11,000 miles distant from the Strait of Sunda.

A year ago the remnant of the Krakatoa volcano was once more beginning to show signs of activity. And no one can foretell when or where the subterranean lightning will strike next. As for the people who live here, they are like all the others who live under similar circumstances. They pay no more attention than a small boy in one of our tenement districts pays to the trucks that are driven right across his baseball game in one of the most crowded streets of the Italian quarter.

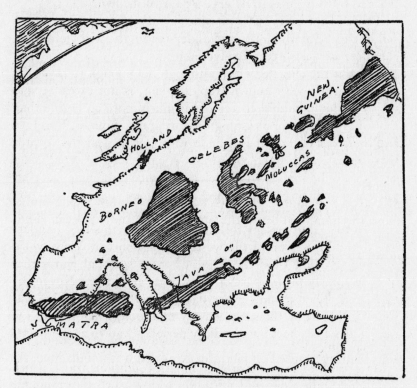

The Dutch East Indies compared to Europe

This fatalistic attitude may be due to the Mohammedan faith. It may also be the result of just plain ordinary contentment with life and the conviction that volcanic eruptions, like foreign dominations or floods or fires, are all of them negligible incidents in life and of small importance to the man who tills his fields, whose ancestors ever since the beginning of the world have tilled these same fields, whose children will till these same fields, and who none of them ever want or expect to go without sufficient nourishment.

This sounds as if I were trying to describe Java as a sort of earthly Paradise. It is hardly that, but it has been so supremely favored by Nature as to deserve a page of its own.

There is the soil, 28% of which is of volcanic origin. That soil, if treated at all kindly and understandingly, will yield three complete harvests every twelve months.

There is the climate, which although hot enough to favor the cultivation of every known tropical plant, is not excessive and which in the mountainous regions is much more agreeable than that of New York or Washington during the summer. For Java and the other islands of Insulinde, although so near the equator that the days and nights are almost equally long, is on all sides surrounded by the sea. It therefore has moisture enough for all purposes and the temperature never goes higher than 96° Fahrenheit, nor lower than 66°, with a mean annual temperature of 79°. The seasons follow each other with sharp regularity. The rainy season of the western monsoon (an Arabic word meaning "season" and the name of those seasonal winds that blow regularly in this part of the world) lasts from November to March. Then it rains every day at a certain hour. This season is followed by the so-called dry monsoon, when it does not rain at all. The short intermediary period is known as the "canting season".

As a result of these favorable climatic conditions, Java, which is only 622 miles long and 121 miles wide (a sort of rectangular breakwater, protecting the islands of the inner archipelago against the violence of the southern Indian Ocean) is able to support 42,000,000 people, while Sumatra and Borneo, although much larger, have only one-tenth of that population. And because of its great fertility, the island has from the very beginning attracted the attention of the white man.

The Portuguese were the first to appear upon the scene. Then came the English and the Dutch, but the English gradually concentrated all their forces upon the exploitation of British

India and left Java and the other Malaysian islands to the Dutch. Having committed every possible mistake of which the European was capable, in dealing with a native populace during the first three centuries of their rule, the Dutch seem at last to have learned a few primary lessons of colonial management. They interfere just as little as possible with the native and are gradually drawing him more and more into the administration of his own country, knowing that the time will come when for good or evil these people will insist upon being given their liberty. With an army of 30,000 men, of which only one-fifth are white, one will never be able to rule a territory fifty times as large as the mother country if the inhabitants have really made up their minds that the foreigner must go. The old days, therefore, of "forced labor" and "government plantations" are gone forever. Schools and railroads and hospitals are taking the place of the old punitive expeditions. If eventually one will have to give up these regions as the sovereign master, one may hope to remain behind as an indispensable part of the economic fabric. The old guard, which was firmly convinced that "a native was all right as long as he knew his place", is slowly giving ground to a younger generation, which knows that facts are mightier than slogans and that this universe of ours was created on the principle of eternal change.

As for the other islands that belong to the Dutch group, none of them is as highly cultivated as Java. Celebes, that queerly shaped, spidery island just west of the Moluccas, the original spice-islands for which the English and the Portuguese and the Spaniards and the Dutch fought each other so bitterly all during the seventeenth century, is being slowly groomed by the Dutch to become a second Java. Today Macassar, the town where the oil came from with which our Victorian grandfathers adorned their locks and which made our Victorian grandmothers knit their endless "antimacassars", is one of the most important cities of the Java Sea, doing a regular business with Surabaya and Semarang, the main ports on the northern coast of Java, and being in regular communication with Tandjong Priok, which is the harbor of Batavia, the capital, just as Weltevreden is the residential quarter and Buitenzorg the seat of government.

The Molucca Islands themselves are not as rich as they used to be, but their inhabitants, the Amboinese, are still renowned for their ability as sailors. Four hundred years ago these same

Java

Amboinese were dreaded far and wide as the most voracious cannibals of the Pacific Ocean. Today they are exemplary Christians although, curiously enough, they have given the Dutch East Indian army its best fighting regiments.

Borneo, the main remnant of the old submerged Asiatic peninsula, suffers from under-population due to the strange native belief that head-hunting makes for holiness. The Dutch have been trying to kill this popular pastime by the most drastic forms of punishment. But in the interior no young man, even today, is allowed to marry until he has at least one head to his credit. This prolonged process of mutual extermination (the Borneo people will exhibit their gruesome conquests as proudly and as unconcernedly as an expert golf player will show you his cups) has kept the number of the inhabitants way below par. But now at last the rivers are being opened up, and oil and coal and diamond companies are constructing roads, and the savages are gradually being persuaded to turn to the more peaceful pursuits of agriculture. Thus the island, in due course of time, may be able to support twenty times its present population without noticing the difference.

The northern part of Borneo belongs to the English. The north-western corner is an independent state, called Sarawak, and ruled by the descendants of an Englishman, the famous Rajah Brooks, who arrived in the island as Sir James Brooks to suppress a local rebellion and who remained to become its independent sovereign.

Another island of tremendous importance is Sumatra in the east, which runs parallel with the Malay peninsula. It is highly volcanic and will grow almost anything, but unfortunately it is cut into two distinct halves by a high mountain-range which has greatly retarded its development until the introduction of railroads. The automobile and the flying machine will do more to open up this territory to western commerce than any other mechanical agency would ever have been able to do.

Between Sumatra and Borneo lie the islands of Banka and Billiton which, being a continuation of the Malay peninsula, are also exceedingly rich in tin. East of Java lies the famous island of Bali, where the ancient native form of life has been best preserved, and then come Flores and Timor, just north of Australia, and finally New Guinea, which is really part of the Australian mainland and of which only the western half is in Dutch hands. The island, which would cover the greater part of central Europe, from Paris to Odessa, has hardly been touched. There are no rivers leading to the interior and the population is very small, due in part to cannibalism and in part to the backwardness of the natives, forever decimated by disease and man-hunting. Here and there in the interior there are remnants of pygmy tribes, indicating that the island must have been settled at a very early age.

But then, this whole part of the world is very old and according to one theory at least, it is in this region that Man first of all bade farewell to his anthropoid cousins, the apes. Hence the skull of that earliest man-like creature, the famous Pithecanthropus Erectus, which was found in the island of Java, and the presence in Borneo and Sumatra of those big, man-like apes which are known as the orang-utan.

This is indeed a curious world, this world of ours. One branch of the family progressed until it was able to build zoos provided with tropical heat. And the other half went to live in them.

XLII

AUSTRALIA, THE STEP-CHILD OF NATURE

SPEAKING of the wasteful methods of Nature and the lack of an apparent purpose in creation, the late Hermann Ludwig von Helmholtz, the famous German scientist, a specialist in the field of physiological optics, is said to have made the remark that if any instrument-maker should ever have dared to favor him with a contraption quite as clumsy as the human eye, he would have denounced the man as an incompetent bungler who did not know his business.

I am glad Helmholtz did not extend his investigations beyond the realm of physiology and electricity for I would hate to repeat what he would have said about the way the deity handled the geographical arrangement of our planet.

Take a country like Greenland. There it lies, almost buried beneath thousands of feet of snow and ice. If those 827,000 square miles could be moved to the middle of the ocean, they might support a population of millions of people. Now they offer a scant living to a few thousand ice-bears and a handful of half-starved Eskimos. But as a sublime example of bad executive management, I offer you Australia. For Australia, although officially registered as a continent, is just about exactly everything a well-regulated continent should not be.

In the first place, its location is so unfortunate that although the Portuguese, the Spaniards and the Dutch had suspected its existence for over a hundred years and had done their best to discover it, the whole of that enormous territory of almost 3,000,000 square miles (as large, therefore, as the United States) was not actually seen by the eyes of a white man until the year 1642, when Abel Tasman, flying the flag of the Dutch East India

Company, circumnavigated the country and took posssession of it in the name of the United Netherlands.

But this visit of state was perfectly useless from a practical point of view. The Dutch were not interested in this wilderness and allowed their title to lapse. When James Cook was sent to the Pacific to observe the transit of the planet Venus in the year 1769 (a century and a quarter therefore after Tasman's voyage) the map-makers of Amsterdam and London were still quite uncertain where exactly they must place this Terra Australis Incognita in the midst of the vast expanse of water that went by the name of the Great Peaceful Ocean.

Not only did Australia suffer from a bad location, but in the second place it had a very unfortunate climate. The climate is fairly good along the east coast and along the eastern part of the southern coast where Adelaide, Melbourne, Sydney and Brisbane, the four big cities, are located. But the northern coast is uncomfortably wet and the western coast is uncomfortably dry, which means that the most inhabitable part is also the furthest removed from the great trade-routes which connect Asia with Africa and Europe.

In the third place, the whole of the interior is a desert without any rain and its subterranean water supply is so badly located that systematic irrigation will always be extremely difficult.

In the fourth place, the highest parts are practically everywhere along the outer edges of the continent. The interior therefore resembles a hollow bowl, and, since water does not flow uphill, it has no rivers worthy of that name. The Darling River, the largest of all Australian rivers (1160 miles long) takes its origin among the mountains of Queensland, not so many miles away from the Coral Sea, a part of the Pacific Ocean. But instead of running eastward into the Pacific, it flows westward to lose itself in Encounter Bay, and for the greater part of the year (remember that it is winter in the southern hemisphere when it is summer in the northern, and vice versa) it consists mainly of a series of pools and is of no earthly use to anybody.

In the fifth place, there were no natives who could be trained

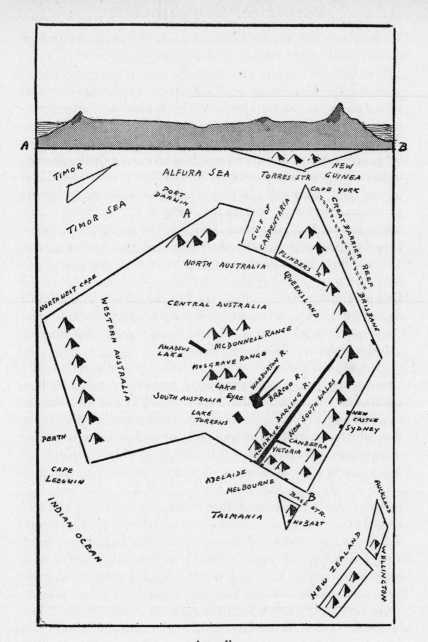

Australia

to do the white man's chores. The unfortunate Australians, about whose origin we are still very much in the dark, might just as well have lived on another planet, as far as their relations with the rest of mankind were concerned. Left entirely to their own devices, they never rose very high beyond the status of some of our more primitive animals. For example, they never learned how to build houses nor how to raise grain nor how to use a spear or an arrow or an axe. They knew how to handle the boomerang, as indeed a great many other people all over the world had done at one time or another. But whereas the others had eventually graduated from that very clumsy weapon to the sword and the spear and the bow, the Australians had remained exactly where they had been shortly after their ancestors had learned to walk on their hind legs without the support of their arms. The most generous way of classifying them would probably be to say that they resembled "the hunting type" of the earliest period of the Stone Age. And even then we are rather hard on the typical stone-age man who was as a rule a much better artist than any aboriginal Australian has ever been.

And finally, this poor continent had apparently been told to shift for itself long before the earth had been covered by those plants and shrubs which have contributed so much to our own comfort and happiness. It had developed a specific dry-climate flora of its own which is undoubtedly of profound interest to our professional botanists but which offers the white settler, intent upon raising a profitable crop of something or other (anything at all as long as it pays him for his trouble), only very slight prospects for a profitable future. Kangaroo grass and salt bush make fairly good food for sheep, but the common prickly spinifex is too much even for the hard-palated camel. And one cannot very well grow rich raising eucalyptus trees, although some of them will grow as high as 400 feet, the only rivals of our own sequoias in California.

As for the farmers who hastened to this new promised land in 1868 when it definitely ceased to be a penal colony, they found themselves faced by a collection of living fossils which

The Atlantic

The Pacific

absolutely refused to let themselves be domesticated. Once more
it was the isolated position of Australia which had allowed all
these curious prehistoric creatures to continue their existence
long after they had been exterminated in every other part of the
world. The complete absence of all the larger and more intel-

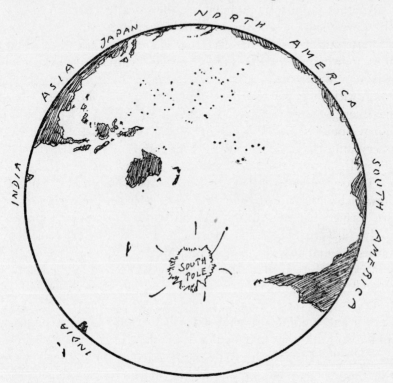

Australia's isolation

ligent mammals of Asia and Africa and Europe had not forced
these Australian quadrupeds to improve their intellectual ca-
pacities or die out. From sheer lack of competition they had always remained as they had been on the day they were born.

We are all of us familiar with the strange animal called the
kangaroo. The kangaroo belongs to the family of the marsupials.
Marsupials are animals which have a pouch in which they carry

their young who are born imperfect and who then grow to perfection inside this pouch. During the tertiary period, the whole earth was inhabited by marsupials. Today there remains only one variety of marsupial in America, the opossum, but Australia has quite a large number of them.

Another prehistoric remnant are the so-called Monotremata, the lowest sub-class of the mammals, creatures which have but a single outlet for all the excretory channels of the body. The best-known among these is the grotesque ornithorhynchus paradoxus or water-mole, a brownish creature some twenty inches long, with short fur and the bill of a duck (which in the young has even got teeth) and web-feet with long nails and a poisonous horny spur on the heels of the males—a walking museum of everything that Nature has ever invented or discarded during the millions of years of her evolutions forward and backward.

As for the rest of the Australian fauna, it contains a most formidable museum of animal curiosities: birds with feathers that are formed like hair; birds that can only walk and are unable to fly; birds that laugh like jackals; cuckoo birds which look like pheasants and pigeons as large as chickens; rats with web-feet and rats with tails that allow them to climb trees; lizards able to walk on two legs; fishes with gills and lungs which date back to the days of the ichthyosaurus and which are really a mixture of fish and amphibian; wild dogs that resemble both a jackal and a wolf and that may be the descendants of pariah dogs imported into Australia by some of the earliest immigrants from the Asiatic mainland; and a whole menagerie of other monstrosities.

But that is not all. Australia also has an assortment of insects of its own and they are more to be feared than tigers and snakes. There are the jumping ants, for Australia is El Dorado of the jumpers. Mammals, birds, insects, they all of them jump in preference to flying or running. There are ants that live in skyscrapers of their own making. There are ants that will eat their way through anything short of a cast-iron door, for they are able to cover ordinary tin and lead boxes with a particular acid which causes the metal to oxidize and allows the ants to dig a tunnel through which they can enter into the interior and then destroy the contents at their own leisure.

There are the flies which hatch their eggs in the skins of sheep and cows, and mosquitoes which make the swampy regions of southern Australia absolutely uninhabitable, and the grasshoppers, able to destroy the labor of years in as many minutes, and the ticks which attach themselves to the flocks and live on their blood, and the cockatoos who look so pretty and so harmless but are able to do terrific damage when operating en masse, as they are apt to do in that part of the world.

But the worst of all these manifold local plagues is not of Australian origin at all but an import from Europe. I refer to Brer Rabbit, a harmless enough creature in his usual haunts, but a terrific nuisance among the sandy wastes of a continent where the creatures can breed *ad libitum*. The first rabbits were introduced from England in the year 1862 for the purpose of a little sport. The colonists were bored. Hunting rabbits would be a pleasant diversion to break the monotony of life in the bush. A few of these rabbits escaped and they set up house-keeping in the well-known rabbit fashion. Astronomers, accustomed to deal with large figures, have tried to compute the number of rabbits that must be at large at the present moment in Australia. They have come to the conclusion that there must be almost 4,000,-000,000 of them. As forty rabbits eat as much as one single sheep, that represents a herd of 100,000,000 sheep. Draw your own conclusions. Entire regions have been devastated by these rodents. Western Australia was so badly eaten by the hungry conies that an effort was made to protect it from further invasions by means of a gigantic fence of chicken-wire, a sort of Chinese rabbit-wall, over three feet high and three feet below the ground, to prevent the vermin from digging holes underneath. But, driven by necessity, they soon learned to climb these fences and the plague continued unabated. Poison was then tried, but also in vain. Wild animals which regulate the rabbit supply in the rest of the world were not to be found in Australia, or refused to adapt themselves to this strange land and died as soon as they were imported. And in spite of all the white man has done, the rabbits continue to multiply as merrily as the sparrow, another European importation which is now the dread of all Australian garden lovers, and as rapidly as the prickly-pear which has taken to the arid Australian soil as a seal takes to water.

Nevertheless, and in spite of these terrific handicaps, the immigrants have succeeded in making Australia the most important

Australia is found

wool-growing country of the world. Today Australia, with almost 80,000,000 sheep, looks after one-quarter of all the wool we wear, and wool accounts for fully two-fifths of the country's exports.

As the Australian mainland is much older than Europe, it is self-evident that it must contain a great variety of minerals. The gold rush of the early fifties drew attention to the Australian gold fields. Since then, lead, copper, tin, iron and coal have also been located, but oil has not yet been found. Diamonds occur, but they are rare. Semi-precious stones, on the other hand, such as opals and sapphires, occur in large quantities. Lack of capital and bad means of transportation have prevented a thorough exploitation of these treasures but that will come in time when Australia shall at last have recovered from years of financial

Australia

mismanagement and shall once more be counted among the
solvent nations.

Meanwhile Australia enjoys the distinction of having been,
next to Africa, the most difficult continent to explore. By the
beginning of the nineteenth century her three main divisions were
fairly well understood. There was the table-land of the west,

The Pearl Diver

which had an average altitude of 2000 feet, although in some
spots it went as high as 3000 feet. This table-land was also the
gold land, but it had no harbors and only one city of any importance, called Perth. Then there were the eastern highlands,
very ancient mountain-ranges which rain and wind had gradually
worn away until the highest top, Mount Kosciusco, was only
7000 feet above sea-level. This was the part of the continent
with good harbors, which therefore attracted the first colonists.

Between these two elevated plateaus lay a wide plain which

never rose above 600 feet and which in the region of Lake Eyre actually sank below sea-level. This plain was cut into halves by two mountain-ranges, the Flinders range in the west and the Grey range in the east which connected in the north with the mountains of Queensland.

As for the political development of the country, it has been peaceful but only fairly successful. The first immigrants were people, who according to the laws of England of the latter half of the eighteenth century, were considered "criminals", but who usually were guilty of no worse crime than that poverty or misery which had driven them to commit some petty offence like the theft of a loaf of bread or a few apples. The first penal settlement was in Botany Bay, so called because Captain Cook, who discovered it, arrived there just when all the little flowers were in bloom. The colony itself was called New South Wales and Sydney was the capital. The island of Tasmania, then part of New South Wales, was converted into a penal station in 1803, and the convicts were gathered together in the neighborhood of the present city of Hobart. In 1825 the city of Brisbane, the capital of Queensland, was founded. During the thirties a settlement at the head of the bay, called Port Phillip, was named after Lord Melbourne and it became the capital of the province of Victoria. Adelaide, the capital of South Australia, dates back to the same period, but Perth, the capital of West Australia, remained an insignificant village until the days of the great gold rush of the early fifties. As for the northern territory, administered by the Commonwealth very much as our own territories used to be administered by Washington, although it has an area of half a million square miles, it has only 5000 inhabitants of whom less than 2000 live in Port Darwin on the Timor Sea, one of the finest natural harbors in the world but without a vestige of trade.

In the year 1901 these six states, with 6,000,000 inhabitants of which three-quarters lived in the east, formed the Commonwealth of Australia and seven years later they decided to build themselves a new capital called Canberra, situated 150 miles south-west of Sydney and not far away from Mount Kosciusco, the highest mountain of all Australia.

In the year 1927 the Dominion took possession of its new headquarters. But the parliament of the new Commonwealth will have to do some very deep thinking ere it can pull the nation out of its present difficulties. In the first place, the Labor Union Government, which had been in control ever since the Great War, has been so needlessly costly that the Commonwealth is no longer able to get any credit from the money-lenders of Europe. It is doubtful whether the new government that has recently succeeded the Labor Party will be able to overcome this financial handicap without making some very serious concessions. In the second place, Australia suffers from a most dreadful under-population. Tasmania and New South Wales have eight people to the square mile. Victoria has twenty. But Queensland and South Australia have only one and West Australia only one half per square mile. And even these have been so thoroughly steeped in labor union lore that they are among the world's most incompetent and indifferent workmen and cannot live without a great many public holidays, devoted to sport and horse-racing.

Well then, who is to do the work that is necessary to keep a nation going?

Italians are not wanted, although they would be perfectly willing to come. But the English middle-class element which is predominant in the political life of the Commonwealth has coined the phrase, "Australia for the Australians", which means the exclusion of everything that is not strictly white and of English middle-class origin. The hardworking Italian is neither, and he is therefore discouraged from crossing the Torres Strait. The Japanese and the Chinese, being yellow of color, are out of the question. The Polynesians and the Malays and the Javanese are of a chocolaty hue and therefore anathema. I repeat the question—who is to do the work? And I add that I do not know the answer. But 3,000,000 square miles of land lie practically uninhabited, and other parts of the world are hopelessly over-populated. This will provide the usual solution.

XLIII

NEW ZEALAND

NEW ZEALAND, together with her newly acquired possessions among the Samoan Islands, is one and a quarter times as large as England and Scotland together. The population is 1,500,000, of whom 143,000 live in Wellington, the capital, which is situated on the North Island.

It was first seen by Abel Tasman in the year 1642 and was called by him after that southern island province of his native land in which the first part of this geography was written. Some three centuries before it had been discovered by the Polynesian canoemen, those marvellous mariners of the Pacific, whose queerly shaped straw maps were so dependable that they could sail thousands of miles from home and always be sure of finding their way back.

These Polynesian conquerors became the ancestors of the warlike and handsome race of the Maoris, of whom there were some 50,000 left in the year 1906, and who since then seem to be again on the increase. The Maoris are evidently one of the few examples of a native stock which has been able to maintain itself against the white man and to adopt some of the more agreeable virtues of western civilization without at the same time drinking itself to death. They have given up several of their ancient habits and customs, such as eating their enemies and tattooing their faces, and they send representatives to the New Zealand parliament and build churches which are in every way as unattractive as the chapels constructed by their white masters, all of which bids well for the future, as far as the racial problem is concerned.

During the first quarter of the nineteenth century both the

French and the English tried to get hold of these islands by means of their respective missionaries. But in the year 1833 the Maoris put themselves under the protection of the English and in the year 1839 the English formally took possession of all New Zealand territory.

If the French squadron had been three days earlier, New Zealand would today be a French colony like New Caledonia and the Marquesas and so many other islands of the Pacific. In 1840 the islands became a dependency of the Australian colony of New South Wales and in 1847 an English Crown Colony. In the year 1901, New Zealand was given a chance to join the Australian commonwealth but, proud of the fact that it had never been a penal establishment, it declined the honor. Since 1907 it has been an independent dominion with an English governor-general but a representative government of its own.

As for the geological aspect of these two big islands, they have probably never been part of the Australian mainland, for the Tasman Sea which separates them is more than 15,000 feet deep and 1200 miles wide. They are probably the remnants of a high mountain-range which once upon a time formed the western shores of the Pacific. But the changes have been so numerous that it is difficult to state precisely how the present islands came into being. What makes their case even more difficult is the fact that they have so little in common with each other. Whereas North Island is a tremendously volcanic region (a sort of Yellowstone Park of the Pacific), South Island, separated from North Island by the Cook Strait, which is only 90 miles wide, is a replica of Switzerland with a few Norwegian fjords thrown in for good measure.

New Zealand is not in any way tropical. It is as far removed from the equator as Italy and enjoys the same sort of climate. This means that it is much more likely to become a permanent European establishment than Australia. All sorts of European fruits, such as peaches and apricots and apples and grapes and oranges, can be cultivated in the valleys, while the mountain sides provide excellent grazing fields for cattle. Flax grows as well here as in the moist climate of the old Zeeland and the slow growing trees of the North Island, exported chiefly from Auckland, make excellent timber.

In the year 1901 New Zealand annexed a number of islands of the Pacific. Among them were the Cook Islands and the Island of Rarotonga from where, according to the Maori belief, New

New Zealand looks very much like Norway

Zealand got its first Polynesian settlers. The Cook Islands are still of volcanic origin but thereupon we leave the volcanic belt and get into the midst of the coral islands.

These are formed by little marine organisms, the Anthozoa or "flower-animals", which die but whose assembled skeletons are responsible for the thousands of reefs and islets which dot this part of the Pacific Ocean. These polyps are fussy creatures. They can only live in fresh salt water of a certain temperature. A single frost will kill them. They cannot descend lower than about 120 feet. Whenever we find coral deposits lower than that, we know that the bottom of the ocean must have sunk from its original level. But they have been building their little islands for millions of years and their work is more enduring than that of the best masons. As they depend upon a constant supply of water-in-motion, the polyps who live in the center of the edifice are apt to die off first. The edges then continue to grow and finally they form a so-called atoll, an island consisting of a narrow ring of solid material with a circular lagoon in the center. There is usually a single entrance to such a lagoon and it is always away from the prevailing winds as the waves on the other side provide the polyps with a more abundant food supply and therefore make them grow faster.

A number of such atolls which grow cocoanuts and produce copra now belong to New Zealand and the German share of Samoa was given to the dominion as a mandate in recognition of the excellent services of the New Zealand troops during the Great War. What they are going to do with it, I do not know.

XLIV

THE ISLANDS OF THE PACIFIC WHERE PEOPLE NEITHER TOILED NOR SPUN BUT LIVED JUST THE SAME

THE Atlantic has hardly any islands at all. The Pacific has by far too many. The Caroline Islands, the Marshall Islands and the Hawaiian Islands lie north of the equator. All the others lie south of the equator. They usually make their appearance in groups. Easter Island, the place where we have found those mysterious gigantic stone statues, is an exception. It lies by itself, but it is much nearer to South America than to Australia.

The Pacific Islands can be divided into three distinct groups. There are the islands which are undoubtedly the remnants of the vast Australian continent of prehistoric geological times. New Caledonia, the French penal settlement, is an example of this sort of island. Then there are others like the Fiji Islands, Samoa, the Hawaiian or Sandwich Islands and the Marquesas, which are of distinct volcanic origin. Finally there are the coral islands like the New Hebrides.

Of all these thousands of islands (many of the coral islands are only a few feet above water) the most important ones are the Hawaiian Islands, where Captain Cook was murdered by the natives on his way home in the year 1779. In the year 1810 they became the center of a large South Sea Empire which continued to exist until 1893, when they were annexed by the United States. Outside of their great fertility they are of tremendous importance as half-way stations between America and Asia.

They are a bit shaky. Kilauea, a volcano with the unusual height of 4400 feet, continues to be active. The volcano on Maui, another island of the group, has the biggest crater of the world. But the marvellous climate easily makes up for an occasional worried glance at the smoke plumes of these old but none too trustworthy friends. Honolulu on the island of Oahu is the capital.

The most important city of the Fiji Islands is Suva, a port of call for all steamers from America to Australia and New Zealand.

The capital of Samoa is Apia.

Another island of which you sometimes hear is Guam in the Ladrones, half-way between Japan and New Guinea and an important American cable station.

Then there is Tahiti, a French possession among the Society

The Coral Island

Islands, where the South Sea movie stories are supposed to come from.

Finally there are dozens and dozens of other islands belonging to the three general groups of Melanesia and Micronesia and Polynesia. They seem to form regular barriers across the Pacific, running in three parallel lines from north-west to south-east, and making navigation in the Pacific something very different from that in the Atlantic where Rockall is the only danger spot between Ireland and the American coast.

It is said that these islands offer a most agreeable home to all those who find our modern machine-made civilization too complicated for their simple tastes and who prefer peace and quiet and agreeable companions to noise and hurry and the angry looks of jealous competitors. I suppose they are more restful than, let us say, the corner of Broadway and Forty-Second Street. But they are so dreadfully far away—and do they really grow an herb that will allow the average man to escape from himself?

XLV

AFRICA, THE CONTINENT OF CONTRADICTIONS AND
CONTRASTS

AFRICA, like Australia, is the remnant of a much older continent, the greater part of which disappeared beneath the waves of the sea a great many million years ago. Until comparatively recent times it was still connected with Europe. Arabia, geographically speaking a continuation of the Sahara, and Madagascar, which has the fauna and flora of Africa, Asia and Australia, seem to indicate that there may have been a land connection between these three continents as recently ago as the era during which life first appeared upon our planet.

It is all very complicated and we shall have to discover a great many more data before we shall be able to say, "It was thus and thus and not otherwise". In the meanwhile it is not a bad idea to mention these theories. They show us that the surface of our planet is constantly changing—that nothing is today quite as it was yesterday and that our descendants a million years hence will look at our maps (if they are still interested in our funny little globe, having long since learned to fly to other and bigger planets) with ill-concealed surprise, just as we contemplate a hypothetical map of the Tertiary or Silurian age and ask ourselves, "Can such things ever have been?"

What finally remained of all this ancient territory and what has not changed since the beginning of our so-called "historical times" consists of two parts, a large square of land north of the equator and a smaller triangle south of the equator. But both the square and the triangle suffer from the same geographical disadvantage. Their outer rims are higher than the interior and as a result the interior resembles a gigantic saucer. Such a condition, as we have already seen in the case of Australia, is very bad for the country at large. The high edges of the saucer prevent the sea winds from penetrating into the interior, which is therefore apt to turn into a desert, and furthermore they deprive that interior of its natural outlets towards the sea. For when the African rivers finally reach the ocean, after having wandered all over the landscape, they must break their way through a series of mountain-ranges. That means that they suffer from water-falls and cataracts where they are least wanted. It means that ships cannot use these rivers to reach the interior of the country. It means that trade must wait until artificial harbors have been constructed and until railroads have been built that circumnavigate the water-falls. In short, it means isolation.

To most of us Africa is merely the "black continent" and we usually associate it with tropical forests and Negroes. As a matter of fact, one-third of the 11,300,000 square miles which the continent occupies (it is therefore three times as large as Europe) are desert and of absolutely no value. The population of 140,-000,000 is divided into three groups of which one, that of the Negroes, is black, while the other two, the Hamites and the Semites, vary all the way from a dark chocolate to the whiteness of polished ivory.

It is natural, however, that the Negro should have forced himself more upon our attention than his lighter-colored neighbors. Not only does he impress us as something queer when we first see him, but the mistaken economic conceptions of our ancestors have dragged him all over the globe as a cheap and docile form of labor, and it is not always pleasant to be reminded of this disgraceful error of judgment. For Negro slavery has been one of the worst misfortunes that could possibly have overtaken both races, that of the white man as well as that of the black. We shall return to it a little later but we must first talk of Africa as it was before the invention of Negro slavery.

The Greeks were familiar with Egypt and with the Hamitic race which inhabited the valley of the Nile. The Hamitic races

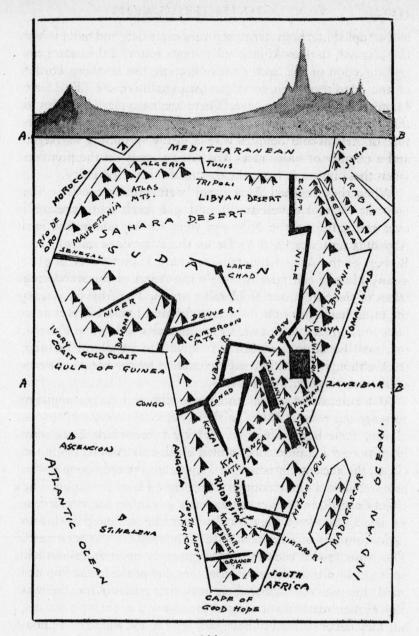

Africa

had occupied northern Africa at a very early date and had pushed
the original, darker-skinned inhabitants southward in the general direction of the Sudan while keeping the northern border
of the Mediterranean for their own exclusive use. The term
Hamitic is a very vague one. There are no typical Hamites as
there are typical Swedes or Chinamen. The Hamites are a mixture of Aryans and Semites with a heavy sprinkling of Negro
and a number of older races that were already on the premises
when these invaders from the east made their first entry.

When they reached Africa they were probably still in the
nomadic stage of development, and as a result they spread all
over the valley of the Nile and went further southward into
Abyssinia and westward as far as the Atlantic seaboard. The
Berbers of the Atlas Mountains are pure Hamites—or as pure
as any Hamite can possibly be—and several of the wandering
tribes of the Sahara are of Hamitic origin. The Abyssinians, on
the other hand, are now so hopelessly mixed with Semites as to
have lost a great many of their Hamitic traits. While the Fellahs,
the small-boned farmers of the Nile valley, are also of Hamitic
stock although mixed beyond recognition by thousands of years
of intermarriage with other races.

As a rule, when we try to classify different races, language
comes to our rescue. But in northern Africa the spoken tongue is
of very little help. There are Semitic tribes which speak only
Hamitic and Hamitic tribes which speak only Arabic, while the
Copts, the ancient Christians of Egypt, are the only people who
have retained a knowledge of the ancient Hamitic tongue. The
Greeks and Romans were apparently just as much puzzled as
we are. They solved the difficulty by calling all the people who
came from this neck of the woods "Ethiopians" or "black faces".
They wondered at their pyramids and at the negroid lips of their
Sphynx (or are the lips Hamitic? Ask the professors!) and ad-
mired the patience of their long-suffering peasants and the wisdom of their mathematicians and the learning of their physicians,
but they never seemed to have bothered to ask where these people might have come from. They spoke of them as Ethiopians.

One word of warning! If you should ever go to north Africa, be careful not to call all these people "Niggers" just because they are often rather dark-skinned. They might resent it and some of them are among the best fighters in the world. They have got the blood in them of those Egyptian warriors who conquered the whole of western Asia. They may even be the descendants of those Semitic Carthaginians who almost deprived Rome of the mastery of the Mediterranean. They may be the great-grandchildren of those Arab conquerors who not so very long ago overran the whole of southern Europe, or the children of those Algerian chieftains who put up such a terrific struggle when France tried to conquer Algeria and when Italy tried to get a foothold in Tunisia. Even if their hair be a little kinky, be careful and remember the fatal day in 1896 when the fuzzy-haired Ethiopians pushed the white-skinned Italians into the Red Sea.

So much for the Hamites, the first people the Europeans saw after they had sailed successfully across the Mediterranean. And little need be added about the Semites, with whom the Europeans came in very painful contact when Hannibal introduced the domesticated elephant to the plains of the Po. But once Carthage had been destroyed, the road to Africa lay open; and it is a curious fact that so few Europeans availed themselves of the opportunity to find out what lay beyond that vast sandy region to which the Romans had given the name of Numidia.

Nero, of all emperors, was the first to take a serious interest in African exploration. His expeditions apparently got as far as that village of Fashoda which some thirty years ago was almost the cause of a war between France and England. But the Nero-Nile expedition does not seem to have been the white man's furthest-south even in those long ago days. It now seems likely that the Carthaginians several centuries before had already crossed the Sahara and had visited the Gulf of Guinea. But Carthage had been destroyed and all knowledge about that central part of Africa was definitely lost. For the Sahara was a barrier which frightened even the hardiest explorers. They might, of course, have followed the coast regions. But these were so completely lacking in harbors that the problem of getting a fresh water supply became an almost insurmountable obstacle. Africa has a coast line of only 16,000 miles, while Europe, one-third its size, has a coast line of 20,000 miles. As a result, navigators who wanted to land anywhere on the African coast were obliged to drop anchor several miles away from land and must then cross the surf in an open row-boat, a procedure so uncomfortable and so dangerous that few of them ever tried it.

And so we had to wait until the beginning of the nineteenth century before we learned a few definite facts about the geography of Africa. Even then these sources of information were merely incidental, for the Portuguese, the first explorers of the African west coast, were on their way to the Indies and had very little interest in the land of the naked blackamoors. Since they could not reach India and China without circumnavigating that big barrier of the south, they felt their way along the African coast as carefully as a blind man trying to get out of a dark room. Without in any way looking for them they stumbled upon several islands, the Azores and the Canary Islands and the Cape Verde Islands. Finally in 1471 they reached the equator. Then in 1488 Bartholomew Diaz spotted the Storm Cape, now the Cape of Good Hope or briefly, the Cape. In 1498 Vasco da Gama rounded that cape and definitely located the shortest route from Europe to the Indies.

When that had been done, Africa once more dropped out of sight. It was a hindrance to navigation. It was too hot and too dry or too hot and too damp. The people were savages. The skippers of the sixteenth and seventeenth centuries, on their way to the Orient, called at the different islands, the Azores, Ascension, St. Helena, whenever scurvy and a high death rate among their sailors forced them to buy a few fresh vegetables. But African land to them was bad land. Give it a wide berth. And the poor heathen of that vast continent might have continued to dwell in peace if it had not been for the kindheartedness of the first man who was ever ordained a priest in the New World.

Bartolomé de las Casas was the son of a man who had accompanied Columbus on his original voyage to America. The son, appointed Bishop of Chiapa in Mexico, received as compensation for his services a piece of land with the Indian occupants attached to it. In other words, he became a plain, ordinary slave-holder. Every Spaniard then living in the New World had a certain number of Indians who worked for him. It was a bad system but, like so many bad systems, it was tolerated because,

On the way to the Slavery Coast

being everybody's business, it was nobody's business. It just happened that las Casas one day clearly realized just how bad the system was and how unfair it happened to be to the original owners of the land, who were now forced to work in the mines and perform all sorts of menial tasks which they never would have touched while they were still free.

He went to Spain to do something about it. The all-powerful Cardinal Jimenes, confessor of Queen Isabella, thought that he was right, appointed him "Protector of the Indians" and sent him back to America to write a report. Las Casas returned to Mexico but found his superiors completely cold on the subject. The Indians had been given unto the Christians to do their bidding, just like the animals of the field and the birds of the air and the fishes of the sea. (See Genesis 1: 28.) Why start something that would upset the entire economic fabric of the New World and furthermore would very seriously interfere with profits?

Then las Casas, who took his God-given task very seriously, had a bright idea. The Indian preferred death to captivity, as had been proved in Haiti where the number of natives had dropped from 1,000,000 to 60,000 in less than fifteen years. But the Negro of Africa did not seem to mind being a slave. In the year 1516 (direful date in the history of the New World) las Casas published the details of his famous humanitarian scheme for the complete liberation of his Indian charges. Each Spaniard living in the New Spain was to be granted the right to import twelve African Negroes and the Indians were to be allowed to return to what remained of their own farms after the immigrants had deprived them of all the better parts.

Poor las Casas lived long enough to come to a true realization of what he had done. His shame (for he was an honest man) was such that he retired to a monastery in Haiti. Afterwards he returned to public life and tried once more to fight the battles of the unfortunate heathen. But nobody listened to him, and when he died in 1556 new plans were under way to bind the Indians even more fully to the soil, and the African slave trade too was in full swing.

What this trade meant to Africa during the 300 years of its existence we can only guess from the few reliable figures that have come down to us. The actual slave-hunting was not done by white men. The Arabs, who could wander at will over the entire northern part which had gradually been converted to Mohammedanism, held a monopoly of that racket. They had sold an occasional shipload of blackamoors to the Portuguese ever since the year 1434, but their business did not assume the gigantic proportions of the later days until the year 1517. There was big money in it. The Emperor Charles V (he of the famous Habsburg chin) bestowed upon one of his Flemish friends a grant which allowed him to carry 4000 African slaves each year

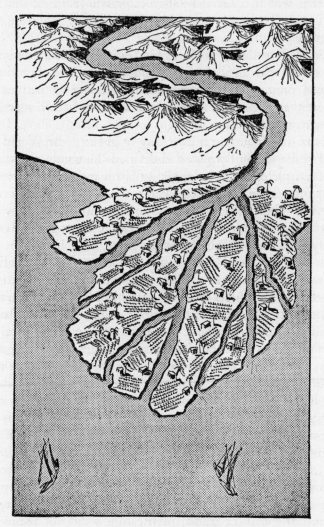

The Delta of the Nile

to Haiti, Cuba and Porto Rico. The Fleming at once sold his
imperial patent to a Genoese speculator who paid him 25,000
ducats for it. The Genoese in turn sold it to a combination of
Portuguese and these Portuguese went to Africa and got in touch
with the Arab dealers and the Arab dealers raided a number of
Sudanese villages until they had about 10,000 slaves together
(one must count on a heavy percentage of loss during the voyage)
who were then packed into the hold of some evil-smelling carack
and dispatched across the ocean.

Rumors of this new and easy way to get rich spread far and
wide. The Papal Bull which had divided the whole world into
two halves, one of which belonged to Spain and one to Portugal,
made it impossible for the Spaniards to visit the "slave coast"
themselves. The actual business of buying and transporting this
black merchandise was therefore left to the Portuguese. But as
soon as the power of the Portuguese had been broken by the
English and the Dutch, slave-running became a monopoly of
these two Christian nations. They continued to provide all the
world with their "black ivory" (as the Bristol and London
merchants playfully called it) until the year 1811 when Parliament finally passed a bill making the traffic in slaves a felony
punishable with a fine and deportation. But it was a long time
from 1517 until 1811 and until even afterwards, for slave-
smuggling continued for fully another thirty years in spite of
all the English warships. It did not fully come to an end until
the early sixties of the nineteenth century when practically all
European and American nations had abolished slavery definitely.
(The Argentine abolished it in 1813, Mexico in 1829, U.S.A.
in 1863, Brazil in 1888.)

How important the trade was in the eyes of Europe's rulers
and statesmen is proved by the efforts they made to gain a
monopoly of the slave traffic for the sole benefit of their own
country. The refusal of Spain to continue a slave contract, thus
far held by a few English merchants, even led to a war between
England and Spain; and one of the stipulations of the famous
peace treaty of Utrecht definitely transferred the West India

slave monopoly from the Dutch to the English. Not to be outdone, the Dutch, who in 1620 had landed the first African slaves
on Virginian soil, hastened to avail themselves of a law passed
during the reign of William and Mary which had opened up the
slave trade with the colonies to all the nations of the world. Indeed the Dutch West India Company, which through its scandalous neglect was responsible for the loss of Nieuw Amsterdam,
only escaped bankruptcy because it made so much money out of
its traffic in slaves.

We have very few statistics upon the subject, for the slavers
were usually not the sort of men who took a scientific interest in
their business; but those we have are appalling. The French
Cardinal Lavigerie, archbishop of Carthage and founder of the
famous Pères Blancs (the missionaries who have done so much
good in northern Africa) and a man therefore thoroughly con-
versant with African affairs, estimated that at least 2,000,000
people per year had been lost to Africa on account of the slave
trade, including those who were killed by the hardships of the
march to the coast, the children who died because they were too
young to be of any value and were therefore left to the mercies
of the wild animals, and those who were actually shipped away
to foreign shores.

Dr. Livingstone, another highly competent judge, put the
actual number of slaves taken away from their homes every
twelve months (regardless of those who died because they were
left behind without any protection) at 350,000, of whom only
70,000 ever reached the other side of the ocean.

Between 1700 and 1786 not less than 600,000 slaves were
brought to Jamaica alive, and during the same period more than
2,000,000 slaves were carried from Africa to the West Indies
by two of the smaller English slave companies. By the end of
the eighteenth century, Liverpool, London and Bristol maintained a fleet of 200 vessels with a total capacity of 47,000
Negroes, which plied regularly between the Gulf of Guinea and
the New World. In 1791 when the Quakers and the enemies of
slavery in general began their agitation against this outrage, a

survey of the slave stations along the Bight of Benin showed 14 English, 15 Dutch, 4 Portuguese, 4 Danish and 3 French. But the British were better equipped and handled one-half of the

The water-hole

whole trade, the rest being divided among the other four nations.

Of the horrible things that happened on the mainland we learned very little until much later, when the British, in order to stamp this business out by the roots, went on shore in search of further violaters. It then appeared that native chieftains had been among the chief offenders, selling their own subjects as unceremoniously as those German rulers of the eighteenth cen-

tury sold their regiments of recruits to the English for the purpose of squelching that little rebellion in Virginia and Massa-
chusetts. But the general organization of the business had always
been in the hands of the Arabs. This is rather curious. The Koran
highly disapproves of such pursuits and Mohammedan law in
general is much more lenient towards the slaves than the Christian edicts used to be. According to the laws of the white man,
the child of a slave by her master was in turn held to be a slave,
whereas according to the Koran, such a child must follow the
status of the father and must therefore be considered as free.

The opening up of the Congo by the unspeakable Leopold of
Belgium and the demand for cheap labor to work His Majesty's
concessions started a temporary revival of the slave trade between the Portuguese colony of Angola and the interior of the
Congo basin. But fortunately when that miserable old man (a
medieval scoundrel on a constitutional throne in a modern democratic country—as strange a contradiction in terms as had been
seen for a long time) died, the Congo Free State had already
been taken over by the Belgian state and that meant the end of
the last attempts to make money out of buying and selling human
beings.

The beginning of the relation between the white man and the
black one was therefore as unfortunate as it possibly could be.
But what followed was just as bad. The reasons for this unfortunate state of affairs I must now describe in as few words as
possible.

In Asia the white man came face to face with races that were
either as civilized as he was himself or more so. Which meant
that they were able to fight back and that the white man must
mind his p's and q's or suffer the consequences.

The great Sepoy rebellion in India of the fifties of the last
century, the terrible insurrection of Diepo Negoro, which twenty
years before had almost deprived Holland of Java, the expulsion of all foreigners from Japan, the Boxer Rebellion of only
a few years ago in China, the present unrest in India and the open
defiance of Europe's and America's notes in regard to Manchuria

by Japan are lessons which the white man could not afford to ignore.

In Australia the white man came in contact with the poor, savage remnants of the early Stone Age whom he could kill at will and with as few pangs of conscience as he destroyed the wild dingos that ate up his sheep.

The greater part of America was practically uninhabited when the white man arrived. The high and healthy plateaus of Central America and the north-western part of the Andes (Mexico and Peru) had a dense population, but the rest was almost empty. The few wandering nomads could be easily pushed aside and disease and degeneration then did the rest.

But in Africa conditions were different, for in Africa, regardless of slavery, regardless of sickness, regardless of bad gin, regardless of bad treatment, the population refused to die out. What the white man destroyed in the morning was replaced over night. Yet the white man insisted upon taking the black man's property. The result has been a holocaust of blood, the like of which the world has rarely seen; and the end is not yet. It is a struggle between the white man's gunpowder and the black man's tropical fertility.

Let us look at the map and give you a general outline of where things stand at the present moment.

Roughly speaking, Africa can be divided into seven parts and these I shall now take up, one by one. We begin in the left upper corner, in the north-west, the infamous coast of Barbary which made our ancestors tremble with fear whenever they had to sail past it on their way from northern Europe to the ports of Italy and the Levant. For it was the land of the terrible Barbary pirates and capture by them meant years of slavery until the family at home had borrowed enough money to set their poor cousin free.

This whole territory consists of mountains, and quite high mountains, too. And these mountains explain why that country had to develop as it did and why even today it has not yet actually been conquered by the white man. They are very treacherous mountains, full of ambushes and deep ravines, allowing a marauding party to make their attack and disappear without any one being the wiser.

Aeroplanes and long distance guns are of comparatively little value here. It was only a few years ago that the Spaniards met with a number of terrible defeats at the hands of the Riff people. Our ancestors knew this, and they preferred to pay an annual tribute to the different Sultans ruling this part of the African coast, rather than risk their navies and their reputations on dangerous expeditions against harbors which no white man had ever been allowed to visit. They maintained special consuls in Algiers and Tunis whose business it was to arrange for the ransom of their captured subjects and they supported religious organizations which had no other purpose than to look after the fate of the sailors who had been unfortunate enough to fall into the hands of the Moors.

Politically speaking, this north-western corner of the African continent is now divided into four separate parts, all of which however take their orders from Paris. The process of infiltration and occupation began in the year 1830. A common, ordinary fly-swatter was the immediate cause of the outbreak of hostilities but the real reason was that old public scandal of the north-western Mediterranean, piracy.

At the Congress of Vienna the European powers had decided that "something must be done" to suppress piracy in the Mediterranean. But of course the different powers could not decide who was to undertake the job, for the hero might keep some territory for himself and that would be unfair to the others— the usual story of all diplomatic conferences.

Now there were two Algerian Jews (all business in northern Africa had been in the hands of Jews for centuries) who had a claim against the French government for grain delivered to the French government in the days before Napoleon—one of those old claims that are forever cropping up in the chancellories of the Old and New World and that have been the cause of so many misunderstandings during the last two centuries. If nations, like individuals, would only pay their bills as they go along, we surely would all of us be much happier and certainly much safer.

In the course of the negotiations about this little grain bill, the Dey of Algiers one day lost his temper and hit the French consul with his fly-swatter. Then there was a blockade and a shot was fired (probably by accident, but such things are always happening where there are war-ships around) and an expeditionary force sailed across the Mediterranean and on the fifth of July of the year 1830 the French marched into Algiers and the Dey was taken prisoner and sent into exile and the war was on in all seriousness.

The mountain people found a leader, a certain Abd-el-Kader, a pious Mohammedan and a man of great intelligence and courage, who held out against the invaders for fifteen years and who did not surrender until the year 1847. He had previously received the promise that he would be allowed to remain in his own country, but this promise was broken and he was taken to France. Napoleon III however set him free on condition that he would never again disturb the peace of his fatherland and Abd-el-Kader retired to Damascus, where he spent the rest of his days in philosophic meditations and pious deeds and where he died in 1883.

Long before his demise the last revolt in Algeria had been suppressed. Today Algeria is merely another department of France. Its people have the right to choose their own representatives and protect their interests in the French parliament in Paris. Its young men have the honor to serve as conscripts in the French army, but that is not entirely a matter of choice. But from an economic point of view, the French have done a great deal of excellent work to improve the living conditions of their new subjects.

The plain between the Atlas Mountains and the sea, called the Tell, raises grain. The Shat plateau, so called after many small salt lakes, is a grazing country, and the mountain slopes are more and more being used for wine-growing, while large irrigation works are under construction to allow the raising of tropical fruit

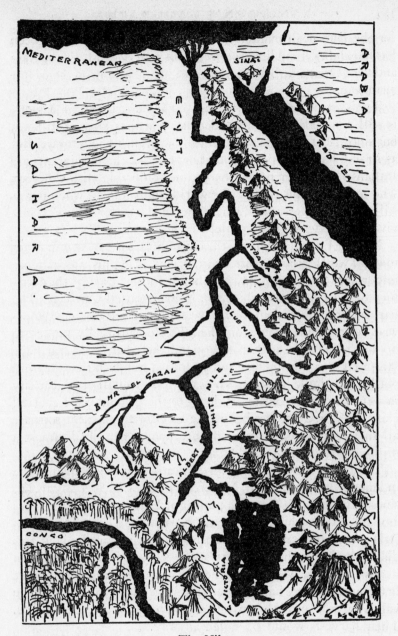

The Nile

for the European market. Iron and copper deposits have been located and railroad lines connect them with Algiers (the capital) and with Oran and Bizerta, the three main harbors on the Mediterranean.

Tunis, immediately to the east of the department of Algiers, is still nominally an independent state with a king of its own, but since 1881 it has been practically a French protectorate. But as France has no surplus population, most of the immigrants are Italians. The latter have a hard time competing with the Jews who moved to this part of the world centuries ago when it was still a Turkish possession, where they had a better chance to survive than under Christian rule.

Next to Tunis, the capital, the city of Sfax is the most important town. Two thousand years ago the land of Tunis was of more importance than it is today for then it formed part of the territory of Kart-hadshat, which the Romans called Carthage. The harbor, which had room for 220 vessels, may still be seen. Otherwise very little remains, for when the Romans really wanted to do a job, they did it thoroughly and their hatred of Carthage (inspired of course by fear and jealousy) was such that they did not leave a single house standing when they finally took the city in 146 B. C. They burned it down to the ground. The charred ruins, lying sixteen feet below the level of the present soil, are all that remains of a city that once upon a time had almost a million inhabitants.

The north-western corner of Africa is officially known as the independent sultanate of Morocco. There still is a sultan but since 1912 he too is merely a puppet of France. Not that he ever amounted to much. The Kabyles, the mountain folk of the Anti-Atlas, were too strongly entrenched to bother much about this distant majesty who for safety's sake varied constantly between his two capitals, Morocco in the south and the holy city of Fez in the north. These handy mountains were such a menace that the valley people never even undertook to cultivate their fields. Their harvests would be stolen anyway.

One can say a great deal against French rule in these parts of

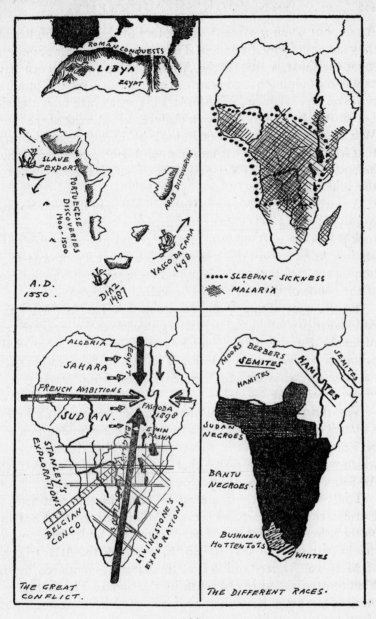

Top-left panel:
ROMAN CONQUESTS
LIBYA
EGYPT
SLAVE EXPORT
PORTUGUESE DISCOVERIES 1400–1500
ARAB DISCOVERIES
VASCO DA GAMA 1498
A.D. 1550.
DIAZ 1487

Top-right panel:
•••••• SLEEPING SICKNESS
MALARIA

Bottom-left panel:
ALGERIA
SAHARA
EGYPT
FRENCH AMBITIONS
SUDAN
FASHODA 1898
EMIN PASHA
STANLEY'S EXPLORATIONS
BELGIAN CONGO
LIVINGSTONE'S EXPLORATIONS
THE GREAT CONFLICT.

Bottom-right panel:
MOORS BERBERS
SEMITES
HAMITES
HAMITES
SEMITES
SUDAN NEGROES
BANTU NEGROES
BUSHMEN HOTTENTOTS
WHITES
THE DIFFERENT RACES.

Africa

Africa, but when it comes to the safety of the public highroads, they have performed wonders. They moved the center of government to Rabat, a city on the Atlantic, where the French navy can lend a helping hand in case of need. Rabat is several hundred miles north of Agadir, another Atlantic port which unexpectedly got into the lime-light four years before the outbreak of the Great War when the Germans sent a gun-boat there to remind France that Morocco must not become another Algiers, an incident which helped a great deal to bring about the final disastrous conflict of the year 1914.

A small corner of Morocco just opposite Gibraltar is a Spanish colony. It was given to Spain as a peace-offering when France took possession of Morocco. The two cities of Ceuta and Melilla are best known from the newspaper stories of recent date mentioning the defeats which the unwilling Spanish troops suffered at the hands of the natives, the so-called Riff-Kabyles.

To the west of the Riff Mountains lies Tangier, the internationalist city where during the eighteenth and nineteenth centuries the European ambassadors accredited to the court of the Sultan of Morocco used to reside. The Sultan did not want them too near his own court and Tangier was therefore chosen as their place of residence.

The future of this entire mountainous triangle is no longer a matter of doubt. In another fifty years, that whole region will be French, together with the second natural division of Africa which we shall discuss now—that of the great brown desert, the As-Sahra of the Arabs, the Sahara of our modern maps.

The Sahara, which is almost as large as the continent of Europe, runs all the way from the Atlantic to the Red Sea and on the other side of the Red Sea it continues under the guise of the Arabian peninsula. In the north, except for the Atlas triangle of Morocco, Algiers and Tunis, the Sahara is bordered by the Mediterranean and in the south by the Sudan. The Sahara is a plateau, but not a very high one, for most of it lies at an altitude of only 1200 feet. Here and there are the remnants of old mountain ridges, worn away by wind and sand. There are a fair number of oases where the subterranean water allows a few thrifty Arabs to lead a not over-abundant existence. The density of population is 0.04 per square mile which means that the Sahara is practically uninhabited. The best known among the wandering desert tribes are the Tuaregs, excellent fighters. The other Saharians are a mixture of Semite (or Arab) and Hamite (or Egyptian) and Sudanese Negro.

The French Foreign Legion looks after the safety of travellers and does this exceedingly well. These French Legionnaires (who, by the way, are never allowed on French soil) may be a bit rough at times, but they have a tough problem on their hands. To police a region as large as Europe with a mere handful of men is no job for saints. Therefore, if we can believe common rumor, very few saints have been encouraged to enlist. The old caravan roads are beginning to lose their importance. The tractor-wheeled automobile has taken the place of the smelly camel. It is much less costly and infinitely more dependable for very long distances. The days when tens of thousands of camels would foregather in Timbuktu to bring salt to the people of the western Sahara are gone forever.

Until the year 1911 that part of the Sahara which borders on the Mediterranean was ruled by a Pasha of its own who recognized the Sultan of Turkey as his over-lord. In that year the Italians, knowing that the French were going to take Morocco as soon as they could do so without provoking a war with Germany, suddenly remembered that Libya (the Latin name for Tripoli) had once upon a time been a very prosperous Roman colony. They crossed the Mediterranean and took 400,000 square miles of African territory and hoisted the Italian flag over it and asked the world politely what it was going to do about it. As nobody was particularly interested in Tripoli (sand without iron or oil) the descendants of Caesar were allowed to keep their new colony and they are now busy building roads and trying to raise a little cotton for the textile factories of Lombardy.

On the east, this Italian experiment in the difficult art of colonizing is bordered by Egypt. This country owed most of its prosperity to the fact that it was really a sort of island cut off from the west by the Libyan desert and protected against the south by the Nubian desert, while the Red Sea and the Mediterranean took care of the boundaries in the north and in the east. The actual Egypt, the Egypt of history, the ancient land of the Pharaohs, which was the great store-house of art and learning and science of the ancient world, consisted of a very narrow strip situated along the shore of a river almost as long as the Mississippi. The real Egypt, not counting the desert, is smaller than the kingdom of the Netherlands. But whereas Holland can feed only 7,000,000 people, the Nile valley is so fertile that it is able to support double that number. When the great irrigation works, begun by the English, shall have been finished, there will be room for many more. But the Fellahs (the tillers of the soil who are almost without exception Mohammedans) will have to stick to their farms, for industry is not easy in a country which has neither coal nor water-power.

Ever since the great Mohammedan conquest of the eighth century, Egypt had belonged to Turkey, under a khedive or king of its own. In 1882 England occupied the country under the pretext that its financial conditions were so hopelessly bad as to warrant interference on the part of a competent European power. But the demand of Egypt for the Egyptians became so strong after the Great War that the English were forced to renounce their claims and Egypt was once more recognized as an independent kingdom which had a right to conclude all sorts of treaties with other foreign powers except commercial treaties, which must first of all be submitted to England. The British troops were to be withdrawn from all Egyptian cities except Port Saïd. Finally Alexandria, which had become the main commercial port on the Mediterranean since Damietta and Rosetta on the delta had lost their importance, must be allowed to remain an English naval base.

It was a generous agreement and a perfectly safe one, for meanwhile England had definitely occupied that eastern part of the Sudan through which the Nile happens to flow. By getting

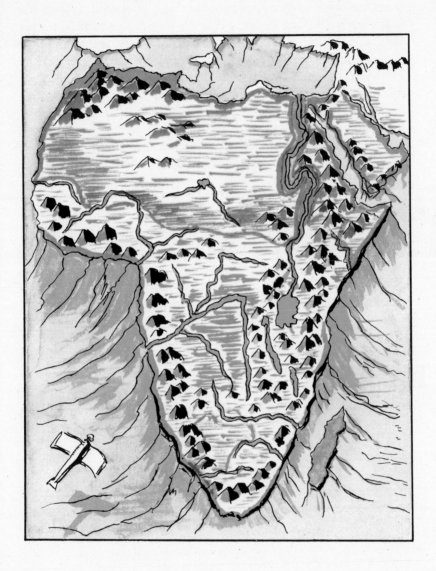

Africa

control over the water of this river upon which 12,000,000 little brown Egyptians depend for their living, England is certain that it can always make its wants more or less understood in distant Cairo.

Any one however at all familiar with political conditions in the Near East will hardly blame England for trying to maintain

Oasis

a strong hold upon this part of the world. The Suez Canal, the short cut to India, runs entirely through Egyptian territory and it would be suicidal for England to let some one else get hold of that salty artery of trade.

The canal, of course, is not of England's making. As a matter of fact, the British government tried as hard as it could to prevent de Lesseps from beginning to dig any canal at all. There were two reasons why England should have opposed this plan. In the first place, England did not have the slightest confidence in the oft-repeated assertions of Napoleon III that the canal, built by

French engineers and with French money, was merely a commercial venture. Queen Victoria might love her dear brother in the Tuileries, who once upon a time had done service as a special London constable when her beloved subjects were on the verge of rioting for bread, but the average Englishman did not care to hear that name which reminded him too much of a certain nightmare of half a century before. And in the second place, England feared that this short cut to the Indies and China and Japan would seriously interfere with the prosperity of her own good city on the Cape of Good Hope.

Nevertheless, the canal was built and Signor Verdi composed his noble opera, "Aïda", in honor of the occasion and the Khedive ruined himself providing free board and lodging and free tickets to "Aïda" to all his foreign visitors, who filled not less than sixty-nine vessels when they went a-picnicking from Port Saïd to Suez, which was the terminus of the canal on the Red Sea.

Then England changed her tactics and her prime-minister, Benjamin Disraeli, who belonged to a race that has never yet been accused of lacking in business ability, managed to get hold of a majority of the canal stock which until then had belonged to the Khedive. And as Napoleon no longer counted and the route proved to be a god-send for the trade between Asia and Europe and produced almost $40,000,000 a year in revenue alone (28,000,000 tons passed through it in 1930, which is almost one-third of the total number of tons that passed through our own Sault Ste. Marie Canal), there have been no further complaints from the side of the British government.

By the way, the famous antiquities of Egypt are situated all over the land. The pyramids you will find in the neighborhood of Cairo where Memphis was once upon a time located. But Thebes, the old capital of upper Egypt, was situated several hundred miles further up the river. Unfortunately the tremendous irrigation works of Assuan have turned the temple of Philae into little islands which are now entirely surrounded by the muddy waters of the Nile and which are therefore doomed to ultimate destruction. The grave of King Tut-ank-Amen, who

died fourteen centuries before the beginning of our era, is also
to be found in that part of Egypt, as are the graves of many other
kings whose former household possessions and whose mummies
are gathered together in the museum of Cairo which is fast becoming a cemetery as well as one of the world's most interesting
collections of antiquities.

The third part of Africa, geographically different from all
other sections, is the Sudan. The Sudan runs almost parallel
with the Sahara but it does not continue quite so far eastward because it is brought to a sudden halt by the high plateaus of Abyssinia which separate it from the Red Sea.

Now in the great international bridge game played with
Africa as a stake, when one nation announces "three spades" the
others at once answer "four diamonds". England had taken the
Cape from the Dutch during the beginning of the nineteenth
century. The original settlers, being Dutch and therefore obstinate, had packed their belongings in their covered wagons,
had inspanned their oxen and had trekked northward (these are
now perfectly good English words. Since the late Boer War you
will find them in any good dictionary.) The English were playing the game the Russians had played in the sixteenth century
during the conquest of Siberia. You will remember how it was
played. As soon as enough Russian fugitives had settled a new
region of Siberia, the Czar's troops went after them and informed
them that since they were originally Russian subjects, the land
they had just occupied was therefore of course Russian property
and the government in Moscow would let them know when to
expect the tax-collector.

The English were forever following the Boers further northward, trying to annex their territory. It had come to several very
disagreeable conflicts, for the Boer farmers, having spent most
of their lives out in the open, were better shots than the Cockney
regiments turned loose against them. After the battle of Majuba
in 1881 (Gladstone, who was eminently fair in this matter, on
that occasion gave a lesson in forbearance which all statesmen
might well copy: "Just because we were defeated last night and

our pride is hurt is no reason why we should insist on the shedding of more blood!"), the Boers gained a temporary respite and regained their independence.

But all the world knew what the end would be of this struggle between the British Empire and a handful of farmers. English land companies, acquiring enormous tracts of land from native chiefs, were creeping up further and further northward. Meanwhile British troops, in order to establish order all over Egypt, were slowly but steadily working their way southward along both banks of the Nile. A famous English missionary was exploring the central region of Africa with the most brilliant results. Plainly the English were digging themselves a tunnel right through the heart of the Dark Continent. They had started building operations simultaneously in Cairo and in the Cape (the usual way for tunnels to be constructed). Sooner or later the two ends would meet in the region of the great lakes where both the Nile and the Congo came from, and then England could run her trains from Alexandria to Table Bay (so-called after the Table Mountain, that curiously shaped mesa that forms a natural background for Capetown) without a change of cars.

What England was so evidently trying to do along a line running from north to south, France now planned to do along a line running from west to east, from the Atlantic to the Red Sea, let us say from Dakar in the Senegal to Djibouti in French Somaliland which was also the port of entry for the whole of Abyssinia and which even then was connected by railroad with the Abyssinian capital of Addis Ababa.

Such gigantic projects take time but not quite as much time as we sometimes feel inclined to believe when we look at the map and contemplate the terrific difficulties that were to be overcome ere that line should ever have reached such a hard-to-get-at spot as Lake Chad, just north of Nigeria—and from there the hardest part of the route would begin, for the eastern Sudan (now the Anglo-Egyptian Sudan) was as inhospitable a region as the Sahara.

Capital, however, in the hands of an energetic modern power,

The Suez Canal

especially if it sees a chance of making one hundred cents on the dollar, will dynamite its way through time and space as lightly and easily and usually as ruthlessly as a war tank going through a flock of geese. The Third French Republic, trying to regain the prestige the Second Empire had lost, was energetic enough, and the stockings and the hidden old cigar boxes of the French peasants produced the necessary capital. The struggle for the right of way from west to east in competition with the right of way from north to south was on in all seriousness and the French, who ever since the beginning of the seventeenth century had been fighting with the English and the Dutch for the possession of the land situated between the Senegal and Gambia Rivers, now used that territory as a political can opener with which to get at the contents of the unlimited area of the whole of the Sudan.

I can't go into the details of all the operations and machinations and the diplomatic steps and the commercial steps and the lying and cheating and horse-dealing and cajoling that had to take place before France could claim the greater part of the western Sudan as part of their African Empire. Even today they keep up the pretense of being merely the temporary administrators of a number of protectorates and mandates, but everybody has gradually learned what that means. The gangsters who have acquired exclusive control over the New York milk racket will probably call their band of cutthroats "The Milk Dealers' Protective Association". European nations, quick to learn even from our humble highwaymen, have coined the word "mandates". But the results are about the same.

Geographically speaking, the French have made a wise choice. Most of the Sudan is very fertile, which of course explains the fact that the natives are by far the most intelligent and industrious of all the different Negro tribes that inhabit Africa. Part of the soil is the same sort of loess as that found in northern China, and as Senegambia (merely another name for Senegal) is not cut off from the sea by a mountain ridge, the interior has sufficient rainfall to allow the people to raise cattle and corn. The African Negro, by the way, is no rice-eater, but a mealie-eater, "mealie" being a sort of second-cousin to our own corn-mush but a little less delicately prepared. They are also very remarkable artists whose curious bits of sculpture and pottery when exposed in our museums never fail to attract the attention of the multitudes

Kilimandjaro

because they look for all the world exactly like the most recent masterpieces of our own futurist painters.

The Sudanese, however, have one great disadvantage from the white man's point of view. They are ardent followers of the Prophet whose missionaries overran and converted the whole of northern Africa. In the Sudan, one race especially, the Fula or Fellatah, a mixture of Negroes and Berbers, who are to be found everywhere south and east of the Senegal River as the dominating class of society, have long been a menace to French authority. But railroads and roads and airplanes and tanks and caterpillar tractors are more powerful than all the Sudras or verses of the Koran. The Fellatahs are learning to drive flivvers. Romance is rapidly making its exit by way of the gas-station.

Before the French and the English and the Germans settled down in the Sudan, the greater part of this territory belonged to those charming native princes who had grown rich stealing each other's subjects and selling them into slavery. Some of these potentates have gained a certain sad fame as among the most picturesque but also the most brutal of by-gone despots. The King of Dahomey with his highly efficient army of Amazons is still fresh in the memory of those who as children saw the last of his troops perform at our country fairs; and that may have been one of the reasons why the natives put up so little resistance when the European war ships appeared. No matter how greedy the new white master might be, he was always a great improvement on the black tyrant who had just been deposed.

The greater part of the southern Sudan is cut off from the ocean by a high mountain ridge which follows the coast line of the Gulf of Guinea. This prevents such rivers as the Niger from playing a really important part in the development of the interior, for like the Congo, the Niger is obliged to take a very roundabout way to avoid the main mass of these hills. Then just before it reaches the coast, it must dig a channel through these rocks with the result that there are a number of cataracts where they are least wanted (that is, near the sea) while the upper part of the river is apt to be navigable enough but there is nobody there to navigate it.

In the case of the Niger even this does not hold true. It is really more of a succession of long lakes and small pools than a regular river, as Mungo Park discovered in 1805 when he gave his life to find the river of which he had dreamed since he was a small boy in Scotland. This may have been responsible for the fact that the Sudanese, deprived of all water-ways, were able to make such a success of their overland trade-routes, and that

Timbuktu, on the left bank of the upper Niger, could become such a very important center of trade, the Nizhni-Novgorod of Africa, where the north and the south and the east and the west came together to do business.

Timbuktu owes a great deal of its popularity to its queer name which sounds like the magic formula of some mysterious African witch-doctor. In the year 1353 it had been visited by the Ibn Batuta, the Marco Polo of the Arab world. Twenty years later it made its first appearance on Spanish maps as a great market for gold and salt, substances which were of almost equal value in medieval days. When the English Major Gordon Laing reached it in the year 1826, after having crossed the Sahara from Tripoli, it was merely the ruins of its former self, having been repeatedly attacked and destroyed by Tuareg and Fellatah marauders. On his way to the coast Major Laing was murdered by the Fellatah of Senegambia, but from that time on, Timbuktu was no longer another mysterious Mecca or Khiva or Tibet, but became a plain, ordinary "objective" of the French forces operating in the western Sudan.

In the year 1893 it was taken by a French "army", consisting of one French naval ensign and six white men, accompanied by twelve Senegalese. The power of the desert tribes had not yet been broken, for soon afterwards they killed off most of the white invaders and almost completely destroyed a relief corps of two hundred men which was coming up from the coast to avenge the defeat of the naval contingent.

But of course it was then merely a matter of time before all of the western Sudan should be in French hands. The same held true of the region around Lake Chad in the central part of the Sudan, which was easier of access because the Benue River, a tributary of the Niger which runs due east and west, is much more navigable than the Niger itself.

Lake Chad, which lies about 700 feet high, is very shallow and rarely deeper than about 20 feet. In contrast to most other inland seas, the water is fresh and not salt. But it is growing smaller and smaller all the time and in another century it will

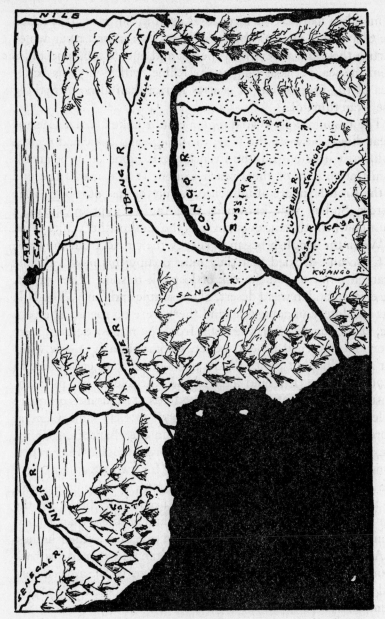

Congo and Niger

be merely a marsh. One river loses itself in this lake. It is called the Shari, and the fact that it is merely an inland river which starts a thousand miles from the sea and ends a thousand miles from the sea, yet is as long as the Rhine, will give you a better idea of the proportions of central Africa than almost anything else I can think of.

The mountainous Wadai region east of Lake Chad acts as the great divide between the Nile, the Congo and the Chad region. Politically it belongs to the French and is supposed to be an administrative part of the French Congo. It also marks the end of the French sphere of influence, for on the east of it begins the eastern Sudan, now known as the Anglo-Egyptian Sudan, a country which the ancients knew as the land of the White Nile.

When the English began to survey their road from the Cape to Cairo and decided that they must occupy this most valuable strategic point or run the risk of losing it to some other nation, the eastern Sudan was a desert, plain, simple and fancy. The Nile was absolutely unnavigable, and there were no roads. The people, at the mercy of all the scum from the nearby deserts, were poor and wretched beyond belief. Geographically it was without any value, but politically its possibilities were enormous. In 1876 therefore, England induced the Khedive of Egypt to entrust the administration of these hundreds of thousands of square miles of "nominal Egyptian territory" to that same General Gordon whom we have already met in the chapter on China, assisting the Peking government to repress the Tai-Ping rebellion. Gordon remained in the Sudan for two years and with the help of a very clever Italian assistant, one Romolo Gessi, he accomplished the one thing most needed: he broke up the last of the slave rings, shot the leaders and set more than 10,000 men and women free and allowed them to return to their homes.

As soon, however, as this stern Puritan had turned his back upon the Sudan, the old terrible conditions of misgovernment and oppression returned. The result was the outbreak of a movement for complete independence, a sort of "Sudan for the Sudanese and all the slave-trading we want". The leader of this

The desert

rebellion was a certain Mahommed Ahmed, who called himself a Mahdi or leader to show the faithful the road of the true Moslem faith. The Mahdi was successful. In 1883 he conquered El Obeid in Kordofan, which is now connected with Cairo by rail, and later in the same year he destroyed an Egyptian army of 10,000 men under Hicks Pasha, an English colonel in the service of the Khedive. Meanwhile, in 1882, England had assumed a protectorate over Egypt and the Mahdi now had to contend with a more dangerous enemy.

But England was too experienced in colonial affairs and knew the difficulties too well to rush into any rash expeditions. For the moment she counselled the Egyptian government to withdraw its troops from the Sudan. General Gordon was once more sent to Khartum to arrange for the withdrawal of the remaining Egyptian garrisons. But no sooner had he reached Khartum than the forces of the Mahdi swept northward and left Gordon and his companions marooned in Khartum. He sent urgent messages for relief. But Gordon was a Puritan mystic. Gladstone, who was then the head of the British government, was an Episcopal mystic. These two mystics, the one in London on the Thames and the other in Khartum on the Nile, did not like each other. And because they did not like each other, it was impossible for them to cooperate intelligently.

Gladstone sent a relief expedition, but much too late, for when it was still several days away from Khartum the town was taken by the forces of the Mahdi, and Gordon was murdered. That happened in January of 1885. In June of the same year the Mahdi died. His successor maintained himself as ruler of the Sudan until the year 1898 when an Anglo-Egyptian army under Kitchener wiped his followers from the face of the desert and recaptured the entire territory as far south as Uganda, which is on the equator.

The English have done an enormous amount of good in improving the condition of the natives by giving them roads, railroads, safety, by stamping out all sorts of hideous and unnecessary forms of disease, the usual things which the white man does

for the black man and for which the white man expects the black
man to say thank you, if he is that foolish, but for which the
black man will shoot the white man in the back just as soon as
he can, as the white man will well enough know if he has had a
couple of centuries of colonial experience.

The railroad southward from Alexandria and Cairo now runs
as far as El Obeid in the west and Port Sudan on the Red Sea
in the east. If in the years to come an enemy should suddenly
destroy the Suez Canal, England can still transport her troops
from east to west via this railroad that runs through the valley
of Egypt and then recrosses the Nubian Desert.

But now we have got to go back a few years and see how the
Mahdi revolt was to have the most far-reaching influence upon
the development of Africa in a way which had nothing at all to
do with the Mahdi himself or his ambitions to become the independent ruler of the land of his fathers.

When the Mahdi uprising began, the Egyptian forces furthest
towards the south were forced to find a refuge in a part of central Africa which was then practically unknown. Speke had
crossed it in 1858 when he discovered Lake Victoria, the mother
lake, so to speak, of the river Nile. But most of the land between
Lake Albert and Lake Victoria was still terra incognita. This
Egyptian force, under command of a German physician, a certain Dr. Eduard Schnitzer, better known by his Turkish title of
Emin Pasha, had disappeared from sight after the fall of Khartum, and the world was curious to know what had become of
its leader.

The job of finding him was entrusted to an American newspaper man by the name of Stanley. His name was really Row-
lands, but he had adopted that of a New Orleans merchant who
had been very good to him when he had first landed in America,
a poor English boy who had run away from the workhouse.
Stanley was already famous as an African explorer for the voyage which he had undertaken in 1871 to find Dr. Livingstone.
Since then England had begun to realize the importance of
keeping at least a few fingers in the African pie and the London

The Zambesi Falls

Daily Telegraph cooperated with the New York *Herald* in defraying the cost of the voyage. This expedition, which lasted three years and which was undertaken from east to west, proved that the Lualaba which Livingstone had suspected of being part of the Congo was in reality the beginning of that river. It also showed the vastness of the territory traversed by the Congo River on its circuitous route to the sea and it brought home tales of strange native tribes, the presence of which no one so far had suspected.

It was this second voyage of Stanley's which drew the attention of the world to the commercial possibilities of the Congo and which made it possible for Leopold of Belgium to found his Congo Free State.

When at last the fate of Emin Pasha became a subject of world-wide concern, it was only natural that Stanley should be selected as the man best fitted to find him. He began his search in 1887 and the next year he found Emin in Wadelai just north of Lake Albert. Stanley tried to persuade this German, who seems to have exercised a tremendous power over the natives, to enter the service of the King of the Belgians, which would probably have meant that the great lake region of Africa would also have been added to the territory of the Congo colony. But Emin seems to have had plans of his own. As soon as he reached Zanzibar (he really was not anxious at all to be "saved") he got in touch with the German authorities and it was finally decided to send him back, well provided with men and money, to try to establish a German protectorate over the high plateau between the three great lakes of Victoria, Albert and Tanganyika. Along the coast of Zanzibar the German East Africa Company had acquired large interests as early as 1885. If the lake region were added, Germany would be able to frustrate the English plans for dividing all of Africa into two parts by a broad strip of English territory running from Egypt to the Cape. But in 1892 Emin was murdered near Stanley Falls on the Congo by Arab slave-dealers who wanted to avenge some of their colleagues deservedly hung by the stern German in his younger days.

Nothing therefore came of the Emin's dream of the new Germany on the high plateau of Tanganyika. As a result, however, of his disappearance, the greater part of central Africa had now been definitely put upon the map. And that brings us to the fifth natural division of Africa, the high mountainous regions of the east.

These stretch all the way from Abyssinia in the north to the Zambesi River in the south where the territory known as South Africa begins. The northern part of this region is inhabited by Hamites, for the Abyssinians and the Somalis, although they have kinky hair, are not Negroes. The southern part consists of Negroes and a great many Europeans.

The Abyssinians are Christians of a very old vintage, having been converted as early as the fourth century, almost 400 years before we had a single Christian community in central Europe. Their Christian sentiments, however, did not prevent them from making perpetual war upon their neighbors. In the year 525 they even crossed the Red Sea and conquered the southern part of Arabia, the Arabia Felix of the Romans (in contrast to the Arabia Deserta of the interior). It was this expedition which had made the young Mahommed realize the necessity for a strong and united Arab fatherland and which had started him upon his career as the founder of a religion and a world-empire.

One of the first things his followers did was to drive the Ethiopians away from the coast towns of the Red Sea and to destroy their business relations with Ceylon and India and far-away Constantinople. After that defeat, Ethiopia became a sort of Japan which took no further interest in outside affairs until the middle of the last century when the different European powers began to cast longing glances in the general direction of the peninsula of Somaliland, not because Somaliland was of any possible value, but because it was situated on the Red Sea which soon would be merely an extension of the Suez Canal. France was the first to arrive upon the scene and to occupy the harbor of Djibouti. The English, after a punitive expedition against the Emperor Theodore of Abyssinia, during which that extraordinary monarch killed himself rather than fall into the hands of his enemies, took British Somaliland which, situated just opposite Aden, gave them command of the gulf of that name. The Italians took a slice north of the French and British possessions with the intention of using the coastal region as a base of supplies from where to conduct a glorious expedition against Abyssinia.

This glorious expedition took place in the year 1896, and on that occasion the Italians lost 4500 white and 2000 native troops, with a slightly smaller amount of prisoners. Since then the Italians have left their Abyssinian neighbors alone although they are now the owners of another part of Somaliland, south of the British settlement.

In the end, of course, Abyssinia will go the way of Uganda and Zanzibar. But the difficulties of transportation, not overcome by the single railroad line from Djibouti to Addis Ababa, and the broken up nature of the entire Abyssinian plateau which makes it a natural fortress, together with the realization that those black men will under circumstances fight back with great bitterness, have so far saved that ancient kingdom from the usual annexation by one of her European neighbors.

South of Abyssinia and east of the Congo lie the three great African lakes. Of those the Nyasa sends tributaries to the Zambesi River, while Lake Victoria is responsible for the River Nile and the Tanganyika Lake connects with the Congo, suggesting that this region must be the highest part of Africa. The investigations of the last fifty years completely bear this out. Kilimanjaro, southeast of Lake Victoria, is 19,000 feet high and Mount Ruwenzori (the Mountain of the Moon of Ptolemy, which Stanley rediscovered some twenty centuries later) is 16,700 feet, with Kenya (17,000) and Elgon (14,000) close seconds.

This whole region was originally volcanic but the African volcanoes have not been working at their trade for a good many centuries. Politically the entire territory is divided into a number of sub-divisions, all of them however under British rule.

Uganda, a cotton-raising country, became a protectorate in 1899.

The former possessions of the British East Africa Company, now Kenya Colony, were made part of the empire in 1920, while the erstwhile holdings of the German East Africa colony became a British mandate in 1918 and are now part of the Tanganyika territory.

The most important town on the coast is Zanzibar, the capital of an old slave-trading sultanate over which the English established a protectorate in 1890. The town was a great center for Arab merchants from all over the Indian Ocean. They were probably responsible for the spread of the Swahili language, the jargon of Zanzibar, which is now spoken all over the east coast of Africa just as Malayan has become the "lingua franca" of the islands of the Dutch East Indies. At the present time a slight knowledge of Swahili is the most valuable asset for anyone wishing to do business along the three thousand miles of the Indian Ocean front and their millions of square miles of hinterland. If he will also bother to learn a little Bantu, the language of all the South African Negroes, he can, with a few words of Portuguese and a smattering of pidgin-Arabic and a sentence or two in Cape Dutch be sure of all of his meals while travelling from one end of the continent to the other.

That closes the chapter on northern Africa, except for the narrow coastal region that lies between the Atlantic and the mountains of the Sudan and the Cameroon Mountains. This strip of land has been known these last four hundred years as Upper Guinea and Lower Guinea. I have already mentioned the Guineas when I spoke of slavery, for it was there that the "black ivory" was gathered ere it was made ready for shipment to the rest of the world. Today that coast belongs to a number of nations, but none of these settlements is of any interest to anybody except a few stamp-collectors.

Sierra Leone is an old English settlement which, like Liberia just to the west of it, was intended to be a homeland for former slaves. Neither Sierra Leone nor Liberia, with its capital city of Monrovia (so-called after our President Monroe) amounts to anything except sad disappointments in the hearts of a good many perfectly honest men and women who had hoped for better things when they generously offered their money to return the black man to the country of his great-grandfather's birth.

The Ivory Coast is French, and Accra will eventually be a harbor of the French Sudanese Empire. Nigeria is English. The capital is Lagos. Dahomey was an independent native state until the French took it in 1893.

Cameroon was German until the war. It is now a French protectorate. So was and is Togo. The rest is part of the French Congo, making the whole of that part of the world a large French equatorial empire with little foreign enclosures which eventually will be acquired by the French in exchange for either cash or for something some other power may want in another part of the world.

The Dutch East Indian Company, in order to shorten the voyage from Batavia to Amsterdam, had maintained an overland route of its own by way of Persia and Syria and Alexandria. But every time there was a quarrel between two Mesopotamian potentates the mails and the caravans were so hopelessly delayed that the bulk of the merchandise continued to be sent by way of the Cape.

In order that nothing might interfere with the steady flow of its Indian products, the Dutch thereupon occupied a few harbors along the coast of Guinea which they could also use as slave ports, took St. Helena and fortified the Cape.

In 1671 the Dutch, who like all good merchants liked to have things in writing (think of the absurd comedy of "buying" Manhattan in exchange for $24.00 worth of gadgets!) bought the land around the fort of Capetown from the Hottentots. That meant the end of the Hottentots for, deprived of their land, they were forced to move northward into the region of the Orange River and the Vaal which was occupied by their hereditary enemies, the Bushmen. It seemed a punishment from Heaven that those same Dutch farmers, who had been terribly cruel in their dealings with both Hottentots and Bushmen, should afterwards have suffered a similar fate. For Capetown was occupied by the English in 1795 and then it was the turn of the Boers to move northward. They repeated this maneuver a number of times until the year 1902, when the last of their two independent republics, the Transvaal and Orange Free State were definitely annexed by the English.

Capetown, however, has remained the most important harbor of the whole triangle. But the coastal region counts for nothing compared to the tremendously rich interior. This interior consists of a high plateau dotted with low hills, a sort of mesa here called kopjes. On the west this plateau is cut off from the Atlantic by the Komas highlands. On the east it is separated from the Indian Ocean by the Matoppo Mountains and in the south it is cut off from the Capetown region by the Drakensberg Ridge.

None of these mountains has any glaciers. All the rivers therefore of this entire region depend upon rainfall for their water supply. As a result they are wild torrents in the winter and dry, hollow roads in the summer, and as they have got to break their way through a mountain ridge ere they reach the sea (with the exception of the rivers in Natal, which therefore is the richest of the different countries that now make up the U. S. A. or Union of South Africa) they are of no possible use as roads of commerce to the interior.

In order therefore that the hinterland might have access to the sea, a number of railways have been constructed. Before the war the most important of these roads was the one between Pretoria and Lourenço Marques on the Delagoa Bay in Portuguese East Africa. Since the war the roads to Swakopmund and Lüderitzland in the former territory of German South-west Africa (now a mandate of the Union) have been finished; and northward one can now go by rail as far as Lake Tanganyika and then, after having crossed the lake by boat, one can take another train from there for Zanzibar.

In order to get that far north, one is obliged to spend an uncomfortable day crossing the Kalahari desert but once this has been left behind, one enters into the hilly territory of Rhodesia, so-called after Cecil Rhodes, the founder of the old British South African chartered company and one of the earliest prophets of a united South Africa under British domination. That dream has partially come true. The different chartered companies and the former Boer republics and the Kaffir and Zulu nations are now all of them part of the Union of South Africa which was proclaimed in 1910. But as the Boer element which lives in the country districts seems to be gaining on the English element which had been chiefly attached to the cities by the discovery of gold around Johannesburg and diamonds near Kimberley, there is a violent struggle going on to decide which of the two rival elements shall be the deciding factor. By way of compromise, Capetown has been made the place where the parliament of the Union meets, but Praetoria, the old capital of the Transvaal Republic, has been promoted to act as the seat of the government.

As for the two unusually large remnants of the ancient Portuguese Empire which continue to separate the U. S. A. from the Atlantic and the Indian Ocean, Angola in the west and Mozambique in the east, they are so badly administered that sooner or later they will be taken over by one of their more powerful neighbors. Just now, with agricultural products at a lower price than ever before and cattle-raising at a complete standstill, the South Africans are not in search of fresh pastures and grain fields. When times return to normal, these Portuguese colonies will be annexed without the firing of a single gun. For South Africa is developing a new race, neither Dutch nor English but purely South African. And it is so rich in mineral wealth, in copper and coal and iron, and the soil is so fertile that it may well develop into a sort of United States on a slightly smaller scale.

At the other side of the Strait of Mozambique lies the island of Madagascar which measures 230,000 square miles and is slightly larger than the Republic of France to which it belongs. The population is about 4,000,000. It is a mountainous island and the eastern part, exposed to the trade-winds, has excellent timber which is exported from the harbor of Tamatave, connected by rail with the capital, Tananarivo.

The people look more like Malays than like Negroes. But Madagascar must have been separated from Africa at a very early period in our geological history for none of the usual African animals are to be found on the island.

East of Madagascar lie two little islands which were of great importance when the India trade still followed the route of the Cape. They are Mauritius and Reunion. Mauritius, an old fresh water vegetable station of the Dutch East India Company, is now English, and Reunion is French.

As for the other islands which, geographically speaking, belong to Africa, I have already mentioned St. Helena, while Ascension, further to the north in the Atlantic, is also a coaling and a cable station. The Cape Verde Islands are Portuguese. They lie a few hundred miles west of the coast of Mauretania, now occupied by the insignificant Spanish colony of Rio de Oro. The Canary Islands are Spanish, and Madeira and the Azores are Portuguese, and Teneriffe, with its well known volcano, is Spanish. As for the island of St. Brandon, in which all honest skippers of the seventeenth and eighteenth centuries believed as firmly as we ourselves believe in the tables of multiplication, that was situated here too. But no one could ever quite find out where because it went to the bottom of the ocean as soon as any vessel came near it and only reappeared when the visitor was gone. That seems to me to have been a very sensible thing to do on the part of an African island. It was the only way in which it could escape being occupied by a foreign power.

Most continents can be reduced to a few simple images. We say "Europe" and we see the dome of St. Peter's and ruined castles on the Rhine and the silent fjords of Norway and we hear the troika bells of Russia. Asia calls forth pictures of pagodas and masses of little brown men bathing in a wide river and strange temples, ten thousand feet up in the air, and the placid symmetry of old Fuji. America means sky-scrapers, factory

Discovery of the South Pole

chimneys, an old Indian on a pony going nowhere in particular. Even far off Australia has its symbols, the Southern Cross, the amiable kangaroo with his inquisitive and intelligent eyes.

But Africa, how shall we reduce that land of contrasts and extremes to a single symbol?

It is a land of torrid heat without any rivers! Yet the Nile is almost as long as the Mississippi and the Congo is only a little shorter than the Amazon River and the Niger just as long as the Hwang-Ho. It is a land of torrential rains and insufferable moisture! Yet the Sahara alone, the dryest of all deserts, is larger than all of Australia and the Kalahari is as big as the British Isles.

The people are weak and helpless, the black man does not know how to defend himself! Yet the most perfectly organized military machine the world has ever seen was developed among the Zulus, and the desert Bedouins and other northern tribes have been known to charge successfully against European troops armed with machine guns.

Africa has no convenient inland seas like the Baltic or our own Great Lakes! Granted, but Lake Victoria is as large as Lake Superior, Tanganyika is as big as the Baikal Sea, Nyasa twice as big as Lake Ontario.

Africa has no mountains! But Kilimanjaro is 5000 feet higher than Mount Whitney, the highest peak of the United States, and Ruwenzori, just north of the equator, is higher than Mont Blanc.

Then what is wrong with this continent? I don't know. Everything is there but nothing seems to be where it could possibly be of any use to anyone. The whole arrangement is wrong. With the exception of the Nile, all these rivers and mountains and lakes and deserts serve no purpose. Even the Nile, which at least flows into a sea of great commercial importance, is hampered by too many cataracts. As for the Congo and the Niger, they have no comfortable access to the sea, while the Zambesi starts where the Orange River should end and the Orange River ends where the Zambesi should start.

Modern science may eventually make the desert bear fruit and drain the marshes. Modern science may find ways to cure the dysentery and the sleeping sickness, which have wiped out entire countrysides in the Sudan and the Congo region, as modern science has set us free from yellow fever and malaria. Modern science may turn the high central and southern plateaus into a replica of the French Provence or the Italian Riviera. But the jungle is strong and persistent and the jungle has a handicap of millions of years. Let modern science relax but for a moment and the jungle and all its atrocities will be back at the white man's throat and will throttle him and it will breathe its poisonous breath into his nostrils until he dies and is eaten by the hyenas and the ants.

Perhaps it is the lightless tropical forest which has put its dreadful stamp upon the whole African civilization. The desert may be frightening but the shimmering dark forest is terrifying. It is so full of life that it has become lifeless. The struggle for existence must proceed quietly lest the hunter himself become the hunted. And so day and night and night and day creation devours itself beneath the high roof of the listless leaves. The most harmless-looking insect has the most deadly sting. The most beautiful flower carries its secret burden of poison. Every horn and hoof and beak and tooth is against every other horn and hoof and beak and tooth. The pulse-beat of existence is accompanied by the crunching of bones and the tearing asunder of soft brown skins.

I have tried to talk of these things with Africans. They laughed at me. Such was life. Life was either stark poverty or overwhelming abundance. There was no golden mean. One either froze or one roasted. One either drank coffee from golden cups with an Arab merchant in Mogador or one took a pot-shot at an old Hottentot woman. She was no good anyway. For this land of contrast seems to do dreadful things to people. It warps their vision. It kills their susceptibilities to the finer sides of life. The ceaseless carnage of the veldt and forest gets into their blood. And a quiet little mousy official, fresh from the stiff respectability of a slumbering Belgian village, turns into a monster who has women flogged to death because they fail to bring an extra pound of rubber; and then quietly smokes his after-dinner cigar while the insects devour some poor black devil, mutilated because he was in arrears with his ivory.

I am trying very hard not to be unfair. Other continents, too, have greatly contributed to the sum total of human cruelty and malevolence. But gentler forms walk across the countryside. Jesus preaches, Confucius teaches, Buddha implores, Mahommed sternly points to his harsh virtues. Africa, alone, has borne us no prophet. Other continents have been greedy and selfish but at times the spirit has conquered the flesh and they have gone forth upon some mighty pilgrimage, the purpose of which lay hidden far beyond the gates of Heaven.

The only sound of marching feet across the African desert and through the shrubs is that of flint-eyed Arabs in search of their human prey, of Dahomeyan Amazons, ready to pounce upon a sleeping village and steal the children of their neighbors to sell them into foreign slavery. In other parts of the world women ever since the beginning of time have tried to make themselves desirable in the eyes of their men that they might attract them and gain their favor. In Africa alone women have deliberately made themselves hideous that they might repel all those who should meet them unaware.

I might continue this bit of special pleading *ad infinitum*. But this book is getting much too long and so you had better try to find an answer for yourself.

People have been faced by the same perplexing question ever since they first gazed upon the useless grandeur of the Pyramids and looked suspiciously at the tracks that lost themselves in the sands of the distant desert. But none of them returned any the wiser.

XLVI

AMERICA, THE MOST FORTUNATE OF ALL

The American continent is the most obliging continent of all. I am speaking, of course, of America as a purely geographical unit, not as an economic factor in the development of industry nor as a political laboratory for experiments in diverse new forms of government. But from a geographical point of view, America is almost everything that possibly could be desired.

It is the only continent on the western hemisphere and therefore has no immediate competitors as Africa, Asia and Europe have. It is situated between the two largest seas of the world and it was settled by white men during a period when the Atlantic had just become the center of civilization.

It reaches from the North Pole to the South Pole and therefore enjoys every sort of climate. That part which lies nearest to the equator is also the highest and therefore enjoys a temperature which makes it fit for human habitation.

It has practically no deserts. It has been blessed with wide plains which are situated in the moderate zone and which are therefore predestined to become the world's granaries.

It has a coast line which is neither too simple nor too complicated and which is therefore eminently fitted for the establishment of deep-sea harbors.

As its chief mountain-ranges run from north to south, its fauna and flora could freely escape the advance of the glaciers of the ice period and had a better chance to survive than those of Europe.

More than almost any other continent it is blessed with coal and iron and oil and copper and those other raw materials which the machine age needs in ever increasing quantities.

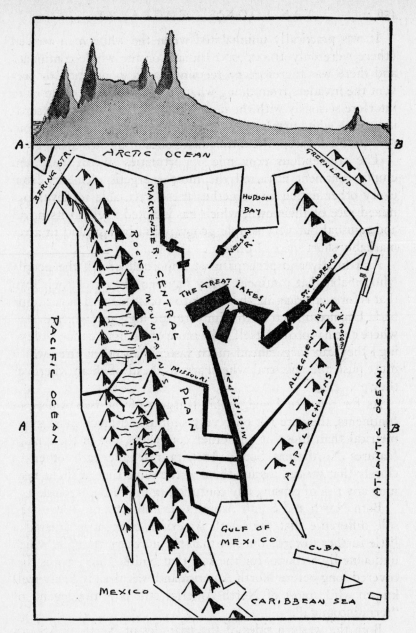

North America

It was practically uninhabited when the white man arrived (there were only 10,000,000 Indians on the whole continent) and there was therefore no teeming native population to prevent the invaders from doing whatever they pleased to do or to interfere seriously with the development of the country according to the white man's plans. As a result America has no serious race-problem except the unfortunate ones of its own making.

The tremendous economic opportunities of the new and empty continent attracted the most energetic elements from every other nation and together these were able to develop a mixed race of their own, which has adapted itself to its novel and unusual but very simple geographical background in a remarkably short space of time.

And finally and perhaps most important of all, the people who inhabit that continent today have no history of their own that is forever dragging them back to a past that will never come back. Unencumbered by that unfortunate luggage (which everywhere else has proved itself to be more of a nuisance than a blessing) they can forge ahead much faster than other races which must push the ancestral wheelbarrow ahead of them wherever they go.

As for the actual geographic features of the two American continents, they are not only very simple and much more symmetrical than those of any other continents, but in their main features North and South America resemble each other so closely that we can discuss them at the same time without running any risk of causing any confusion in the reader's mind.

Both North and South America resemble triangles with the sole difference that the South American triangle is situated a little further towards the east than the northern triangle, which undoubtedly accounts for the fact that South America was discovered long before North America and was already fairly well known while most of North America still bore the legend of "terra incognita".

Both the western sides of the triangles of North and South America consist of a mountain ridge which runs sharply from the north to the south and which occupies approximately one-third of the surface while the other two-thirds in the east consist of a wide plain, separated from the ocean (in both cases) by two shorter mountain-ranges, the hills of Labrador and the Appalachians in North America and the mountains of Guiana and the Brazilian highlands in South America.

In the matter of their rivers, too, the two continents behave similarly. A few of the less important ones run northward while the St. Lawrence and the Amazon run almost parallel with each other, and the Parana and the Paraguay imitate the Mississippi and the Missouri by meeting each other halfway and then running the rest of their course at right angles with the St. Lawrence and the Amazon respectively.

As for Central America, the narrow strip of land which runs from east to west, geologically speaking it is really a part of the northern continent. Then suddenly, in Nicaragua, the landscape and the fauna and flora begin to change and it becomes part of the southern continent. The rest of Central America consists of high mountains, which is one of the reasons why Mexico, although as near the equator as the Sahara Desert, is a densely populated country with an excellent climate.

South America, of course, is much nearer to the equator than North America and the Amazon River practically follows the line of the equator in the course of its magnificent career from the Andes to the Atlantic. But speaking in very general terms (as I am now doing) here we have a magnificent case wherewith to study the influence of the geographical surroundings upon Man and of Man upon his geographical surroundings.

Nature built herself two large states and finished them both in practically the same way. A main entrance on the right, a high wall on the left, and a large open space in the middle provided with a richly stored larder. Then she gave the northern stage to a company of Germanic strolling actors, who thus far had played the smaller theaters in the provincial towns, a troupe of humble origin, accustomed to long hours and the plain roles of butchers and bakers and candlestick-makers. But the southern

stage she rented out to noble old tragedians of the best Mediterranean school, who were accustomed to perform only in the
presence of royalty and each one of whom could handle a sword
or a rapier with a grace entirely unknown to their northern colleagues whose arms were stiff from the handling of spade and

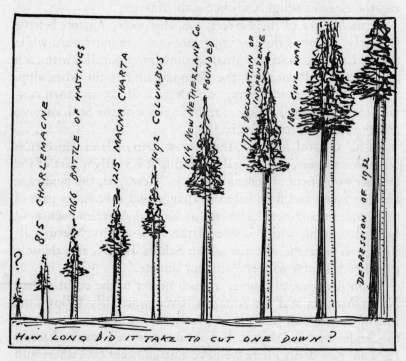

The sequoia as historical contemporary

axe, whose backs were prematurely bent by their ceaseless
struggle with an unyielding soil.

Then she raised the curtain on both stages at almost exactly
the same moment and bade the world come in and watch the
entertainment. And behold, ere the first act was half over,
neither stage looked quite the same as it had done when the
opening lines were spoken. And when the second act began, such
a change was noticeable among the ladies and gentlemen and

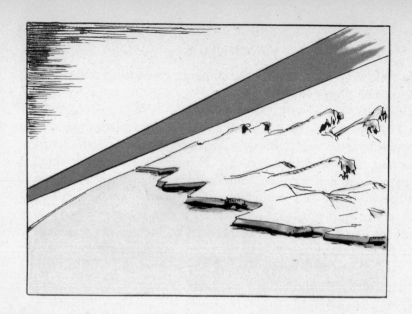

The Polar Regions

The Equator

the children of the cast that the audience gasped and whispered, "Can such things be?"

The vessels of the old Vikings looked very picturesque but they were exceedingly clumsy vehicles when it came to the actual business of sailing them across a choppy sea. As a result those hardy Norsemen were continually blown out of their normal course, for they had neither compass nor log and their sailing rig was as clumsy as that of those Egyptian feluccas which you may still admire on a roll of papyrus painted in the valley of the Nile, 3000 years ago.

Now if you will kindly look at the map of the Gulf Stream (there are several in this book) you will see that the Gulf Stream, after having crossed the ocean from Africa to America, recrosses the northern part of the Atlantic from the south-west to the north-east in a leisurely fashion, bestows its blessings upon the coast of Norway, visits the Arctic Ocean, and then decides to go home by way of Iceland and Greenland, where it changes its name and its temperature, to travel southward once more, first as the Greenland current and next as the Labrador current, that accursed stream which sprinkles chunks of Greenland's azure glaciers all over the northern part of the Atlantic.

The Norsemen, sailing by God and by guess, as my own ancestors used to call this procedure, had reached Iceland as early as the ninth century. Once, however, regular communications had been established between Iceland and Europe, the discovery of Greenland and America became inevitable. Just as a Chinese or Japanese junk, blown out of its course, must inevitably reach the shores of British Columbia or California, being carried thither by the Kuro Siwo, the Gulf Stream of the Pacific, so a Norseman, bound from Trondheim to Iceland and being prevented by fog from locating his place of destination (and even today with all the instruments in the world, a fog is a terrible thing), would sooner or later find himself on the east coast of Greenland, or, if the fog continued and his luck held out, on the very coasts of the great land-barrier to the east which those early visitors called Vineland, because it raised a kind of grapes from which they could make an excellent sort of wine.

Now it is well to remember that there have been a great many discoveries made of which the world at large never heard at all. The average skipper has an instinctive fear of making a fool of himself before his colleagues by telling them a yarn which none of them will believe anyway, and which afterwards may prove

Greenland

to have been the result of an hallucination, or of low clouds mistaken for a mountain-range, or a strip of sunlight, maybe, interpreted as a flat coast. Australia was undoubtedly seen from the distance by a number of French and Spanish sailors long before Abel Tasman set foot on shore and cut himself a new goosequill to report to the authorities in Batavia about the monstrous size of the natives. The Azores and Canary Islands were discovered and forgotten and re-discovered so often that our school books have a hard time trying to find out just exactly when they should be first mentioned among the world's great discoveries. French fishermen had undoubtedly found their way to the Grand Banks of Newfoundland centuries before the days of Columbus. But they merely told their neighbors that the fishing was good and let it go at that. Fish interested them. Another piece of land was just another piece of land. There was enough land in Brittany for everybody. Why worry about something that lay so far away from home?

Newfoundland

As in everything I have ever written I have steadfastly defended the doctrine that humanity comes ahead of nationality, I shall not lose myself in the usual acrimonious disputes concerning the desirability of celebrating Columbus Day or Leif Ericsson Day or a day in honor of some French sailor who eventually may be dug out of the archives of Normandy. Suffice it to say that we have documentary evidence proving that the Norsemen visited these shores during the first ten years of the eleventh century and that a small group of sailors, preponderantly Spanish but with certain foreign admixtures, and more or less obeying the commands of an Italian captain, visited these shores during the last ten years of the fifteenth century, and that when they arrived here they found out that they could not possibly be the original discoverers because the country was already inhabited by people who were of unmistakable Asiatic origin, wherefore, if the honor of "having been there first" must go to any specific group of people, the Mongolians are the logical candidates for all our future commemorative tablets.

We have a monument to our Unknown Soldier. Another and slightly larger pile of marble erected to our Unknown Discoverer would not be out of place. But as the relatives of that poor man are now forbidden by law to set foot on the soil of our continent, I fear me that nothing will ever come of this plan.

Concerning the descendants of those first intrepid explorers who undoubtedly hailed from the Far East, we know a great deal, but the one thing that would really interest us will probably remain a mystery until the end of time. And that one thing is this—how did the people of Asia actually reach the American continent? Did they sail across the narrow northern part of the Pacific Ocean, or did they walk across the ice of the Bering Strait, or did they come at a time when America and Asia were still connected by a narrow bridge of land? Well, we just don't happen to know. Nor can I see that it matters very much. When the white man reached these distant shores he came in contact with a race which, except in a few isolated spots, had barely passed out of the late stone age and which had not yet reached that stage of development when the wheel was used to relieve the human back of its manifold burdens or when the domesticated animals had set their owners free from the everlasting drudgery of gaining a meagre daily livelihood by means of hunting and fishing. Even with his bows and arrows the copper-colored man was no match for the white man who was able to kill his enemies at a distance by means of a gun.

The red man, reduced from the rank of a host to that of a

The Three Discoveries of America

guest, will continue to exist for a few centuries longer. Then he will be completely absorbed by his former enemies and will only survive as a vague historical memory. That is too bad, for the red man had many very excellent qualities, both of body and mind.

But that is the way things happen and I don't see what we can do about it.

And now let us for the last time look at a map.

From the Bering Strait to the Isthmus of Panama the west coast of America is protected against the Pacific Ocean by a barrier of high mountains. This barrier is not everywhere of the same width and parts of it consist of parallel ridges, all of which, however, run in the same direction, that is to say, from north to south.

In Alaska this mountain-chain is clearly a continuation of the mountains of eastern Asia. It is divided into two sections by the wide basin of the Yukon River, the main river of this northern territory, which was part of the Russian Empire until the year 1867 when the United States acquired these 590,000 square miles of wilderness in consideration of 7,000,000 American dollars.

The reason Russia was satisfied with so little was probably due to her ignorance about the country's potential riches. Seven million dollars for a few fishing villages and a chaos of snow-covered mountains seemed quite a good bargain at that time. But in 1896 gold was discovered in the Klondike, and Alaska got on the map, as the popular saying has it. The trip of a thousand miles from Vancouver to Juneau and then via Skagway and the Chilkoot and Chilkat passes to Dawson, the center of the Klondike territory (carrying one's pack on one's own back, as animals were very expensive and could hardly wade through the dense snow at the elevation of 3500 feet just south of the Polar Circle), was about as inconvenient as any trip ever undertaken by mankind in search of material wealth. But a pot of gold at the end of the trail awaited the early arrivals, and on

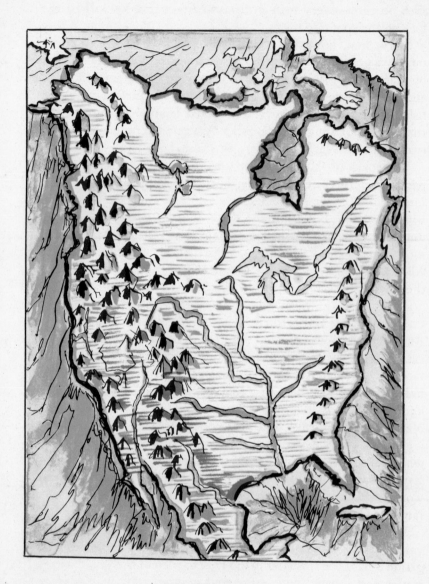

North America

such occasions every man is always certain that he will be the first on the spot.

Since then, however, it has been found that Alaska is not merely a gold land (as well as the country most densely covered by glaciers) but that it also has a great deal of copper and silver and coal, besides being an ideal country for fur-trapping and fishing. As a result the revenue derived from it during the first forty years of its existence as an American territory has been twenty times as large as the original cost.

Just south of Alaska, the mountain-range gets split into two parts of which the eastern branch, the Rockies, turn further inland, while the western branch continues to run exactly parallel with the ocean. But while the Rockies never change their name until they lose themselves among the highlands of Mexico, the mountains of the Pacific slope, after they have bade farewell to Mount McKinley, the highest mountain of the Alaska range and the highest peak on the whole North American continent (20,-300 feet) are known by quite a number of different names. In Canada they are called the St. Elias Range and the Coast Range. But after they have passed Vancouver Island (a rocky island cut off from the mainland by Johnston Strait and the Strait of Georgia) they are divided into two parts, of which the western half is still called the Coast Range while the eastern hills are known as the Cascades in Washington and Oregon and the Sierra Nevada in California. The wide open space between the two is the valley of the Sacramento River and the San Joaquin River which meet in the middle just before they run into San Francisco Bay, the widest and deepest and the best sheltered harbor of the world, which connects with the Pacific Ocean by means of the famous Golden Gate.

When the advance guard of the Spanish pioneers reached the valley, it was absolutely uncultivated. Today by means of irrigation it has been turned into the fruit garden of the world where apples and peaches and plums and oranges and apricots grow and prosper in exchange for a very reasonable amount of labor.

This valley proved to be a veritable godsend to California,

for when the great gold rush of the forties of the last century had come to an end, the miners and their followers discovered that they could hope to make quite a comfortable living by merely changing their profession and by becoming fruit farmers instead of prospectors. In Alaska and in Australia, once the veins of gold had been exhausted, there was no possible chance of feeding the multitudes, and they disappeared as fast as they had come, leaving behind them their empty towns and villages and tin cans. But California, instead of being impoverished by its golden treasures, as most gold-providing countries have been, was actually enriched by them, and the fact should be noted down as unique in the history of mankind.

When it was shown that way down deep below the soil there lay vast reservoirs of oil, the future of the state was entirely insured. It is true that this entire region is a bit shaky and that the deep incision of the Gulf of California may cause an occasional shifting of the different layers of rock which are apt to be dangerous (especially when followed by fire) but earthquakes are only temporary inconveniences while sunshine and an agreeable and even climate are permanent blessings. California has only started upon its career as one of the most densely populated spots of the entire northern continent.

Between the Sierra Nevada and the actual range of the Rockies lies an enormous valley consisting of three parts. In the north lies the Columbia plateau which sends the Snake River and the Columbia River to the Pacific and in the south it is bordered by the Wasatch Mountains and the Colorado plateau through which the Colorado River has dug its famous canyon. Between these two plateaus lies the depression known as the Great Basin which the Mormons chose as their permanent place of residence after they had been forced to flee from the eastern part of the United States and which in spite of its lack of moisture (the Great Salt Lake is full of water but it is much saltier than the ocean) they have in less than a single century been able to turn into a most profitable venture.

That this entire region is of a highly volcanic nature and that

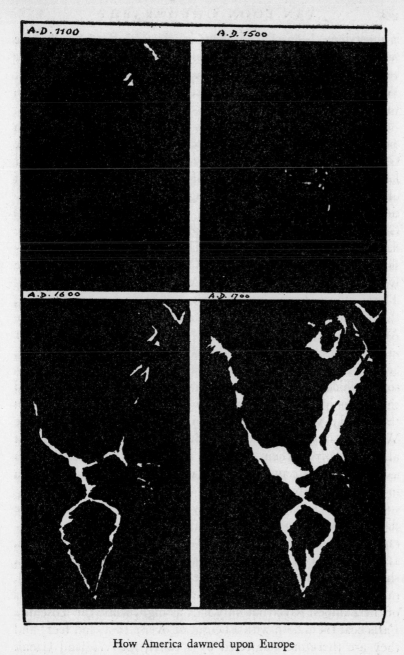

How America dawned upon Europe

it must have been shaken about considerably is shown by the fact that from the bottom of the Death Valley, which is 276 feet below the surface of the ocean, one can see the top of that Mount Whitney which is the highest peak of the entire United States (14,496 feet).

To the east of the Rockies lies that tremendous plain which on the north is bounded by the Arctic Ocean, on the south by the Gulf of Mexico and on the east by the Laurentian Highlands of Labrador and the Appalachians of the United States. That part of the world alone could, if brought under the proper cultivation, feed the whole population of our globe. The so-called Great Plains (where the Rockies gradually slope off into the flat country) and the Central Plains through which the Mississippi and the Missouri and the Ohio and the Arkansas and the Red Rivers flow to the Gulf of Mexico, are one vast granary. The northern part is less well favored because here the rivers, the Mackenzie and the Athabasca and the Saskatchewan and the Albany River, all lose themselves either in the Arctic Ocean or in the Hudson Bay and are therefore only of local importance, being frozen up for the greater part of each year. But the Missouri, which rises near the Yellowstone Park in Montana and the Mississippi (together with the Missouri the longest river in the world), which takes its origin on the divide between Lake Winnipeg in Canada and Lake Superior, are navigable almost all the way from their sources to their deltas and pass through a region that in centuries to come will resemble eastern China in its density of population.

The other lakes of this slightly elevated region which is the divide between the Hudson Bay (or the Arctic Ocean), the Atlantic and the Gulf of Mexico, are Lake Michigan, Lake Huron, Lake Erie and Lake Ontario. The latter two are connected by a short river which is unnavigable on account of a water-fall, called Niagara (Niagara is a little wider than the Victoria Falls of the Zambesi River but only half as high, while the Yosemite Falls beat them both with a height of over a thousand feet) and they are therefore connected by a canal, the Welland Canal.

The Huron Lake and Lake Superior are also connected by a
canal, the Sault Ste. Marie Canal, which has more tonnage pass
through its locks than the Panama Canal and the Suez Canal and
the Kiel Canal put together.

The waters of these lakes then pass into the Atlantic Ocean
through the St. Lawrence River, emptying into the St. Lawrence

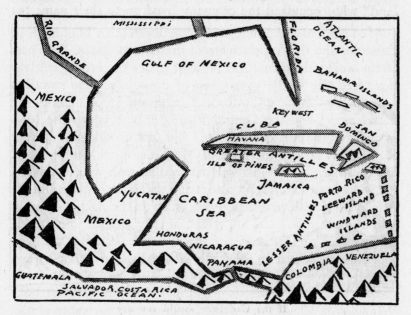

The Caribbean

Bay which is a sort of inland sea, situated between the Canadian
mountains in the west, the island of Newfoundland in the east
(it was "New" when John Cabot found it in 1497 and in 1500
when it got its first Portuguese governor-general) and Cape
Breton Island and Nova Scotia and New Brunswick in the
south. The Cabot Strait, separating Newfoundland from Cape
Breton Island, bears witness to the fact that this region was first
visited by an Italian.

As the northern part of Canada, the so-called Northwestern
Territory, is too cold to be entirely suited to the white man's oc-

cupation, we rarely hear of it except in connection with its picturesque local police force. It is a land of lakes and most of it used to belong to the Hudson Bay Company. This company was founded in 1670, exactly fifty-nine years after Henry Hudson, the discoverer of the bay that bears his name, had been murdered there by his mutinous sailors. The "adventurers of England" who organized the company lived up to their name but

If the Caribbean should run dry

without much discrimination. Had they been given another half century they would have killed off all the live stock of the lakes and forests (even during the breeding season the slaughter of fur-bearing animals did not cease) and the Indians, most liberally supplied with fire-water, would have exterminated themselves completely by way of the gin bottle. Wherefore the Queen's Most Gracious Majesty finally intervened, annexed most of the company's sovereign territory to Her Majesty's dominions in Canada and left the Hudson Bay Company behind as an historical curiosity which still (though greatly diminished in size) continues to do business in the same region (262 con-

The Panama Canal

secutive years under the same management—no mean record, if you please, for any business house!) but no longer on the old, irresponsible scale of former times.

The Labrador peninsula between the Hudson Bay and the St. Lawrence is too near the cold currents that come from Greenland's icy shores to be of any value to anybody. But the Dominion of Canada is only at the threshold of its enormous future and today suffers chiefly from a very serious lack of population.

Politically Canada is one of the most interesting remains of a former dream of empire. We are apt sometimes to forget that when George Washington was born, the North American continent belonged for the greater part to France and to Spain and that the English colonies along the coast of the Atlantic were only a small Anglo-Saxon enclave surrounded entirely by hostile nations. As early as 1608 the French had established themselves at the mouth of the St. Lawrence River. Then they had turned their attention to the interior, first of all travelling due west until Champlain reached Lake Huron. They explored the entire region of the Great Lakes, Marquette and Joliet found the upper part of the Mississippi, and La Salle in 1682 descended the river to the sea and took possession of its entire valley which he called Louisiana after King Louis XIV. By the end of the seventeenth century, the French were laying claim to all the land as far as the Rocky Mountains, beyond which the territories of His Most Catholic Majesty of Spain were supposed to begin. The Alleghenies, which were a real barrier in those days, separated this enormous French colonial empire from the English and the Dutch possessions along the Atlantic seaboard and from Florida which was another colony of Spain.

If Louis XIV and Louis XV had known a little more geography; indeed, if a map had ever meant something more important to these artistic monarchs than a color scheme that could be worked out very nicely in a new Gobelin, the people of New England and Virginia would now probably speak French and the whole of North America would be administered from Paris. But those who decided the destinies of Europe did not realize what the New World meant. As a result of their indifference, Canada became English, Quebec and Montreal ceased to be French cities and a few generations later, New Orleans and the whole of the Far West were sold to the Republic that had been recently founded by a few rebellious little English provinces along the Atlantic seaboard. And even the great Napoleon thought that he had done a clever stroke of business when he looked at the stack of American golden dollars which he had got in exchange for what is now the richest part of the United States.

In 1819 Florida was added to these newly acquired domains, and in 1848 Texas and New Mexico and Arizona and California and Nevada and Utah were taken away from Mexico; and less than a hundred years after it had seemed certain that the northern half of the continent was to be a hinterland of two Latin powers, it had completely changed hands and had become an extension of the great north European plain.

As for the subsequent economic development of those heterogeneous parts which the chances of war, but above all things the indifference and lack of foresight of the original owners, had so suddenly and unexpectedly thrown together, it took on such proportions as the world had never seen. As soon as the first railroads had been constructed and the first steamers had been built, hundreds of thousands of immigrants followed the water routes to the Great Lakes or crossed the Alleghenies to take their share of the Great Plains and make them ready for human habitation and raise that wheat which was to make Chicago the most important grain center of the world.

When the triangle between the Great Lakes, the Alleghenies and the foothills of the Rockies were found to contain coal and oil and iron and copper in unprecedented quantities, this region became the great factory area of the new commonwealth with cities like Pittsburgh and Cincinnati and St. Louis and Cleveland and Detroit and Buffalo attracting laborers from all over the world to assist the earlier arrivals in exploiting these hidden treasures. And as these towns needed harbors from which to export their steel and iron and their oil and their automobiles, the old colonial settlements of the Atlantic seaboard, New York and Boston and Philadelphia and Baltimore achieved positions of eminence which they had never enjoyed before.

Meanwhile the southern states, at last emerging from the dark days of the reconstruction period (infinitely more disas-

The first railroad track

trous than the Civil War itself had been), were scraping together enough money to begin raising their cotton crops without the assistance of slave labor. Galveston and Savannah and New Orleans returned to life. The railroads and telegraph lines and telephone wires turned the whole nation into one enormous farm and factory. 60,000,000 Europeans crossed the ocean in less than half a century and joined the earlier arrivals in planning and building and making and selling and such a workshop as they set up the world had never seen before. But neither had Nature ever given a nation such unlimited opportunities as we enjoyed—

a gigantic plain with an excellent climate and an excellent soil, protected on both sides by convenient mountain-ranges and practically uninhabited—almost inexhaustible resources—handy water-ways to which history had added an almost more important gift, one nation and one language and no past.

What these advantages really mean to a nation we realize as soon as we go a little further down south and reach Mexico and Central America. Mexico, with the exception of the peninsula of Yucatan, where the ancient Mayans lived, is a mountainous region which slowly increases in height from the Rio Grande towards the south until in the plateau of Sierra Madre and that of Anáhuac it reaches peaks of sixteen and seventeen thousand feet. Most of these higher mountains like Popocatepetl (17,543 feet) and Orizaba (18,564) and Ixtaccihuatl (16,960) are of volcanic origin, but Colima (13,092) is the only active volcano at the present moment.

On the Pacific side, the Sierra Madre rises sharply from the coast; but on the Atlantic side the mountains slope down more gradually and since the European invaders came from the east it was easy enough for them to find their way to the interior. The advance guard arrived during the first years of the sixteenth century. That was the time of Spain's great disappointment because the new discoveries of that damnable Genoese had proved to be a flop, a howling failure, no gold, no silver, naked savages who lay down and died when you tried to make them work, and endless mosquitoes.

Then rumor began to spread that beyond the mountains of the nearby mainland there lived an emperor of a people called the Aztecs, who dwelled in golden castles and slept in golden beds and ate from golden plates. Ferdinand Cortez and his three hundred adventurers landed in Mexico in the year 1519. With the help of one dozen cannon and thirteen blunderbusses he conquered the whole realm of poor Montezuma who was strangled to death ere he could witness the complete annihilation of what only a short time before had been a nation not much less effi-

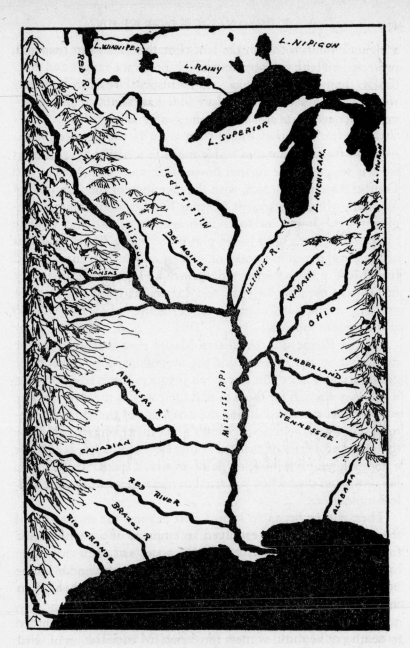

The Mississippi

ciently administered than the realm of the Habsburg monarch in whose name he was murdered.

After that and for almost 300 years, until 1810 to be exact, Mexico remained a Spanish colony and was treated as such. Several of her native products were no longer allowed to be cultivated for fear that they might compete with the less acceptable

Yosemite

products of the mother country. And most of the wealth which the soil produced disappeared into the pockets of a few rich landowners or was set apart for the benefit of those religious establishments which even today are fighting to retain their hold upon the common lands.

Then, during the middle of the last century, shortly after the grotesque adventure of poor Austrian Maximilian, who had hoped to become Montezuma's successor with the help of the

French, it was discovered that Mexico was not only a very rich agricultural country but that her soil contained as much or perhaps more iron and oil deposits than the United States. Thereupon the 15,000,000 Mexicans, of whom nearly 40% were still of pure Indian stock, were almost as badly off as they had been when Cortez first visited them. For now the big banking interests took a hand in their internal affairs and arranged for revolutions, which were then answered by counter-revolutions on the part of

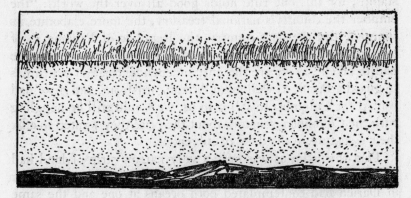

The Soil of the Plains

the natives, until the record of a hundred years (it averages twenty revolutions per year) was broken just before the Great War and it seemed that the whole country would dissolve into murder and bloodshed. Fortunately during the Great War, when the big financial interests were otherwise occupied (that war cost a great deal of money), Mexico had a breathing space, and today a few strong men are trying to undo the harm of three centuries of neglect and sickness and analphabetism and apparently with success, for Vera Cruz and Tampico (the two harbors on the Gulf) are reporting larger and larger export figures. For half a dozen years Washington and Mexico City have not merely been on speaking terms, but have actually spoken to each other almost politely and with a smile.

The isthmus of central America which connects the two continents is exceedingly fertile, raises coffee, bananas, sugar and whatever else foreign capital is willing to plant there; but the climate is hard on the white man, and the black man is not particularly interested in working for the white man, and the volcanoes, which abound in this region, are hard on both the blacks and the whites.

To most people Guatemala, Honduras, Nicaragua and Costa Rica are merely romantic names, unless they collect postage stamps, for this one rule holds good all over the world: "the emptier the country's national treasury, the more elaborate its stamps". But the next country, the Republic of Panama, is of importance to us. It is a child of our own, though I suppose we had to take it, as we are the only independent nation which has to guard a Pacific as well as an Atlantic sea-front, and if we had waited for Colombia to sell it to us, we would still be haggling with the Colombian senators about the price they wanted to affix their signature to the deed of surrender.

That this isthmus was only a very narrow strip of land had already been known to the Spaniards after Balboa from his peak in Darien had contemplated both oceans at one and the same moment. And as early as the year 1551 the Spaniards were playing with the idea of digging a canal of their own. Since then every generation was to hear of new plans. Every man of any importance in the realm of science favored the world with at least one set of blue-prints showing how the puzzle could be best solved. But digging a canal through almost thirty miles of hard rock was a serious problem until Alfred Nobel made his unfortunate invention and gave us that dynamite with which he expected to remove tree-stumps and boulders from a farmer's fields but which he never intended to be used for the more common purpose of killing one's neighbors.

Then came the California gold rush when thousands of people hastened to Panama so as not to be obliged to make the long detour via Cape Horn; and for them the trans-isthmus railroad was built in 1855. Fifteen years later the world heard of the unexpected success of the Suez Canal. Ferdinand de Lesseps, its author, now decided to try his hand at connecting the Pacific with the Atlantic. But the company he founded was scandalously mismanaged and his engineers had made so many errors in their calculations and his workmen died so miserably from malaria and yellow fever, that after eight years of struggle against the forces of Nature and the less direct but even more disastrous forces of

The Interior of a Volcano after the outer crust has
eroded away remains behind as a solid mountain

the Paris Exchange, the French company went most disreputably out of existence.

Then nothing was done for almost a dozen years and palm trees grew out of the smokestacks of the locomotives left behind by de Lesseps, until finally in the year 1902 the United States government bought the rights of the bankrupt French concern. Thereupon Washington and the Republic of Colombia began to haggle about the price that America would eventually have to pay for a strip of land wide enough for her canal. Until Theodore

Roosevelt, tired of the delay, arranged for a private little re-bellion of his own in that somewhat out-of-the-way part of the world, recognized the new and independent Republic of Panama in less than twenty-four hours, and began to dig. That happened in the year 1903 and in 1914 the job was finished.

This changed the Caribbean Sea from an inland sea to part of the commercial highway between Europe and Asia and it greatly increased the value of the islands which cut it off from the At-lantic Ocean. The Bahamas, which are English, and Cuba are a little too far out of the way, as is of course Bermuda, another English possession half way between New York and Florida. But Jamaica (English) and Haiti and San Domingo (nominally independent but ask Washington!) are in a better position to derive some benefits from the canal. So is Porto Rico and so are all the Lesser Antilles, the small islands to the east and the south, which face the Greater Antilles, Cuba, Haiti, Jamaica and Porto Rico.

These Lesser Antilles were of much greater value to the Eu-ropean nations of the seventeenth century than the American mainland. For they were hot and sufficiently moist to raise sugar-cane and the slaves, once on shore, could not disappear in the jungle. Today they still raise sugar and cocoa and coffee but most of them would be deeply grateful if they could make a few extra pennies as halfway stations for ships bound from Europe to the Panama Canal. In order of their appearance these are first of all the so-called Leeward Islands, St. Thomas, Santa Cruz, St. Martin, Saba, St. John, St. Eustatius (a small rock, chief port for smuggled supplies during the Revolution), Guadalupe, Dominica, Martinique (very volcanic like most of the others and almost destroyed by Mt. Pelée in 1902), St. Lucia and St. Vin-cent and Barbados.

The Windward Islands consist of Blanquilla (which belongs to Venezuela), Bonaire, Curaçao and Oruba, which are Dutch. All of these islands once upon a time were part of the outer ridge of a mountain chain that connected the Guiana Range of Venezuela with the Sierra Madre of Mexico. That mountain ridge was destroyed but the high individual tops remained behind.

From an industrial point of view, none of these islands is doing any too well. The abolition of slavery has destroyed the former riches of all of them and today they are best known as winter resorts or coaling stations or oil-distributing centers. Only Trinidad, just off the delta of the Orinoco, retains some of her prosperity because its volcanoes have favored it with large asphalt deposits, worked by Hindus, who came here to take the place of the old slaves and who now form one-third of the total population.

During the war when we learned more geography and in a shorter space of time than we had ever done before (to forget most of it just as rapidly when we no longer were under any necessity of knowing where Kut-el-Amara and the Isonzo might possibly be located) it was quite customary for the younger generation to switch from German (which soon was to be a dead language anyway) to Spanish, on the ground that there was "a great future for that language in South America". That future did not particularly manifest itself while the actual fighting was going on. Indeed, business transactions with that vast continent suffered a very serious slump.

Afterwards we discovered the reason. All the technical details of foreign trade in Peru and Brazil and Ecuador and whatever these other countries might be called had thus far been entrusted to patient little German clerks who were supposed to be familiar with that sort of thing, which was most unfortunately beyond the mental reach of their employers. When South America joined the Allies (for most of them had a few German ships in their harbors and needed loans) these poor Teutonic ink-slingers had been sent to concentration camps and the foreign correspondence of those South American commercial establishments had come to a sudden end, to be resumed as soon as peace had been declared and the Heinies were back at their ledgers.

Gradually the truth then began to dawn upon us. Although South America was a continent of tremendous natural wealth, it was so hopelessly underpopulated and in many respects so far behind the rest of the world that it would take at least another half century before it would be of the slightest value to any one

The oldest mountains are by no means the highest

except the few rich families who had either retained their possessions from the days of Spanish domination or had gained them afterwards in their quality of uncle or nephew to one of the quick-change South American presidents.

Now if in the present volume I devote only a few pages to South America, do not suspect me of anti-Latin feelings. On the contrary, being of northern descent myself, I am able to appreciate the many virtues of the southern races much better than they

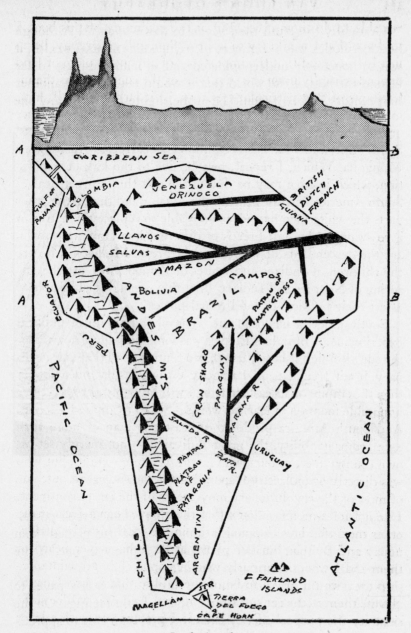

South America

are able to do themselves. But at the beginning of this book I told you that I would try to write a "human" geography, being firmly convinced that the importance of any given piece of land depends entirely upon the sum total of the contributions the inhabitants of that particular territory, be it large or small, have made to the sum total of human happiness in the form of science or commerce or religion or one of the arts. From that angle, alas, South America so far has been almost as barren as Australia or Mongolia. Which, I repeat, may be due to the lack of population, which in turn may be due to the fact that a great deal of South America lies just beneath the equator and that in the other parts the white man has never been able to replace the native or is so swamped by half-breeds of different hue (mulattoes, who are the descendants of whites and Negroes, Mestizos, who are the children of Indians and whites or Zambos, who are the offspring of Negroes and Indians) that they are never quite able to assert their political or intellectual powers.

South America has been the scene of some strange political experiments. A Brazilian Empire was something quite new under the sun although it lasted less than a century, and that extraordinary Jesuit free state in Paraguay (which lasted much longer than the empire on its eastern front) will probably always receive honorable mention in learned works devoted to applied Utopias. And South America produced at least one man of more than extraordinary ability, the great Bolivar who not merely set his own country free, as our own George Washington did, but who was directly or indirectly responsible for the successful outcome of most of the revolutionary movements of the entire continent. I do not for a moment doubt that there have been a great many other men who have loomed large in the local histories of Uruguay and Bolivia, but our planet at large has never heard of them and I wonder seriously whether upon close acquaintance-ship they would prove to be of the calibre that is necessary to elevate them to the rank of world figures. And so it will be sufficient for the purpose of this book if I present you with a brief

catalogue of mountains, rivers and states and promise you faithfully that I will fill in the human details a thousand years hence.

The entire western coast of South America consists of a continuation of our own Rockies and of the Mexican Sierra Madre
and it is known as the Cordilleras de los Andes or the Andes for
short. The Andes was the Spanish name which the conquerors
had given to those irrigation canals which the Indians had built
all over the slopes of their native hills. By merely destroying
those canals and dams, the Spaniards were afterwards able to let
many tribes starve to death and since the Conquistadores had
taken the long and dangerous trip across the ocean to get rich
quick and not to found a permanent home in a new world, this
was as good a way of robbing the natives of their possessions as
any other.

When approaching the South Pole, the Andes break off into a
number of islands of which Tierra del Fuego is the best known.
Between Chile and Tierra del Fuego lies the strait which Magellan navigated with such great difficulty on the white man's first
trip around the world and which is still called after him. The
southernmost point of the island is Cape Horn, so called after
the native town of the man who discovered it (the little town of
Hoorn in Holland) and not after a cow, as so many people seem
to believe. The Strait of Magellan is of course of great strategic
importance. Hence the Falkland Islands which guard it are
British territory.

The Andes, like the whole of this enormous mountain-range
that runs from the Arctic to the Antartic Circle, are volcanic.
The Chimborazo in Ecuador (now extinct) is 20,702 feet high.
The Aconcagua in the Argentine beats them all with 22,834 feet.
While the Cotopaxi with 19,550 feet (also in Ecuador) holds
the record for being the highest active volcano of the entire
planet.

The South American Andes resemble their North American
sisters in two other respects. The high mountain ridges enclose

several wide plateaus which form the natural confines for such states as Bolivia or Ecuador. Furthermore there are very few convenient passes so that the railroad between Argentine and Chile, the only trans-Andean railroad, has to climb to a height

The Railroad across the Andes

which far surpasses that of the Swiss mountain passes like the St. Bernard or the Gothard ere it can bore its tunnels.

As for the mountains of the east, the Appalachians of South America, they consist of the Guiana Ridge in the north and the Brazilian Highlands of the east, each one containing a number of independent Sierras and Serras of its own, and forming the remnants of a much vaster range which was gradually cut in two

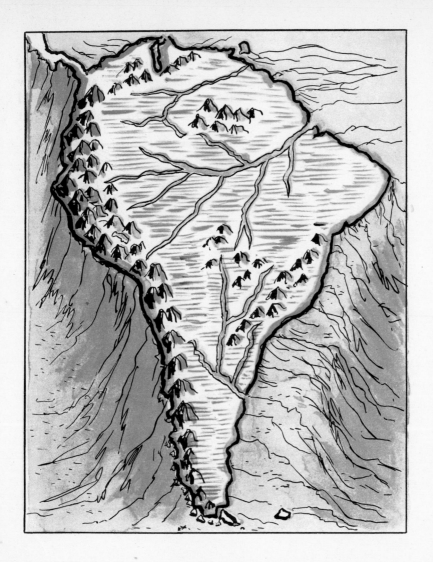

South America

by the valley of the Amazon. The Amazon is not the longest
river in the world but the river that takes care of more water than
any other. It literally has hundreds of branches of which more
than fifteen are quite as long as the Rhine, while several others,
such as the Madeira and the Tapajos, are a great deal longer.

North of the Guiana Mountains there is another valley, that
of the Orinoco River. The Orinoco, which is actually connected
with the Amazon by way of the curious Rio Negro (imagine the
Ohio being part of the Mississippi and the Potomac at the same
time!) is much better suited for navigation than the Amazon.
For it does not have to break its way through the mountains just
before it reaches the sea, as the Amazon is obliged to do, and its
mouth is almost twenty miles wide, while the river itself, a
terrific water-carrier, maintains a steady depth of 300 feet for
several hundred miles inland, which is of great convenience to
sea-going vessels.

As for the Parana, the north–south river of South America, on
the way to the sea it picks up the Paraguay and the Uruguay
rivers and then becomes the Rio de la Plata on which Monte-
video, the capital of the state of Uruguay is situated. Like the
Orinoco, the Parana is a good inland water-way.

In one particular respect, South America is much better off
than most of the other continents, except Europe. It has practically no deserts. Except for northern Chile, most of her country
enjoys a sufficient amount of moisture, while the Amazon region
and the whole of the eastern coast of Brazil are drenched by
equatorial rains which make the Amazon territory much more
densely and evenly wooded than that of the Congo. But as a
result of its steady rainfall, the rest of the continent, especially
in the southern part, which is not quite so near the equator, is
excellently suited for purposes of agriculture, and the Argentine
pampas and the Orinoco llanos and the Brazilian campos are
close rivals of our own Great Plains.

As for the countries which we find on South America today,
few of them grew out of what we might call historical inevita-
bility. They were the unexpected and haphazard results of suc-

cessful revolutions rather than the products of slow growth and development. The United States of Venezuela with a population of 3,216,000 is a little too near the equator to develop a very energetic race of men. But around the Lagoon of Maracaibo in the north oil has been discovered and that has made Maracaibo the most important harbor of Venezuela, a position thus far held

The Llanos of Venezuela

by La Guaira, the port of Caracas, the capital, which lies rather inconveniently just behind a low mountain ridge that separates it from the sea.

On the west of Venezuela lies Colombia with the capital city of Bogota, which lies so far inland that it was a most inconvenient place to reach until the introduction of a regular airplane service with Barranquilla at the mouth of the Magdalena River. Colombia is fertile and has great natural wealth and furthermore, like the United States, it is situated on two oceans. But it will need lots of immigrants from northern Europe before it can begin to develop any of its natural resources.

Ecuador is also a poor country and, although the port of

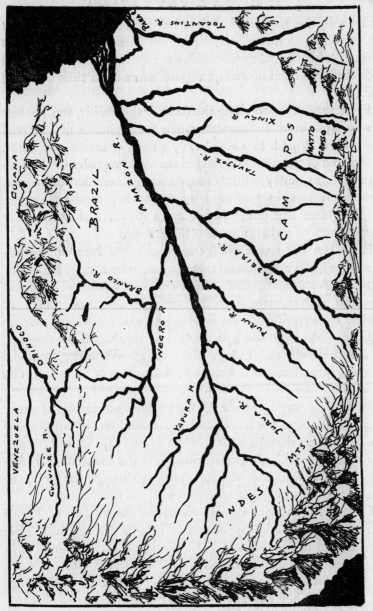

Amazon River

Guayaquil, the harbor of Quito, the capital, has done a great deal better since the opening up of the Panama Canal, there is nothing to report about this nation except that it used to export a lot of quinine and nowadays exports more cocoa than anything else.

Peru, further south along the coast of the Pacific, was the seat of a very powerful Indian state when the Spaniards first arrived in the New World. It was ruled by a caste of nobles, the Incas, or children of the sun, who elected the supreme ruler or the Inca of the whole country, who thereupon was granted despotic rights. Nevertheless and in spite of or because of their feudal character, the Peruvians had developed a much higher and much more human form of civilization than the Aztecs.

But when Pizarro reached these parts, the Inca empire was more than 400 years old and that is a long time for any particular form of government to last. There were many political parties in the land and there was rivalry between different groups of nobles. Pizarro played one side against the other and then in 1531 conquered the whole country. He imprisoned the reigning Inca and turned the Indians into slaves. Whatever could be stolen or plundered was dragged away and sent to Spain. The ruins of the old Incas, the remnants of roads and castles around Lake Titicaca way up in the Andes (3300 square miles of water 12,875 feet above sea-level) and endless old bits of pottery and other bits of art show us what was lost when a capable and competent race was suddenly transformed into the indolent and miserable natives who now wander aimlessly through the streets of Cuzco, the old capital, or take part in some revolution.

Lima is the modern capital where the future fate of Peru's treasures in silver and copper and oil is to be decided, unless the President of the Republic and his foreign banking friends have long since removed the contents of these mines and have deposited them in the vaults of the Banque de France. Such things are possible. They explain why this chapter can be so short.

Bolivia, the poor land-locked state, was not always a land-locked state and La Paz, the capital, once upon a time had direct

access to the sea. But during the famous saltpetre war of 1879–
1882 when Peru and Chile fought for the Arica district, Bolivia
was foolish enough to side against Chile. When Chile won the
war, Bolivia lost her coastal region. Bolivia is a very rich country.
Among other things it is the third tin-producing country of the
world, but a density of population of less than five per square
mile, a total population of less than 3,000,000 and most of those
Indians who remained behind when the Inca Empire was destroyed—no, it will take a great deal of time to do anything with
or for that unfortunate land.

The two southernmost states, Chile and the Argentine, are by
far the most important of the entire continent but their prosperity
is a direct result of their geographical situation. They lie in the
temperate zone. Hence they have fewer Indians (the tropics
make them breed faster) and they have attracted a better class
of immigrants.

Chile is richer in natural wealth than the Argentine. Arica
(from where you take the railroad for Bolivia), Antofagasta,
Iquique and Valparaiso are the four most important harbors of
the west coast of South America, just as Santiago, the capital, is
the largest city of that entire region. The southern part of Chile
is beginning to raise cattle which is slaughtered and frozen and
sent to Europe from Punta Arenas on the Strait of Magellan.

As for the Argentine, it is the great cow-country of South
America. The flat territory along the Parana River, almost as
large as one-third of Europe, is the richest part of the entire
continent. Meat and wool and hides and butter are exported in
such quantities that they have been able to affect our own prices
for those commodities in a most unpleasant fashion. The steady
immigration of Italian laboring men and farmers during the last
ten years will make the Argentine one of the greatest grain and
flax producers of the western hemisphere, while the sheep culture
makes Patagonia one of the most dangerous competitors of
Australia.

The capital of the Argentine is Buenos Aires, also on the Rio
de la Plata, just opposite the small state of Uruguay which has

very much the same soil and climate as the Argentine and which, having rid itself of the last of its Indian population, does in a small way, but very successfully, what the Argentinians are doing on such a very large scale that very often they run the risk of coming to grief through over-speculation and bad financial management.

If the Straits of Magellan should run dry

Paraguay finally, the third of the Rio de la Plata states and in many ways the most favored of them all, would now be prosperous if it had not been for the disastrous war of 1864–1870 when the poor Indians, trained in military service by their former Jesuit masters (who however in 1769 had lost the country to the Spanish crown), had gone on the war-path in behalf of a crazy man who also happened to be their President. This poor man, having quite needlessly declared war on all his three powerful neighbors, continued the fight until five-sixths of the male population of the entire country had been killed. At the end of this period of slaughter, conditions were so bad that the Paraguayans had to revert to polygamy to get their country repopulated. It will take another century however ere this rich little state shall have fully recovered from that catastrophe.

There remains one more country to be discussed—Brazil. As a colony it was badly neglected, first by the Dutch and afterwards by the Portuguese who forbade the natives and the settlers to deal with any one except a few accredited merchants of Lisbon and who kept this entire region in a state of almost complete economic bondage until the year 1807 when the royal family of Portugal was forced to flee before Napoleon and moved over the Rio de Janeiro. Then the tables were turned and for almost a dozen years the despised colony ruled the mother country. And when His Portuguese Majesty sailed for Lisbon in 1821 he left his son, Dom Pedro, behind as his representative. A year later the son proclaimed himself Emperor of an independent Brazil. And since then the Portuguese language is the only tie that binds the colony to the erstwhile mother country, for the house of Braganza, which had probably given Brazil the best government any South American state had ever enjoyed, was forced to abdicate in 1889 as the result of a military upheaval, and the last of the American emperors left for Paris and the cemetery.

Brazil, with 3,285,000 square miles of territory and therefore as large as the United States and covering half of the entire South American continent, is at the same time the richest of all the different countries south of the equator. It is divided into three parts,—the Amazon lowlands or the valley of the Amazon; the coastlands of the Atlantic; and the highlands, where Santos is the town which provides half of the world with its daily coffee. Besides coffee Brazil grows rubber in the Pará or Belem district, just south of the mouth of the Amazon, and in Manaos where the Rio Negro joins the Amazon. Then there are the tobacco and the cocoa of Bahia on the east coast and the grazing fields of the high plateau of Matto Grosso. And finally there are the diamonds and the other precious stones of the darkest interior, gems which are so difficult to reach that they have never been very thoroughly exploited. And the same holds true for the iron ore and the other metals which are all of them awaiting the building of more railroads.

And finally there are three little European colonies in South America, the only remnants of the old colonial possessions of the seventeenth and eighteenth centuries. They are British Guiana or Demerara; Dutch Guiana or Surinam, which the Dutch got in exchange for the New Netherlands and the city of Nieuw Amsterdam; and French Guiana or Cayenne. If the French had not chosen Cayenne as one of their penal colonies and if we did not see an occasional scrap of unpleasant scandal coming from that lost and unhealthy swamp and attaching itself right to the center of our front pages, we would feel tempted to forget that the Guianas existed. Which would probably be just as well for they contribute very little to either the prosperity or the sum total of happiness of the human race, and they are the living reminders of the day when the whole of South America meant but one thing to the visitor from over the seas—a rich store-house to be plundered at will.

Waste: The deserted mine

XLVII

A NEW WORLD

I WANTED to find out how high Kilimanjaro was. After a book has been written and rewritten five or six times, rows of figures are apt to do strange things. What with copying and recopying and infinite corrections scribbled all around them, they have a way of playing hide-and-seek with themselves. One moment they are one thing. The next moment they are something else. If you have ever been snow-blind, you will know what I mean.

"But," you will answer, "that really can't be much of a problem. Look it up in some reliable handbook of geography or in an encyclopedia or in an atlas and copy it."

That would be very simple if these blessed geographies, encyclopedias and atlases were ever able to agree upon any given fact. But apparently they are not. I have got most of the standard volumes on geography right here on my desk and they are a subject of constant delight. Not that they are particularly amusing reading. Geography is not supposed to be a very amusing subject. But when it comes to doing tricks with mountain tops and oceans they are sublime. River basins and the drainage areas of inland seas stretch and shrink and shrink and stretch. The mean average temperature of any given part of the world never stays mean or average very long but makes the mercury of the different meteorological stations behave like a stock-market ticker during a panic. And the bottom of the ocean heaves and sighs like Noodle's tummy after a particularly exciting chase after a cat.

I don't want to destroy any further illusions in a world that has already lost its faith in so many things. But I come out of this struggle with "the facts of geography" having a profound doubt about all further vital statistics. I suppose that this unfortunate diversity of opinions is the result of our incurable vice of nationalism. Every little country must have a few figures all its own, so as to be really able to manifest its sovereign independence.

But that was merely a detail. There were other problems, of which I shall enumerate a few. One half of the world measures weight and distance according to the decimal system. The other half sticks to the duodecimal system. To revaluate meters and kilometers into yards and miles accurately, not merely approximately, is no easy matter, as the gun manufacturers of the Great War learned to their intense discomfort. However, with the help of a competent mathematical assistant (I am no genius at that sort of thing) the necessary calculations can be made. But how about the proper names of countries and mountains and rivers? How should these be spelled? The Gulf of Chili—Gulf of Tjili —Gulf of Tschili—Gulf of Tshi-li—take your choice, my friends! Hindu-Kush — Hindoe-koesch — Hindu-Kutch — Hindu-Kusj—which one do you prefer? But that would not be so bad if at least the different big language groups had been able to agree upon the proper way of spelling Russian or Chinese or Japanese or Spanish names. But every major tongue has at least two and sometimes three conflicting systems of transcribing these strange tongues into the native vernacular.

To add to this confusion of tongues, every tiny scrap of land that can boast of a dialect of its own now claims full and equal rights for "the sacred language of the ancestors", and the map of Europe that used to be fairly simple before the war has recently blossomed forth with a multicolored linguistic flora which makes the reading of Mr. Cook's old and reliable "Continental Railroad Guide" a labor only to be compared to the efforts of Champollion while tackling his first half-dozen Egyptian hieroglyphics.

I am not trying to formulate an alibi. What I have writ, I have writ, but please be lenient with some of my heights and depths. When eminent encyclopedias and statistical handbooks

contradict themselves three or four times on three or four different pages, what is the poor amateur going to do?

I suppose in the end he will do what I did. He will call a
plague upon all these learned tomes and buy himself a copy of
the "World Almanac" and he will say: "I am going to stick to
this one book, and if anybody wants to sue me because I have
made Kilimanjaro 19,710 feet high (in the Britannica it is 19,-
321; in Andrews' Geography, 19,000; in Tarr and McMurry,
19,780; in the Oxford Advanced Atlas, 19,320; in the World
Almanac, 19,710) I shall tell him to go and see the publishers
of the *World-Telegram,* Inc., and let him fight it out with
them."

But what I was going to say when I started upon this Kilimanjaro—Kiliman'djaro—Kilimantscharo—Kilimansjaro topic was
this. I was looking for my World Almanac which had inad-
vertently hidden itself behind a dozen atlases, and during that
search I got hold of a pamphlet that had been sent me a short
while before. It was a pamphlet devoted to the life and the work
of Sir Ronald Ross. In very polite terms the author hinted that
Sir Ronald, if not absolutely in want, was so far removed from
affluence that we might do something about making him at least
reasonably comfortable during the rest of his days—and may
they be many. Of course his needs were not exorbitant. Scientists
rarely count their reward in dollars and dimes. But having completely ruined his health in the pursuit of his studies, he could
do nicely with a more convenient sort of invalid's chair.

I put the pamphlet aside and thought of our own Walter
Reed. I have forgotten what our grateful country has done for
his widow. If I remember rightly the good lady was given a
"mailing frank" (such as any twelve-in-a-dozen congressman
enjoys), and of course she receives the pension that is usually
paid to the widows of officers in the Medical Corps, and there is
a hospital somewhere called after him.

Well, being in a meditative sort of mood, I looked for a
volume on the history of epidemics. And then suddenly I was
struck by an idea. These two men, Reed and Ross, of whom no

one ever seems to have heard, have done more for the development of this earth than hundreds of explorers whose names are familiar to every child in the lowest grades of our grammar schools. By discovering the cause of malaria and yellow fever and by showing us the way in which the world can be set free of those pestilential afflictions, they have opened up more new territory than we shall be able to develop during the next hundred years. The million-murdering mosquito has at last been called to a halt. Anopheles has been driven into a corner and has been forced to listen to the reading of his own death sentence.

It would be easy to add several pages to this chapter on the "Influence of Medicine upon the Geography of the World." Small-pox, beri-beri, sleeping sickness and dozens of other ailments have had to be conquered before the greater part of our world could be made fit for man's permanent habitation. But all this is a little outside of my own "field", so to speak. I know too little about that subject. Nevertheless, the names of those two doctors have set me thinking and wondering.

There is a great deal of unrest in this world. When one looks at the map, one finds little bits of red appearing everywhere. Discontent is breaking out like a severe case of the measles. And books by the ton are being written in an effort to diagnose the case and to suggest suitable remedies. I had never thought very much about it (an author leads such a sheltered life) until I came to write this book. Then suddenly the whole problem became so very simple and Ross and Reed were responsible.

Day-dreaming over a map is really a very pleasant and instructive pastime. There lies Rhodesia—a whole world by itself. Cecil Rhodes was a promoter. He made a few people rich. He killed a great many natives. He turned brigand and started a little war of his own and lost. He turned statesman and started a big war and won. There are a great many monuments to murdered women and children which could bear the legend: "C.R. sculpsit", but a grateful country overlooked these trifles and called a vast new province after him.

A little further northward lies the Congo with its Stanley-villes and Leopoldvilles and the unmarked graves of countless natives tortured to death because they were behind on their rubber quota or slow in bringing in elephant tusks.

Hudson gave his name to a bay which in turn bestowed its

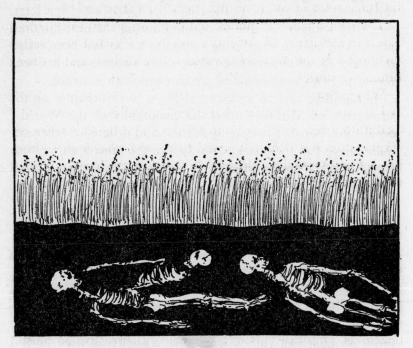

We have fertilized by far too many of our fields in
this way

name upon a rich land company. What that land company did to the original inhabitants makes another terrible chapter in the sad volume devoted to the Martyrdom of Man. But we need not go so far abroad. We ourselves have never yet kept a single treaty with our Indians. What my own ancestors did unto the brown men of those far away spice islands which they conquered three hundred years ago is usually not taught in the public schools of Holland and it is perhaps just as well. What happened in the Putomayo region of South America is still in everybody's memory.

The crimes the different native potentates of Africa and the Arab slave-dealers committed in the silent Senegambian forests make us wish that Dante had reserved a special department of his Inferno for monsters of that particular variety.

The man-hunts with horses and dogs, organized to exterminate the aborigines of Australia and New Zealand are rarely mentioned in the histories devoted to the early years of these distant territories.

Why go on?

I am merely repeating what everybody already knows.

But what few people seem to realize is that the Great Era of Exploitation has definitely come to an end, that most of the present unrest is due to the unwillingness of the former victims to play that role any longer.

There is very little use in sitting in high judgment upon the Errors of the Past. It is more profitable to collect our thoughts and devise ways and means by which we shall be able to avoid a few of the mistakes of the future. Well, the men and women of the type of Reed and Ross are there to show us the way.

Sentimental meditations upon the glories of a problematic Utopia will get us nowhere. To say that since we have spent dozens of centuries "taking away" we must now spend other dozens of centuries "giving" will hardly solve the problem. Charity is as bad as brigandage. Charity is really just as unfair to the recipient as to the donor. To set the Indian native free from the tyranny of the English Raj and then leave him undefended to the mercy of the Moslem mountaineers would be merely another blunder.

Nor would it benefit the Chinese or the Javanese or the Burmese if we should suddenly pack up all our little railroads and flivvers and flying machines and remove our telephone booths and our filling stations and bid them go back to the blessings of the Gandhi's loin-cloth and the crocodile-gnawed sampan. The machine has come to stay. The natives have adapted their

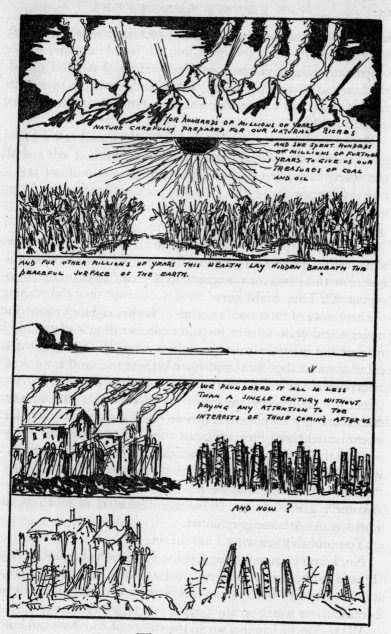

What is the answer?

lives to fast means of transportation and communication. They have fallen into the habit of calling on the white man's doctor when the child develops diphtheria rather than send grandmother to the voodoo priest. When they want to visit their friends, they prefer a jitney-bus to a ten-hour walk across a painful track.

And a world accustomed to money and to bank-notes is not going back to the pails of honey and the spoonfuls of salt and all the other clumsy trivialities of the ancient system of barter.

For better or worse, this planet of ours has become one large, going concern, and the date over the doorway is 1932, not 932 or 32 B. C.

There is, however, a solution, and the labors of Reed and Ross show us the general direction of the road we shall have to follow. For these two men neither "took" nor "gave"—they "cooperated". They could never have done what they did without the assistance of thousands of others. Neither did they stamp out malaria and yellow fever for the exclusive benefit of the black man or the white man or the yellow man. Without regard to color or creed they bestowed their blessings upon the whole of humanity. When Goethals and Dr. Gorgas dug the Panama Canal (Goethals drew the blue prints and Gorgas gave him the man-power with which to translate his drawings into cubic feet of excavated rock) they were not thinking of either the Pacific or the Atlantic alone, nor of America alone, but of the world as a whole. When Marconi invented his wireless, he did not stipulate, "Only Italian ships must be allowed to use the radio in case of disaster". The Zanzibar tramp was benefited as much as the fastest trans-Atlantic greyhound.

You probably see what I am driving at.

No, I am not going to suggest the formation of a new society. That is not necessary. The problem will take care of itself. If it does not, there won't be any problem in a couple of centuries because there won't be any people left to worry about it.

We no longer live in a world the future of which we can leave to itself. That policy went out when steam and electricity came

in and when Patagonia and Lapland, Boston and Han-kow became neighbors, able to confer with each other in less than two
minutes. We are no longer manufacturing goods for ourselves
alone or raising grain for the home village. Japan can make our
matches cheaper than we can ever hope to do and the Argentine
can grow enough wheat to keep the whole of Germany from
starving and at much smaller cost.

We no longer can offer the Chinese Coolie or the Rand Kaffir
one-twentieth of the wages we would pay a white man, because
Moscow has a broadcasting station that carries very far and a
staff of polyglot announcers who inform the black and the yellow
man that he is being cheated out of something that really belongs
to him.

We are no longer able to plunder and filch and rob as heartily
as our fathers did because—well, if you really want to know—
because our conscience won't let us or if we ourselves should
have happened to be born without that spiritual compass, because the collective conscience of mankind has at last reached
the point where it is beginning to get a first flickering suspicion
that honesty and common decency are as inevitable in international affairs as they are in those of private citizens.

No, I am not going to preach a sermon. I am not going to send
you home with a "message". But if you have read this far, I
would like to ask you to sit quite still for another half hour and
draw your own conclusions.

Thus far we have always lived as if we were a sort of accident
—as if our stay on this planet was only a matter of years or at
best of centuries. We have behaved with the indecent greed of
passengers on a passenger-train who know that they will only
have ten minutes for the three-course dinner to be served at the
next halting-place.

Gradually we are beginning to realize that we not only have
been here quite a long time but that we are going to stay here
almost indefinitely. Why the hurry and why the rush? When
you move to a town where you expect to spend the rest of your
days, you plan for the future. So do your neighbors, the butchers

and bakers and grocers and the doctors and undertakers. If they didn't, the whole place would be in such hopeless disorder that it would be uninhabitable in less than a week's time.

When you come to think of it, is there really such a very great difference between the world at large and your own native village? If there is any difference, it is one of quantity rather than quality. And that is all!

You will say that I have wandered all over the place, from Kilimanjaro by way of Dr. Reed and Dr. Ross to planetary-planning for the future.

"But What," as Alice might have asked, "is the use of a Geography without a little Travelling?"

Paris, April, 1931
New Orleans, May, 1932

A FEW FACTS

Area of the earth: 196,950,000 sq. m.
" " " land: 57,510,000 "
" " " water: 139,440,000 "

Area of continents

Asia	17,000,000	sq. m.
Africa	11,500,000	"
North America	8,000,000	"
South "	6,800,000	"
Europe	3,750,000	"

Area of oceans

Pacific	68,634,000	sq. m.
Atlantic	41,321,000	"
Indian	29,340,000	"

Equatorial circumference of the earth: 24,902 miles.
Meridianal " " " " 24,860 "
Diameter through equator: 7,926.667 "
" " poles: 7,899.988 "
Highest mountain: Mt. Everest 29,141 feet
Deepest hole: between Philippines and Japan 34,210 "

Population of continents

Asia	950,000,000
Europe	550,000,000
N. & S. America	230,000,000
Africa	150,000,000
Australia	7,000,000

Population of the earth:
in round figures 2,000,000,000.

Highest mountains of each continent

Asia	Everest	29,141 ft.
S. America	Aconcagua	22,834 "
N. America	McKinley	20,300 "
Africa	Kilimanjaro	19,710 "
Europe	Elbrus	18,465 "

Longest rivers

Mississippi-Missouri	4,221 miles
Nile	4,000 "
Amazon	3,900 "
Ob	3,200 "
Yangtsze	3,100 "

Largest cities

London	7,742,212
New York	6,930,446
Berlin	4,297,000
Chicago	3,376,438
Paris	2,871,039
Osaka	2,453,573
Buenos Aires	2,153,200
Tokio	2,070,913
Moscow	2,025,947

(There are only 9 cities in the world with a population of over 2,000,000. Of these, 4 are in Europe, 2 in the U.S.A., 1 in South America and 2 in Japan.)

505

INDEX